HANDBOOK OF RURAL SKILLS AND TECHNOLOGY

Edited by Vic Marks

Cloudburst 1
Revised Edition
Illustrated by Ted Turner

Cloudburst 2
Illustrated by Cindy Davis

Cloudburst Press

Published
in Canada by:
Cloudburst Press Limited
Mayne Island, B.C. V0N2J0

Published simultaneously in the U.S.A. by:
Cloudburst Press of America, Inc.
2116 Western Avenue
Seattle, Washington
98121

Cloudburst 1

Credits

Thanks are extended to the following authors and publishers as sources of the articles listed below.

Harnessing the Small Stream reprinted courtesy of Popular Science Monthly, 355 Lexington Avenue, New York, N.Y. ©1947 by Popular Science Publishing Co. Inc.

The Michell Turbine reprinted from Low-Cost Development of Small Waterpower Sites, VITA, College Campus, Schenectady, N.Y.

Frost Damage Prevention reprinted from Five Acres and Independence by M.G. Kains, Greenburg, N.Y.

A Treadle Driven Wood Turning Lathe reprinted from 40 Power Tools You can Make, Popular Mechanics Press, Chicago, Illinois.

How to Build an Indian Berry Picker reprinted from the Northwest Passage, P.O. Box 105, S. Bellingham Station, Bellingham, Washington

A Solar Dryer adapted from How to Make a Solar Cabinet Dryer from Agricultural Produce by T.A. Laward. Available from: Brace Research Institute, Faculty of Engineering, McGill University, Montreal 2, P.Q., Canada.

Table of Drying Times and Methods in *A Solar Dryer* article reprinted from Mother Earth News, No. 10, Box 90, Henderson, North Carolina.

How to Build a Juice Press reprinted from Farmer's Bulletin, No. 114, Canada Department of Agriculture, Ottawa, Canada.

The Smoke Curing and Salting of Fish reprinted from Smokehouses and the Smoke Curing of Fish by Iola I. Burg, Washington Department

of Fisheries, Olympia, Washington.

How to Salt Fish reprinted from Village Technology Handbook, VITA, College Campus, Schenectady, N.Y.

Cheesemaking by Monica Rice, Elsie Evelsizer and Helen Valentine, reprinted from the Northwest Passage, P.O. Box 105, S. Bellingham Station, Bellingham, Washington, and The Green Revolution, Heathcote Road, Freeland, Maryland.

Rural Water Works reprinted from Farmer's Bulletin No. 927, U.S. Department of Agriculture, Washington, D.C.

A Hand Operated Washing Machine reprinted from Village Technology Handbook, VITA, College Campus, Schenectady, N.Y.

Cloudburst 2

Credits

Thanks are extended to the following authors and publishers as sources of the articles listed below.

A Colonial Spinning Wheel appears by permission of Popular Mechanics, Chicago, Illinois ©1929 by Popular Mechanics Press.

A Large Wood Burning Oven is reprinted from VITA pamphlet no. 5700.9. *A Carding Machine* is reprinted from VITA pamphlet 9400.7.

A Hand Powered Drill Press reprinted from Popular Science with permission. ©1945

(1948) Popular Science Publishing Company.

Log Falling and Bucking is adapted from the Fallers and Buckers Handbook published by the British Columbia Workers Compensation Board.

Building a Hydraulic Ram by Don Marier reprinted from Alternate Sources of Energy, Vol. 1, No. 1.

The Popular Science Ram reprinted from Popular Science with permission. ©1945 (1948) Popular Science Publishing Company

Foot Powered Scroll Saw reprinted from Popular Mechanics with permission. ©1929 Popular Mechanics Press

A Simple Wood Fired Kiln by Ivan Englund and *A High Temperature Wood Burning Kiln* by Ivan McMeekin reprinted by permission of Pottery in Australia, Lonqueville, N.S.W.

A Controlled Smokehouse by Iola I. Berg reprinted by permission of Washington State Department of Fisheries, Olympia, Washington.

The Chicken Guillotine, A Home Made Hay and Leaf Baler, A Home Made Honey Extractor, and *Sprouting Trays* appear with the permission of Larry McWilliams and Countryside Magazine ("The" magazine for smallholders to subscribe to), Rt. 1, Box 239, Waterloo, Wisconsin 53594; $9.00. year; $10./year in Canada.

Cloudburst 1

A
HANDBOOK OF RURAL SKILLS
AND
TECHNOLOGY

Contents
Cloudburst 1

Contents for Cloudburst 2 following page 128

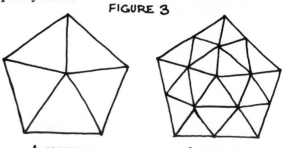

by Jim Bohlen
& Russ Chernoff

The 16ft. Personal Dome

The Personal Dome was designed to offer privacy and flexibility for internal arrangements of space. Its structure allows for interconnection with other domes (fig. 1).

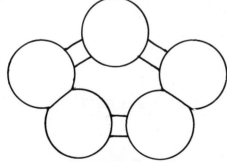

FIGURE 1

The Personal Dome geometry was derived from the dodecahedron, which consists of 12 pentagons (fig. 2a). This polygon was chosen as it yields strut locations which allow access to the interior with minimum disturbance of the structural elements. The Personal Dome is 6/10 of a spherical dodecahedron or a "6/10 sphere" (fig 2b), which is a "natural" division and requires dealing with only one odd-length strut. A rather large number of subdivisions of the triangles was selected, as it facilitates installation of such things as doors, windows, sheathing, insulation, and affords geometric similarity. The side struts rising from the foundation are essentially vertical, and provide generous standup room along the dome perimeter on the inside. The geometric similarity permits five evenly-spaced access portals, which are important to have when considering the community assembly of domes. Individuality of design will result from solutions to localized environmental problems. For instance, consider a community of personal domes, joined with passageways: the form and shape of the passages will be determined by the terrain and the unique social aspects of each community.

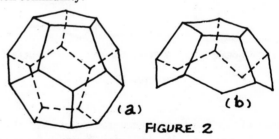

FIGURE 2

The Dodecahedron

Before proceeding farther, we should define the elemental geodesic terms. *Frequency* denotes how each pentagon is broken down. The Personal Dome is a two frequency dome.

FIGURE 3

1 FREQUENCY   2 FREQUENCY

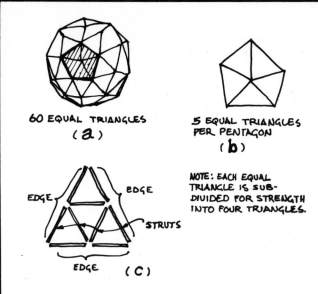

60 EQUAL TRIANGLES
(a)

5 EQUAL TRIANGLES
PER PENTAGON
(b)

EDGE   EDGE

STRUTS

EDGE   (C)

NOTE: EACH EQUAL TRIANGLE IS SUB-DIVIDED FOR STRENGTH INTO FOUR TRIANGLES.

FIGURE 4

A spherical one frequency dodecahedron consists of 12 pentagons or 60 equal triangles—each pentagon containing 5 of the 60 triangles (figs. 4a and 4b). In a two frequency dodecahedron, each of these triangles breaks down into 4 smaller triangles, making 240 triangles total. To visualize this, start with one of the 60 triangles in the one frequency dodecahedron. It has three edges (fig. 4c) and it is subdivided into four smaller triangles by dividing each edge in two (this is done in such a way that the edges will begin to curve outward—fig. 5.). Dividing each edge in two gives you more strength. As you increase the frequency, you get closer to a sphere (and increase the stand-up floor area as well).

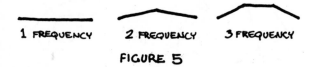

1 FREQUENCY   2 FREQUENCY   3 FREQUENCY

FIGURE 5

The *struts* are the pieces of material out of which the geometric framework is constructed; in figure 4c for example, each line is a strut and there are nine struts altogether.

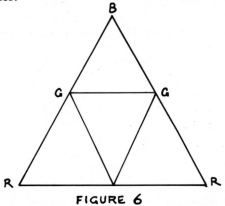

B

G   G

R   R

FIGURE 6

The *strut length* is determined by deducting a uniform dimension from each hub-to-hub distance. This dimension is determined from the specific hub design (figs. 8, 9, and 10).

For the two frequency dodecahedron there are 4 strut lengths (fig. 6 and table 1). Multiply the chord factor (column 3, table 1) by the radius in inches; then deduct 6-1/4-in. from that number. This will be the strut length for the hub design which is included. In this same manner, any size dome may be calculated.

The struts are connected to each other by *hubs*. These connecting hubs are made of 3/4-in. exterior-grade plywood (e.g., used concrete forms). The connectors are made of hardwood dowels which are shaped into 3/4-in. diameter pegs. The hubs are inserted into the sawn slots at the ends of the struts, and the pegs are pushed into place (fig. 7). The holes are all pre-drilled to give the necessary precision and therefore to assure ease of assembly and structural integrity.

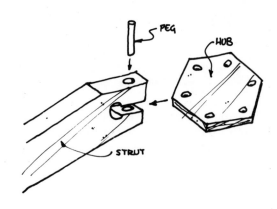

PEG

HUB

STRUT

FIGURE 7

Strut Construction

The struts are made from 2 x 4's cut to the exact strut length (table 1). Code the ends B, G, or R, as the case may be. Try to cut the material so that knots in the wood are avoided at the ends where the slots, the slot holes, and the peg holes will be cut (fig. 7). After making a few of the complete struts, place them on the plan (fig.-12) to conform with the outline of the strut end as shown to check your workmanship. Inaccuracies in the beginning will be paid for later when assembling the dome frame in the field.

If dowels cannot be purchased, they can be made by driving a stick of hardwood through a block of steel which has the proper size holes drilled in it. Another feature of the hub design is that poles may be substituted for dimension lumber. This alternative can be important in the bush.

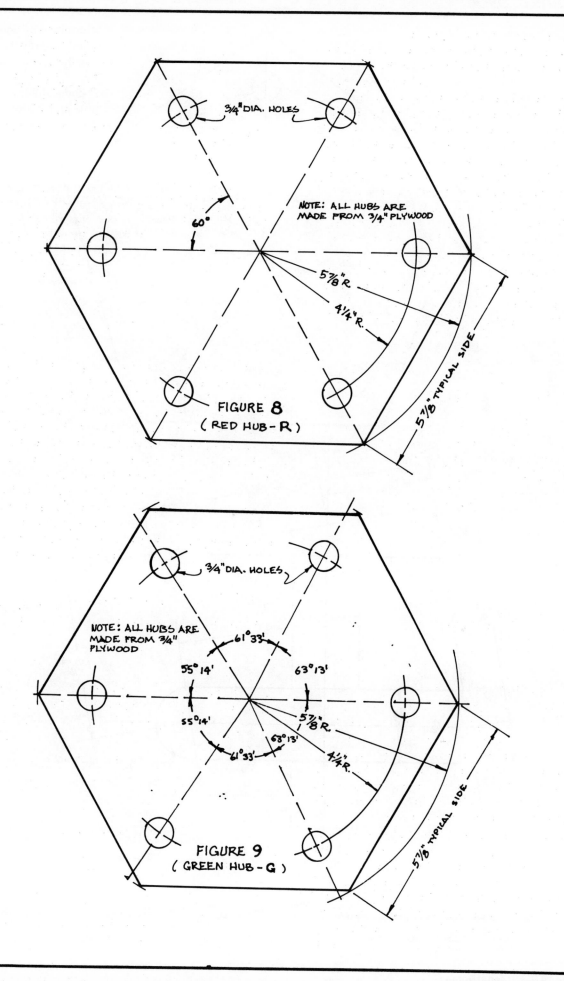

3/4" DIA. HOLES

60°

NOTE: ALL HUBS ARE
MADE FROM 3/4" PLYWOOD

5 7/8" R.

4 1/4" R.

5 7/8" TYPICAL SIDE

FIGURE 8
(RED HUB - R)

3/4" DIA. HOLES

NOTE: ALL HUBS ARE
MADE FROM 3/4"
PLYWOOD

61° 33'

55° 14'   63° 13'

55° 14'

5 7/8" R.

61° 33'   63° 13'

4 1/4" R.

5 7/8" TYPICAL SIDE

FIGURE 9
(GREEN HUB - G)

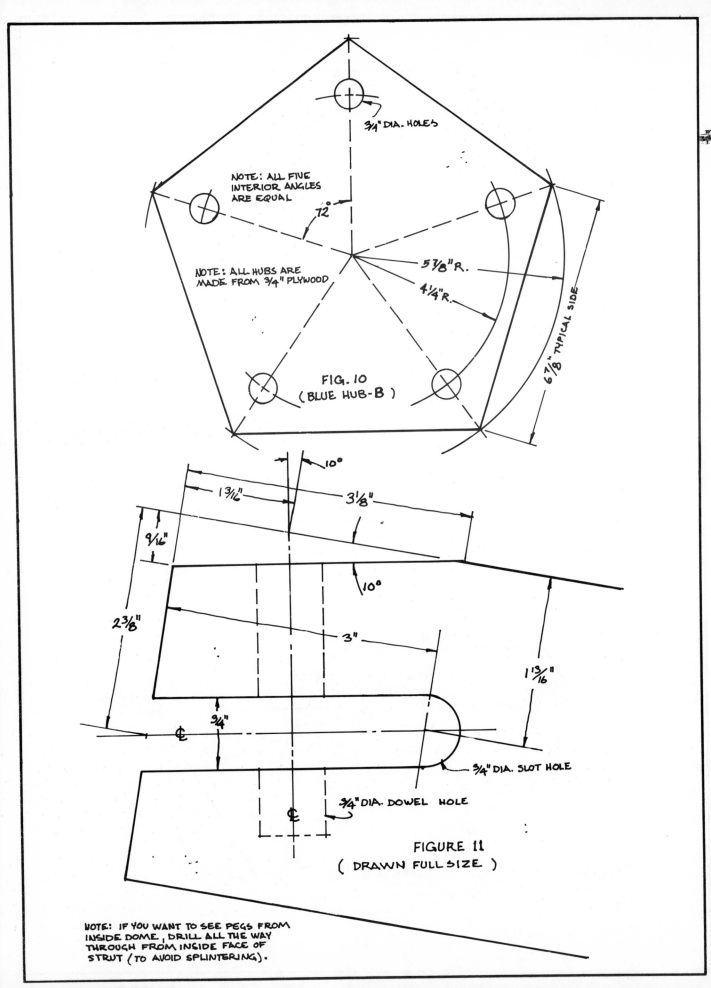

3/4" DIA. HOLES

NOTE: ALL FIVE
INTERIOR ANGLES
ARE EQUAL

72°

NOTE: ALL HUBS ARE
MADE FROM 3/4" PLYWOOD

5 7/8"R.

4 1/4"R.

6 7/8" TYPICAL SIDE

FIG. 10
(BLUE HUB-B)

10°

1 3/16"

3 1/8"

9/16"

10°

2 3/8"

3"

1 13/16"

C⃥

9/4"

3/4" DIA. SLOT HOLE

C⃥

3/4" DIA. DOWEL HOLE

FIGURE 11
(DRAWN FULL SIZE)

NOTE: IF YOU WANT TO SEE PEGS FROM
INSIDE DOME, DRILL ALL THE WAY
THROUGH FROM INSIDE FACE OF
STRUT (TO AVOID SPLINTERING).

To get a better idea of what the Personal Dome looks like, trace figure 12 onto a piece of paper; glue this to a piece of cardboard and make yourself a miniature dome.

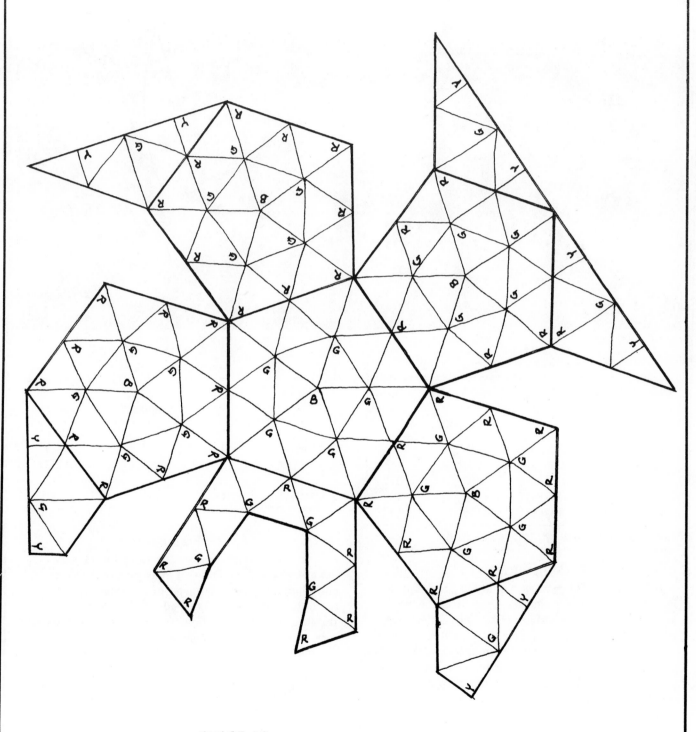

FIGURE 12

TABLE 1 STRUT SPECIFICATIONS				
Type	Number Required	Chord Factor	Hub Centre to Hub Centre	Strut Length
BG	25	.297781R	28⁹⁄₁₆″	22³⁄₈″
GG	28	.346155R	33¼″	27″
GR	103	.351623R	33¾″	27½″
RR	38	.362842R	34¹³⁄₁₆″	28⅝″
RY	10	.187601R	18⅛″	14⅞″
NOTE: RY is the odd or "truncated" strut				

TABLE 2 HUB SPECIFICATIONS			
Colour Code	Type	Number Required	Interior Angles
blue	B	5	all 72°
green	G	33	55°14′
			61°33′
			63°13′
red	R	34	all 60°

Making the Hubs

Cut plywood hubs according to the plans (figs. 8, 9, and 10). Make three master templates from the plans and then transfer the outlines of the hubs and hole centres to the plywood panels. Two 3/4-in. 4-ft. x 8-ft. panels are sufficient to make enough hubs for one dome. The G hub is to be installed directionally, meaning that the part of hub on which the holes are drilled more closely together must point towards the blue (B) hub. The R hub holes are evenly spaced and therefore have no specific directionality. The same for the blue (B) hub.

The hub, strut, and peg system (Peg-A-Strut*) has been tested to failure at five times the design load by the B.C. Tecology Centre in Vancouver, B.C.

* Registered T.M.

The Foundation

One of the basic reasons for using domes is their light weight and the fact that loads on the shell bear evenly along the whole perimeter of the dome. Consequently, very small design loads are imposed on the floor framing and the foundation. To minimize the foundation cost, a raised platform supported on posts is recommended. Here, the small dome philosophy of design demonstrates economy. Since the floor spans are short, very lightweight joists may be used. To support a 40 lbs./sq.-ft. live load, 2-in. x 6-in. joists are adequate. Or, if 2-in.-x 4-in. studs are more commonly available, an inverted T-beam may be fabricated from them.

The joists connect to ten 6 in. diameter posts, which are buried in the ground. A centre-post serves to divide the floor span so the 8-ft. joist may be used. All joists are installed radially, like the spokes of a wheel, and inter-

mediate nailing joists are installed on 2-ft. centres, which give the finished floor frame the appearance of a spider web (fig. 15).

After the foundation and floor framework have been erected, the bottom of the floor joists may be sheathed with insulating board, by nailing to the bottom of the joists. Where inverted T-beams are used, the insulating board is fitted between the radial joist and is supported by the T-flanges. The tops of the joists are covered with conventional flooring materials. This floor system may enable the space between the joists to be utilized as a return air plenum for a space-heating system.

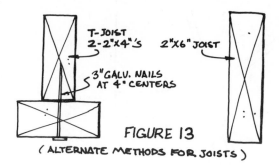

T-JOIST
2-2"x4"'s

2"x6" JOIST

3" GALV. NAILS
AT 4" CENTERS

FIGURE 13
(ALTERNATE METHODS FOR JOISTS)

The plywood hubs are fastened on top of the foundation floor (fig. 16).

The dome can be assembled using the partially assembled framework itself as the scaffold. After assembly and alignment of the completed frame, the bottom hubs are securely nailed to the foundation posts (fig. 14).

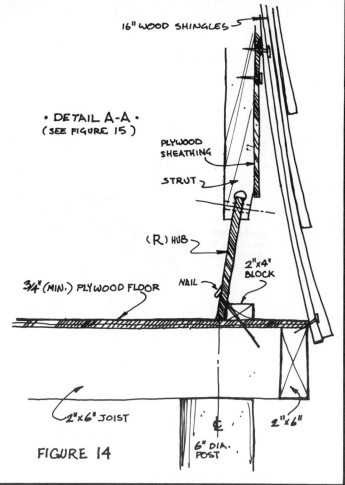

16" WOOD SHINGLES

• DETAIL A-A •
(SEE FIGURE 15)

PLYWOOD
SHEATHING

STRUT

(R) HUB

2"x4"
BLOCK

NAIL

3/4" (MIN.) PLYWOOD FLOOR

2"x6" JOIST

6" DIA.
POST

2"x6"

FIGURE 14

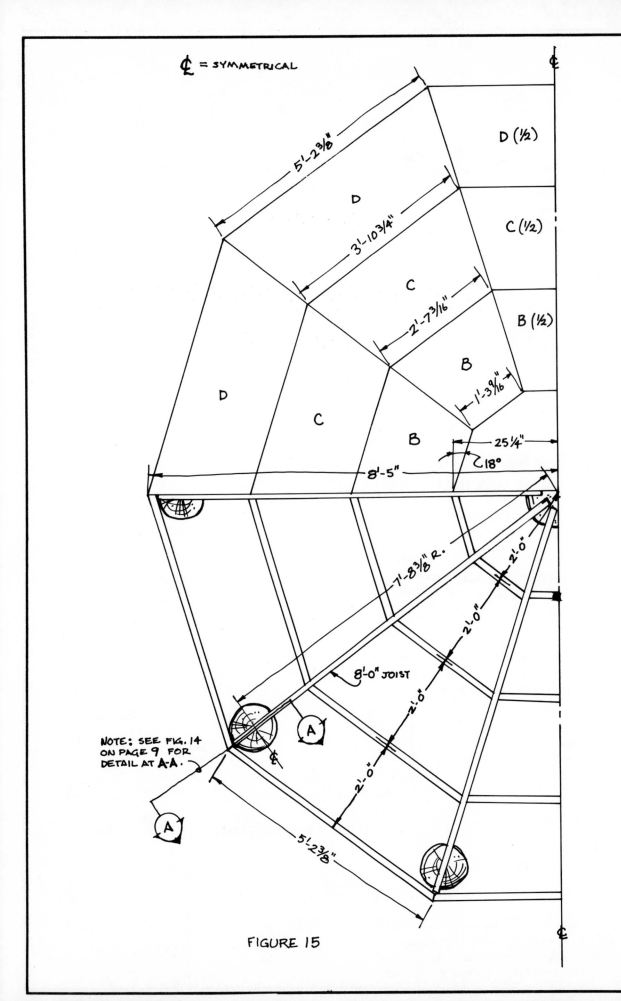

℄ = SYMMETRICAL

D (½)

C (½)

B (½)

D

C

B

5'-2⅜"

3'-10¾"

2'-7³⁄₁₆"

1'-3⁹⁄₁₆"

25¼"

18°

D

C

B

8'-5"

7'-8⅜" R.

2'-0"

8'-0" JOIST

2'-0"

2'-0"

2'-0"

A

A

℄

NOTE: SEE FIG. 14
ON PAGE 9 FOR
DETAIL AT A-A.

5'-2⅜"

℄

FIGURE 15

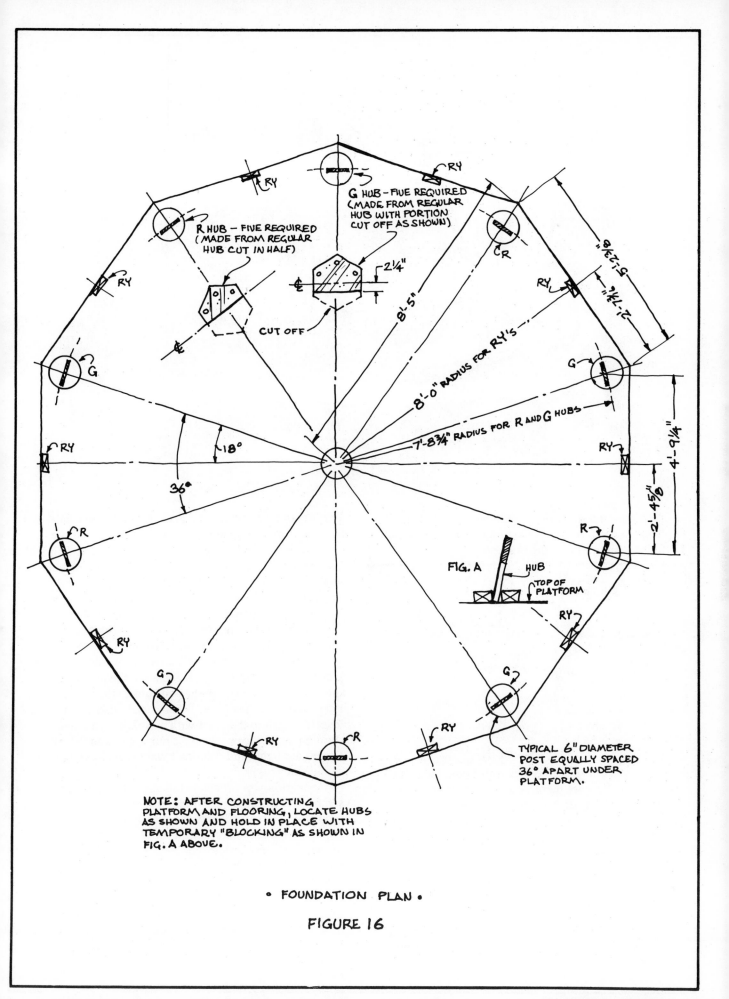

G HUB – FIVE REQUIRED (MADE FROM REGULAR HUB WITH PORTION CUT OFF AS SHOWN)

R HUB – FIVE REQUIRED (MADE FROM REGULAR HUB CUT IN HALF)

2¼"

CUT OFF

8'-5"

8'-0" RADIUS FOR RY's

7'-8¾" RADIUS FOR R AND G HUBS

18°

36°

5'-7⅝"

2'-7¾"

4'-9¼"

2'-4⅝"

FIG. A

HUB

TOP OF PLATFORM

TYPICAL 6" DIAMETER POST EQUALLY SPACED 36° APART UNDER PLATFORM.

NOTE: AFTER CONSTRUCTING PLATFORM AND FLOORING, LOCATE HUBS AS SHOWN AND HOLD IN PLACE WITH TEMPORARY "BLOCKING" AS SHOWN IN FIG. A ABOVE.

• FOUNDATION PLAN •

FIGURE 16

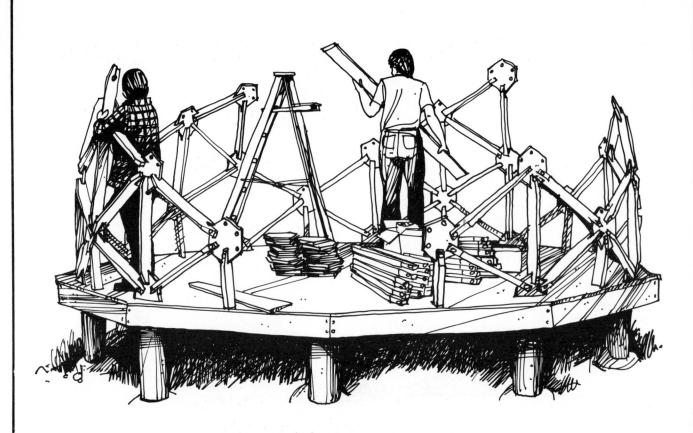

The plywood sheathing should be cut from 4-ft. x 8-ft. sheets in a pattern similar to that illustrated in figure 17. Refer to figure 15 for the exact sizes.

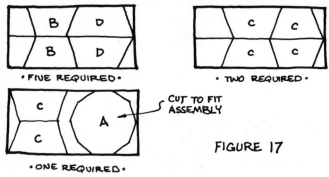

• FIVE REQUIRED •

• TWO REQUIRED •

CUT TO FIT ASSEMBLY

• ONE REQUIRED •

FIGURE 17

The Assembly

The struts have been colour coded (you did, didn't you?) so that they are merely put in place from the bottom hubs up. No scaffolding is needed, because the dome can be assembled with the structure itself used as the scaffold. Install the struts in a sequence with the bottom row and working upward in sort of a spiral direction. Use the folded paper model (fig. 11) as your assembly guide. To make an easy job of peg insertion, dry them out thoroughly by suspending them over coals of a wood fire or warm them at 200°F. in an oven for eight hours. This will shrink the pegs and allow them to be easily inserted. After they are in place, moisture pickup from the air will cause the dowel to expand and lock into place.

Don't plan on removing the pegs at some future date, because it won't happen. Have a picnic on top of the dome frame after driving the last peg into place. This will be your structural test. Upon completing the assembly, you may notice some hubs appear twisted. This will be due to the dome not sitting level on the foundation or you may have put some struts in the wrong place. Check this out, and if everything looks OK, twist the hubs to their correct position. This will level the dome. To check for level, place a 4-ft. carpenter's level on a straight 2 x 4 or piece of evenly-cut plywood, and align the level edge of the wood with centres of any two hubs in the row immediately above the base row. When certain that the frame is level, fasten it to the posts with dowels or drive spikes through the platform, the base hubs, and into the posts. Domes are light, and you don't want them floating away some windy night.

Sheathing (plywood or shiplap) is applied to the struts after the door and window are framed. Breather-type building paper covers the sheathing, over which is applied the finish material. Flashing is used where required. The smoke pipe and toilet vents are installed and flashed. The sheathing should be at least 5/16-in. or preferably 3/8-in. plywood. Flashing may be obtained by cutting up old auto bodies, gallon oil cans, or thin rust-proof metal. Galvanized iron or aluminum flashing may be purchased at any building supply store. The windows are then inserted, and puttied or caulked to keep out the weather.

Framing the Door

Part of the geometry is removed from the dome to facilitate placement of a door. The structural integrity is maintained by the method of framing the door. Columns are installed from the floor to the two topmost hubs. These columns take the load down to the floor, which in turn transmits the weight to the posts. This framing allows the use of an ordinary rectangular door. An old recycled door could be cut to size and installed in a frame that is also modified.

Framing the Windows

A window detail which *does* keep the rain out has been worked out and tested (fig. 18).

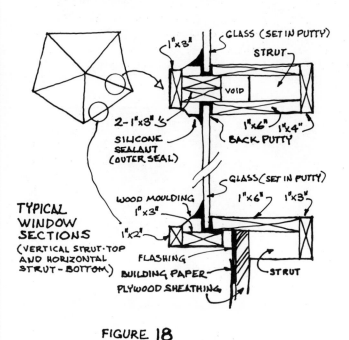

FIGURE 18

The structural strength of the dome does not depend upon the plywood sheathing or any other skin material for structural support. Therefore, you may install glass anywhere you prefer. However, do not remove any struts, unless you are prepared to substitute proper bracing, such as is done for the door opening. The importance of attending to details while installing window glass cannot be overemphasized, in view of the lack of conventional overhanging eaves. Use sealing compounds liberally, and only those of the highest quality.

The Sheathing Skin

As shown earlier, each pentagon is divided into five identical triangles, which are subdivided into four triangles, two of which are identical (fig. 19).

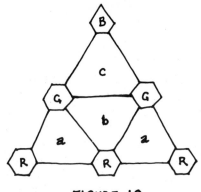

FIGURE 19

Triangles a, b, and c represent the areas to be covered by the sheathing. The templates to be made are as follows:

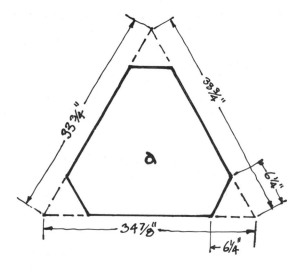

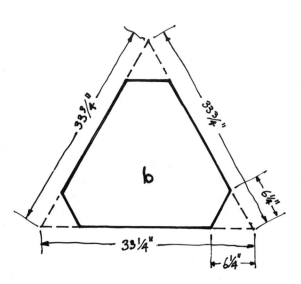

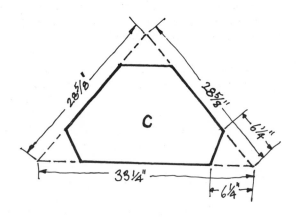

FIGURE 20

One of the reasons that we chose the 16-ft. dome with this breakdown (two frequency dodecahedron) was because it could very efficiently utilize 4-ft. x 8-ft. sheets of plywood (3/8 in. thick or more) for the skin sheathing. A cutting plan (fig. 21) has been worked out. Just for fun, cut a few triangles of different sizes out of your stock of plywood to see how everything fits—you'll feel more confident.

The alternation of a panels and b panels (fig. 21) is necessary for only seven 4-ft. x 8-ft. panels. This situation arises because 28 b's and 68 a's are required. The number of c's would be 25 or less, depending on how many windows are to be included. Along the foundation, partial panels are necessary: 10 half b's and 8 half a's.

Sheath the dome from the top down. This will allow you to use the frame as scaffolding. Sheath in a spiral pattern. The reason for this is to keep the plates (hubs) as straight as possible. The plates have a tendency to twist when stood upon, so the sheathing eliminates this problem. Maintain a constant surveillance to ensure that the hubs are not twisting. If a hub is twisted, it must be straightened or the covering material will not fit properly. Cover the sheathing with *breather-type* building paper, installing it with either staples or roofing nails. Make certain that no gaps are left and that the top section laps (by at least 8 in.) over the bottom sections. Avoid laps which end on seams in the plywood.

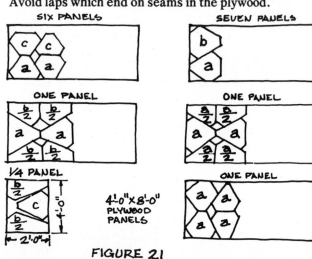

FIGURE 21

Cedar Shingle Skins

Skin designs should hopefully be of materials that are close at hand and/or are inexpensive, at the same time being waterproof and resistant to the elements. The framework is able to take the entire design load, so the skin has only to keep out the undesirable elements.

Red cedar shingles are a good solution: (a) they provide a certain degree of insulation as a result of their cell structure; (b) they are durable because of their resistance to rot; (c) they add strength to the structure and are not too difficult to install, if you follow directions.

Shingles are sold in *bundles,* four bundles making a square. A square covers approximately 100 sq. ft.. Red cedar shingles come in three lengths (16, 18, and 24 in.) and three grades (1, 2, and 3).

Exposure is the amount of shingle that is exposed to the weather. It's really important to have the right exposure or you're chancing leakage problems. The amount of exposure required is determined by the *pitch* of a roof, the pitch being the slope of a given surface. Shingles should never be less than three layers thick on a roof, and the exposure should never exceed 1/3 the length of the shingle (see table 3) for recommended exposures.

TABLE 3

Pitch	Shingle Length (in.)	Exposure (in.)
5" in 12" or steeper	16 18 24	5 5.5 7.5
Greater than 3" in 12" and less than 5" in 12"	16 18 24	3.75 4.25 5.75
Less than 3" in 12"	Cedar shingles are not recommended	
Vertical surface 60°	Exposure should not be greater than half the shingle minus one-half inch (single course). Double course up to ¾ exposure.	

Shingles provide a nice, warm, watertight surface, if you take the time and effort to use them correctly. Before use, keep them covered, if not inside. They should never be laid when they are wet. A table (table 4) of exposure and coverage for the dome has been compiled, so that you can make the best use of a given situation. The table is for use with the 16-ft. two frequency dodecahedron *only.* The 16-in. No. 3 grade shingle is the best shingle for covering this dome in terms of cost, as well as in terms of covering a curved surface. The shorter length means that there will be smaller gaps under the butts of the shingles, as a result of the angles created on the curved surface.

TABLE 4

Surface Segment	Area (sq. ft.)	Grade	Length	Exposure (in.)	Coverage (sq. ft.)	Quantity Shingles (squares)
(a)	285	No. 1	16 18 24	7 8 11	140 145.5 146.5	1.32 1.27 1.26
		No. 2	16 18 24	7 8 11	140 145.5 146.5	1.32 1.27 1.26
		No. 3	16 18 24	6 6 10	120 109 133	1.54 1.85 1.39
(b)	85	No. 1, 2 or 3	16 18 24	5 5.5 7.5	100 90.5 100	.85 .94 .85
(c)	87	No. 1, 2 or 3	16 18 24	3.75 4.25 5.75	75 77 77.8	1.16 1.13 1.12

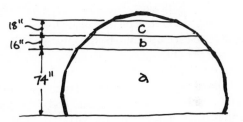

(a) treat the first 74 in., from the base to the top of the doorway, as wall, because the angle is 60° or greater.
(b) treat the next 16 in. as roof with 5 in 12 slope or greater.
(c) treat the following 18 in. as roof with less than 5 in 12 pitch.

Note: we suggest that 5d hot-dip galvanized nails be used for the entire dome to ensure adequate nail holding for the shingles.

Before starting to shingle make sure that you've got *breather-type* building paper over the plywood sheathing. The bottom shingle layer should be *double* (fig. 22). Shingle from the bottom up. If you're unsure about the methods, ask any old timers in the area, because they've likely covered many a roof in their time. It's helpful to use a board tacked to the surface or a chalked line as a straight-edge to line up shingles.

FIGURE 22

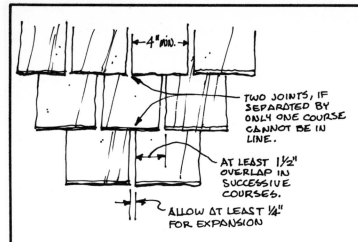

FIGURE 23

If there is a flat grain in the shingle, it is advisable to place it so that the bark side (side nearest the bark) is exposed. The shingle will then be less likely to become waterlogged or to turn up at the butt. Only two nails should be used per shingle.

These are nailed no more than 3/4 in. from the edges, and above the butt line of the next course (row) they should be nailed no more than 2 in. (1-1/2 in. preferably) and no less than 3/4 in. (fig. 24).

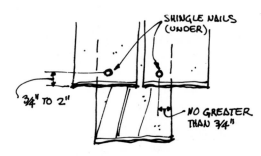

FIGURE 24

Nails should be driven flush with the surface of the shingle, but should not crush the wood (fig. 25).

FIGURE 25

A study done on old shingled farm structures (in the central U.S.) found that:
(a) exposures greater than 5.5 in. contributed greatly to the number of leaks, so be conservative on your exposures.
(b) edge grain shingles significantly reduced the percentage of roofs with warped and loose shingles.
(c) more leaks occured with 16-in. shingles as opposed to 18-in. shingles.
(d) 6 in. to 8 in. in width appears to be the best, as shingles wider than 8 in. showed more warpage, breakage, and a slight increase in leaks.

Handsplit Cedar Shakes

Handsplit shakes can be made as well as installed by you do-it-yourselfers. All that is needed is a saw to cut the logs the proper length, a heavy steel blade called a "froe," and a wooden mallet of some sort. The complete process is explained on page 21.

Shakes look great and have the same good qualities as shingles; they keep the weather outside where it's supposed to be. Overlapping shakes seems to be the best way of covering a curved surface such as the Personal Dome. Table 5 shows the most optimal usage possibilities for this 16-ft. diameter dome *only*.

TABLE 5						
Surface Segment	Area (sq. ft.)	Grade (in.)	Length	Exposure (in.)	Coverage (sq. ft.)	Quantity Shakes (squares)
(a)	285	m	18	7.5	80	3.6
		n	24	10	100	2.9
(b) (c)	172	m	18	5	55	3.1
		n	24	7	70	2.5

Note: 6d nails should be adequate.

m = 18" handsplit and resawn
n = 24" handsplit and resawn

The 18-in. shake is the best of the commercial shakes for this dome, because the shorter length will provide for smaller gaps at the butts on the curved surface. Commercial shakes come in three lengths: 18 in., 24 in., and 32 in. Table 6 indicates the correct exposures as recommended by the Red Cedar Shingle and Handsplit Shake Bureau.

TABLE 6			
For roofs	Maximum Exposure (in.)	For walls Max. Exposure	Best 3-ply Roof (in.)
18" shakes	8.5	8.5	5.5
24" shakes	10	11.5	7.5
32" shakes	13	15	10

Other possibilities for the skin are asphalt shingles, wire mesh and stucco, or perhaps ferro-cement. With the ferro-cement, it might even be possible to omit plywood sheathing.

Ventilation

Ventilation can be very nicely obtained by means other than installing opening windows. This is one advantage with domes, in that one can regulate the flow of air to a fine tolerance, unlike conventional dwellings. However, this is not a pure science, and one cannot provide a universal solution to ventilation problems.

You must provide means for fresh air to enter the dwelling and for used air to leave the dwelling. We may be way off base on this concept, but it appears good theory to us. Cut five vent slots about 6 in. x 18 in. in the floor, equally spaced around the perimeter. Make the slot openings adjustable by installing a sliding cover operating on a simple wooden track. These floor vents are for air intake. To provide for exhaust, or through ventilation, erect a cupola on top of the dome, beginning from the hubs surrounding the centre pentagonal hub. Do not remove any struts, or the dome will be substantially weakened. Install five vents of equal area to those in the floor. The top of the cupola may be shingled, or domed with clear plastic or glass and used for penta-star gazing. Whatever you do, be liberal with the caulking compound. The cupola also serves to shed rain which might work under rooftop shingles lying almost parallel to the ground, thus inviting sister rain to enter. Screen all vents, both

intake and exhaust. We hope that necessity will enable you to arrive at simpler solutions than those we have come up with.

Heating and Insulation

Any kind of wood burning stove is OK for heating. You can insulate between the struts with fibreglass batting, which comes equipped with aluminum foil pasted to one side. Cut the insulation, which comes in 24-in. rolls, into triangles which are slightly larger than the dome triangles. Then, when you push the cut insulation into the openings between struts (with the aluminum side towards the inside of the dome), friction will hold the insulation in place.

Two inches of fibreglass will suit the requirements for heating insulation in areas where up to 8,000 degree-days* are encountered. For up to 12,000 degree-days, 3 in. of fibreglass is required.

When installing the chimney for the stove, remember that the chimney pipe can get red hot. If you don't insulate the pipe from the dome structure, you stand a good chance of having your hard-earned labours go up in smoke. Any hardware store should have the insulating "thimble" and roof flashing which is required to afford protection and assure a watertight seal around the pipe.

To avoid downdrafts, the chimney pipe should extend 3 ft. above the roof surface or structure within a horizontal distance of 10 ft. from the chimney. This means that you should make the chimney so that it extends 2 ft. above the highest point of the dome, which includes the cupola, should you have one.

Lining the Inside of the Dome

Gyprock (drywall) 3/8 in. thick is cheap and easy to work with. It is also fire resistant. Natural material can be used as well: cedar planks, burlap, used weathered planks, driftwood, woven reeds, and bulrushes. Just keep the combustible areas away from the stove by at least 4 ft.

*Each degree that the mean daily temperature is below 65° F. is a degree day.

NOTE: TO PROTECT VENTS FROM WEATHER, CONSTRUCT AT LEAST A 6" OVERHANG; DON'T FORGET THE FLASHING AROUND THE PERIMETER WHERE CUPOLA JOINS THE DOMS.

SHINGLED CUPOLA

AIR EXHAUST VENTS

SHINGLES

VENT

6" OVERHANG

FLASHING

SHINGLES

SHEATHING

FIGURE 26

TABLE 7 MATERIALS LIST		
Material	Type	Quantity
2" x 4" fir, spruce, or cedar	economy grade or better	550 lineal feet
4' x 8' x ¼" exterior plywood	waterproof sheathing grade	2 panels
2" x 4" or 2" x 6" fir for T-beams	no. 3 grade	20 pcs., 7'10" to 8' and 50' random length
4' x 8' x ⅜" exterior plywood	waterproof sheathing grade	18 panels
2" x 4" fir or cedar	economy grade or better	100 lineal feet in random lengths
6" diameter cedar		11 posts
¼" diameter doweling	fir or hardwood	40 lineal feet
roofing paper	asphalt impregnated breather-type	5 - 100' rolls
shingles	refer to tables as required	
insulation		

Splitting Shakes

The varieties of timber adapted to making shakes are few. The wood should split easily and true; when exposed to the weather on the building, it should not warp from its place or "curl" up. The durability of the timber is a secondary consideration—shakes wear out more than they rot—and the varieties which would be least subject to these changes might not, for good reasons, be at all suitable for roofing purposes. Pine is doubtless the best, but hemlock, cedar, and chestnut are excellent. The trees should not have passed their prime when cut, but should be vigorous in growth and sound at the heart, so that the wood will not be "brash."

The first work to be done when we commence shake making is to get out the bolts. Saw the trunk of the tree with a cross-cut saw into sections, each one of the length you intend to make the shingles. Sixteen inches is sufficient length for any easy splitting wood, and if it be tough or "brashy," twelve will do. The shorter the shingles, the less space you can lay to the weather, and the more time and nails it will take to make them into a roof. These sections of the trunk may then be set on end and split into bolts.

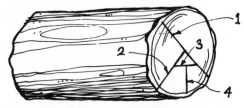

The numbered lines in the drawing show the place and order in which the section should be split. Line 1 divides it through the centre; line 2 quarters it; line 3 takes off the heart block; and line 4 finishes the shingle bolts. If the tree is large, however, so that these bolts are wider than it is practicable to make the shakes, they can be further subdivided. The splitting may be done rapidly with the axe and a light maul, drawing the axe first carefully along the longest lines, and tapping it lightly with the maul, until the block is "checked," when a blow or two on the axe placed in the centre will open it as desired. The bark should next be removed from the bolts, and they should be piled under cover so that the sun and wind will not "season check" them.

Having the bolts in the shop, next proceed to split them into rough shakes with the mallet and froe.

Splitting the Bolts

The figure shows the proper way of splitting a bolt. First, split it at line A; this should take off a piece thick enough for four shingles. Next divide this piece through the centre, as shown by line B; the pieces are then wide enough for two shakes. These are split through the middle, which finishes them. If you undertake to split off each shake separately from the side of the bolt, you will almost invariably "run out," and the timber be wasted.

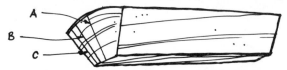

A large-sized shaving-knife and a shaving horse or bench are necessary to shave and complete the shakes.

The froe is formed of a heavy steel blade, eight or ten inches long and two wide, having a dull edge; the handle is a foot long, and projects from one end of the blade at right angles to it. When the blade is driven into the bolt and partially splits it, the handle can be forced over to one side with the hand or by a blow from the mallet, and the leverage force thus exerted splits off the shake. In this operation, skill and practice in the art come most into use. If the check or split runs out, the shake will be too short, and therefore worthless, and the timber wasted. The operator must change his block, end for end, as circumstances require, and work carefully. Three-eighths of an inch is the proper thickness for the shakes.

Shaving Bench and Knife

Shave the butt-end of the shake first; this will require but a stroke or two, since it is already of the desired thickness if properly split. Next, edge the shake on the right or left hand side, as most convenient, taking off, when you meet it, all of the sap wood. Change ends of the shake, shave both sides, thinning it gradually from the butt-end to the top, straighten the other edge, and it is finished. A smart workman will split out and shave one thousand in a day.

The shakes should be packed away in tiers, lapping them as in the common bunches which you see for sale, and a plank put on the top of the pile and weighted down, so as to keep them in proper shape until seasoned.

Pit Privies

by Vic Marks

Pit privies have proved themselves useful for quite a few centuries and, having changed little in such a long time, still have a lot to offer us hardy souls who find them preferable to the septic tank. There are two types of pit privies: those that don't recycle the wastes and those that do. The types that don't recycle the wastes are the most common, but not necessarily the best.

A Healthy Privy

There is no rule which you can apply to determine how far the privy must be from your water source. The privy should be located downhill from any wells or streams. This lessens the possibility of bacterial pollution to your drinking water. A level place is acceptable and, if you *must* put it uphill from the water source, place it at least 100 ft. from the well or stream. Fifty feet is the minimum distance under favourable conditions.

Another factor to be aware of is the depth of your well. In homogeneous soil (uniformly structured), your chance of ground-water pollution is virtually nil if the bottom of the pit is 5 ft. above the ground-water table. But be careful in areas containing fissured rocks or limestone formations, since pollution may be carried directly through solution channels and without natural filtration to distant wells or other sources of drinking-water supplies.

The Pit

The pit acts as both a storehouse and isolation chamber for all germs connected with human wastes.

The standard privy should last anywhere from 4 to 15 years (see table below) without being filled up, depending on how deep the pit is and how many people are using it. A decomposition process takes place in the pit which decreases the volume of wastes deposited by about 50 per cent. It's been found that each person leaves a legacy of about 3 cu. ft. of excreta each year.

PIT VOLUME AND DEPTH* FOR A PRIVY WITH AN AREA OF 9 SQUARE FEET TO BE USED BY 5 PEOPLE		
Service Life	Depth (ft.)	Volume (cu. ft.)
4 Years	6.7	60
8 years	13.3	120

*Depth given is effective pit depth, and 1 to 2 feet are usually added to obtain overall depth of pit.

Privy Size

A 3-ft.-sq. pit is the normal size, although there is no standardized pit size. If you're in an area where the pit might cave in, *line it*. Even in solid soil it's a good idea to line the top two feet of the pit to prevent caving in from the weight of the floor and superstructure. Try to use whatever natural materials are around for this purpose (integrate the outhouse into the environment); stone, roughhewn logs, home-made bricks, lumber, or concrete blocks. Try to find some recycled material to suit the purpose.

The Base

The base serves as a solid foundation upon which the floor can rest. It helps to prevent the exit of hookworm larvae and other crawlies which snap at your arse. Properly made, of hard durable material, it also helps to prevent the entrance of burrowing rodents and of surface water into the pit. The foundation should be at least 4 in. wide on top in order to provide a stable contact with the ground. If it's located where there's a possibility of flooding, the base should be at least 6 in. high. (A mound of dirt approximately 2 ft. high should also encircle the privy.) The base can be made of plain or reinforced precast cement (see illustrations), soil cement (5 to 6 per cent mixed with sandy clay soil), clay bricks, stone masonry, or rough-cut logs (preferably hardwood).

A Hewn Log Privy Base

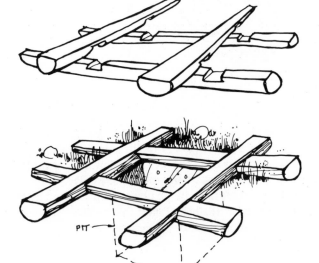

Build a wooden form in which you can pour a concrete ring sill that is 4 in. thick, with outside dimensions of 4 ft. 4 in. x 4 ft. 4 in., and with a hole in its centre measuring 3 ft. x 3 ft. Pour the ring sill.

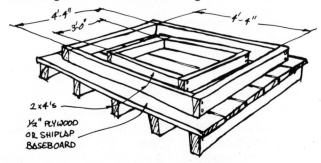

· WOODEN FORM FOR RING SILL ·

Next, build another form in which to pour a slab of concrete 3 ft. 8 in. square (2-1/2 to 3 in. thick), having a hole in its centre to suit your own design. A wooden riser box with cover will have to be constructed and mounted on the slab later.

All concrete should be suitably reinforced with steel rods, and with eye and anchor bolts embedded in the sill and slab.

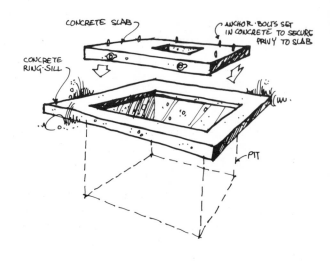

The Floor

The floor should fit tightly to the base, with a minimum of small cracks and openings between base and floor. Concrete is preferable, but wood is OK if you fit the boards tightly together or use the type with a tongue and groove.

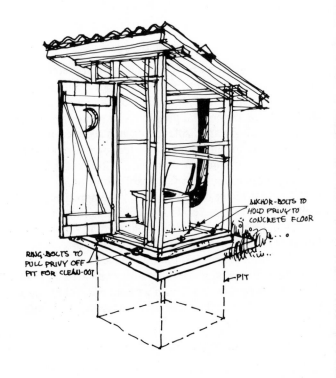

The House

The house should fit the dimensions of the floor or slab. You should keep in mind the fact that when the pit fills, you're going to have to move the house (or construct another house, which is somewhat of a waste). So try to make it strong and flexible enough to be moved; this is especially important if you have a compost privy.

It's a good idea to make openings 4 to 6 in. wide at the top of the walls to allow proper ventilation.

It's always nice to have lots of light in the outhouse, but you should always provide enough shade over an uncovered seat or hole in order not to attract flies.

A good habit to get into, if you have a wood burning stove, is to add some ashes occasionally to keep the smells down. If you're bothered by mosquitoes breeding in the pit, pour a cup of kerosene down the hole once a week.

The provision of a pit or seat vent is a good idea. There is sometimes quite a difference in temperature between the air in the pit and the outside air. This temperature difference causes condensation on the under side of the seat cover. It's also believed that a vent induces a draught of air which helps to keep the pit materials dry and small in bulk.

The Compost Privy

The use of human wastes as a compost material has been practiced in China for centuries. There is no reason why it can't be done in North America.

The composting is extremely important. Never use excrement raw for fertilization. The high temperature created by decomposition is necessary to destroy bacteria and worm eggs.

The privy pit, slab, location, and other features need be no different from those previously described. However, the compost privy should be provided with the largest possible capacity so that it will not fill too fast. For this reason, you might want to enlarge the pit. Do this by doubling the length of the pit, therefore having part of the vault outside the house, but covered with a tight-fitting and durable cover.

The composting method is based on anaerobic decomposition of organic wastes, which are left undisturbed during a period of at least six months to ensure destruction of pathogen and ova of helminths. The best procedure is:

(1) Dig a pit, making sure that the bottom of it is above ground-water level: don't take chances of polluting drinking water.

(2) Before the slab is put in place, cover the bottom 20 in. of the pit with grass cuttings, fine leaves, garbage, paper, etc.; but don't allow rubbish such as metal cans, glass bottles, or other non-organic matter.

(3) Place the slab, and build the house, keeping in mind that they will both be moved periodically to other sites.

(4) In addition to depositing human wastes, throw the daily organic garbage into the pit, along with cow, horse sheep, chicken, or pig manure, as well as urine-soaked earth or straw. The latter materials are important, as urine is rich in nitrogen, an essential plant nutrient.

(5) About once a week, throw about five pounds of grass

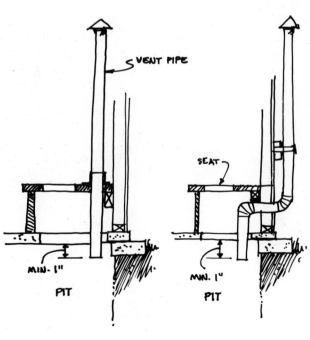

• VENTING PIT PRIVY •

clippings and fine-textured leaves into the pit. If you don't have grass clippings but have access to seaweed, use it instead. It will require a bit of experimentation to get the optimal fertilizer, so use whatever materials are available. Refer to Rodale's *Encyclopedia of Organic Gardening or Composting* for composting mixtures.

(6) When the pit's contents reach a level of 20 in. below ground, dig a new pit 5 to 6 ft. away (more if desired), and move the house and slab over it. Level the first pit with 6 in. of grass clippings and leaves, and the top 14 in. with well-tamped earth.

(7) When the second pit is filled in the same manner, uncover the first pit and remove the compost. It should be stable, and will provide a good fertilizer which can be applied immediately to the fields or stored.

The size of the pit depends on your needs for fertilizer and the number of people using the privy. The proportion of excrement that can be added to refuse for satisfactory composting *should* be about one to five by volume. From the table (p. 22) it can be seen that a family of five will produce 60 cu. ft. of partly digested excrement in four years. Therefore, 1/5 of a pit of 60 cu. ft. capacity would be filled in approximately 9 to 10 months, which is a good cycle for a compost privy.

Rather than build two pits and move the structure back and forth, you might want to build a double privy or double "vault" privy. This consists of a large vault divided into two compartments, each of which is topped by a slab and a hole. The house is likewise partitioned into two houses with separate entrances. In practice, the vaults are filled and emptied alternately in the same manner as previously described. But people, being what they are, tend to use both privies, so if you're going to use this method get a padlock for the one not in use.

Bibliography

Excreta Disposal for Rural Areas and Small Communities,
E.G. Wagner and J.N. Lanoix
World Health Organization
United Nations
New York, N.Y.

Village Technology Handbook
VITA
College Campus
Schenectady, N.Y.

The Mother Earth News
TMEN Inc.
P.O. Box 38
Madison, Ohio

Little Extras that Make Privies more Pleasurable

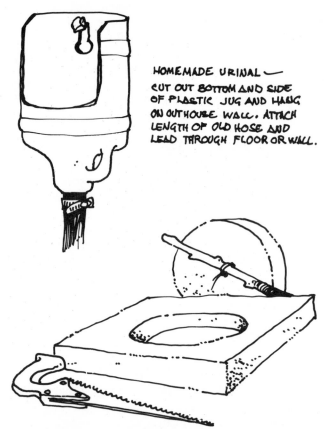

HOMEMADE URINAL — CUT OUT BOTTOM AND SIDE OF PLASTIC JUG AND HANG ON OUTHOUSE WALL. ATTACH LENGTH OF OLD HOSE AND LEAD THROUGH FLOOR OR WALL.

WARM SEAT — ON THOSE COLD, WINTRY DAYS (OR WORSE, NIGHTS) A SECTION OF STYROFOAM WITH A HOLE CUT IN THE CENTRE WILL WARM UP WHEN YOU SIT ON IT! CUT THE HOLE WITH A KEYHOLE SAW OR HACKSAW BLADE AND YOU CAN USE THE CENTRE PIECE FOR A LID.

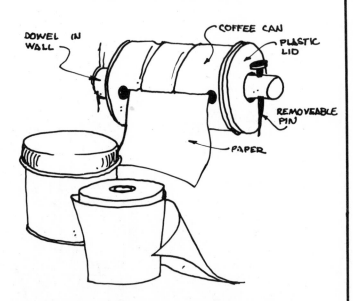

DOWEL IN WALL

COFFEE CAN

PLASTIC LID

REMOVEABLE PIN

PAPER

TOILET-PAPER CONTAINERS — TOBACCO TINS OR COFFEE CANS MAKE GOOD PROTECTION AGAINST DAMP OR ANIMALS.

How to Store Your Fruits & Vegetables

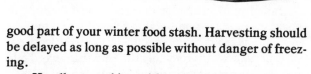

by Vic Marks

A lot of people, both country and city folk, are growing their own vegetables and fruits. With each passing season, the composted and mulched gardens are producing more abundant crops and, as the crops increase, so does the desire to eat healthy organically-grown produce all year round. A storage cellar of some sort is a vital necessity to anybody who lacks either the climate or a greenhouse to ensure fresh vegetables at all times of the year, and wishes to enjoy home-grown produce during those long wintry months.*

Vegetable Classes

Vegetables fall into three classes or groups, determined by their perishableness:

(1) The *quickly perishable:* green peas, green limas, corn, asparagus; green vegetables such as spinach, chard, and lettuce.

(2) The *perishables:* broccoli, cauliflower, late cabbage, and onions.

(3) The *keepers:* potatoes, turnips, beets, carrots, and similar root crops; as well as pumpkins, late squash, and celery.

These classes aren't sharply divided, so look at table 1 to find the approximate lifespan of each.

Store only sound vegetables of good quality. Can or eat in the fall any that don't look too healthy. If they rot in the shelter and you don't happen to notice, you'll lose a

* The cellars, pits, and outbuildings described in this article are practical only where the outside temperatures during winter average 30 F. or below.

good part of your winter food stash. Harvesting should be delayed as long as possible without danger of freezing.

Handle everything with care to avoid cuts and bruises, especially if you wash the vegetables. Let excess water evaporate before storing.

Successful Fruit Storage

How well your fruits are going to keep in storage depends on:

(1) The quality of the produce. The fruits should be without decay, disease, insects, and bruises caused by handling. One bad (i.e., rotten or bruised) apple can destroy the lot.

(2) Storing the right varieties. Ones that mature late are the best.

(3) Harvesting at proper time (refer to preparation section).

(4) Keeping the right temperature and humidity in the storage room (refer to storage conditions section).

(5) The temperature and humidity of the storage space.

Placing fruits and vegetables in storage, before cold weather starts in the fall, is a frequent cause of early spoilage. One of the most difficult steps in sorting your produce is to keep it in prime condition from the time of maturity until the night temperature is low enough to cool the storage area. If *possible,* store fruits in a different storage space from the vegetables, because odours and undesirable flavours can be picked up from the strong-smelling ones such as potatoes, turnips, and cabbage.

Proper Storage Temperatures and Humidity

The humidity and temperature requirements of produce vary greatly, some requiring warm dry conditions (sweet potatoes, tomatoes) and others cold moist conditions (cabbage, apples, root crops). Refer to table 1 to determine the best conditions.

Without proper moisture (humidity), stored vegetables and fruits shrivel, lose quality, and eventually become too god awful to eat. Two common methods used to maintain the proper humidity are:
(1) The use of water to raise the humidity of the storage air.
(2) The use of ventilated polyethylene or cellophane bags and box liners.
The first method is accomplished by frequently sprinkling the floor with water, or by placing large pans of water under fresh-air intake vents (not as effective), or by covering the floor with wet materials such as straw, sawdust, or a combination of these. However, these methods won't stop the root crops from shriveling up on you. The best way to stop root crops from shriveling is to put them in polyethylene bags or box liners, *but* polyethylene is virtually indestructible, non-biodegradable, and possibly passes cancer along in foods that are stored in them for long periods of time. Use cellophane bags instead. Cut a few 1/2 to 3/8 inch holes in the sides of the bags, stuff them full of produce, tie the tops (don't seal them), and prepare yourself for some mighty fine winter eating.

As far as temperature is concerned, get at least two good thermometers (preferably the kind that record minimum and maximum temperatures), placing one in the coldest spot in your storage room and the other outdoors.

You'll probably find that it's necessary to daily regulate the temperature by opening or closing the ventilators. If temperatures consistently drop below 0°F., you may have to install a small heater of some sort. If you have electricity, a small 600-watt heater with a thermostat will suffice.

Plant late all that will be stored. This way you'll be able to solve the problem of how to keep the produce from rotting before the weather gets cool enough to keep the storage room cold. See that the vegetables and fruits are as cool as possible when you put them in storage. Harvest early in the morning, or let the crops cool outdoors overnight before storing them—and don't bother waxing anything, because it just doesn't help.

Dried beans and peas (including lima and soy beans) can easily be stored, as long as you make a few preparatory steps. First, dry the beans in one of two ways:
(1) Pick the pods as soon as they mature and spread them in a warm dry place until they are thoroughly dry, or
(2) Pull and dry the bean plants like hay, after most of the pods are ripe.

After drying the beans, shell them, and either refrigerate them at 0°F. or below for three or four days, or heat them in an oven at 135°F. for 30 to 60 minutes, in order to protect them from destruction by moths or weevils.

Head lettuce, leeks, and *endive* can be footed in dirt in the storage cellar, watered occasionally, and sometimes kept until Christmas or later. Root crops such as cauliflower and brussel sprouts can be handled in the same fashion.

Root crops such as carrots, turnips, beets, parsnips, chard, rutabagas, etc. shouldn't be harvested until late fall (November). Leave them in the ground as long as possible, as light frosts won't hurt them. Dig your root crops when the ground is dry, and cut the tops off about an inch above the root. Don't wash them. You'll find that root crops will keep fresher when bedded in layers of moist sand, peat, or sphagnum moss, or packed in boxes (or cans) surrounded by straw. Cellophane or polyethylene bags can also be used.

Kohlrabi can be stored after removal of leaves and roots. An area of high moisture (95 per cent humidity) and low temperature (32° to 34°F.) is best.

Parsnips, salsify, Jerusalem artichokes, and often *carrots* can be left in the ground throughout the winter. To make digging easier, cover the rows with about one foot of leaves or straw before the ground has frozen.

Onions must be cured. Leave them (after pulling) on the ground for at least two to three days, then place them in crates in an open shed (or somewhere similar) for several weeks to complete curing. Remove the tops and store them in bins or stringbags in a dry, well-ventilated place, such as an attic or unheated room. Light freezing won't hurt onions, as long as you don't handle them while they are frozen.

Late potatoes are much easier to store than early varieties, mainly because you can leave them in the ground until the cool temperatures are around. For several months after harvesting they can be held in almost any storage location, as this is their normal resting period, but they *must* be stored in the dark. After this period, temperatures between 34° and 41°F. are necessary to prevent sprouting, so as soon as temperatures permit, put them in the storage area. If you find the potatoes are a little sweet tasting after a couple of months of storage (low temperatures turn starch into sugar), let them sit in your kitchen cupboard (or some equally warm place) for a week before you use them. *Never* store potatoes with apples, as flavours will mix.

Sweet potatoes should be free from injury, and need to be cured (see early potatoes) before final storage. Lots of air circulation and high temperatures over a period of 10 days to 3 weeks are necessary. After curing, sweet potatoes should be placed in a warm (50° to 60°F.) room.

Early potatoes are usually harvested when temperatures are high, so you have to take precautions if you want them to keep. After harvesting (early morning is best), cure the potatoes by storing them in moist air for 10 days to 3 weeks where the temperature is between 60° to 75°F. Lots of air circulation is important. The curing eliminates excess water and heals skinned areas and cracks. This helps to prevent decay, but isn't altogether

TABLE 1
FRUIT AND VEGETABLE STORAGE

Commodity	Freezing point	Place to Store	Storage Conditions Temperature	Humidity	Length of storage period
	°F.		°F.		
Vegetables:					
Dry beans and peas	---	Any cool, dry place	32° to 40°	Dry	As long as desired
Late cabbage	30.4	Pit, trench, or outdoor cellar	Near 32° as possible	Moderately moist	Through late fall and winter
Cauliflower	30.3	Storage cellar	" "	" "	6 to 8 weeks
Late celery	31.6	Pit or trench; roots in soil in storage cellar.	" "	" "	Through late fall and winter
Endive	31.9	Roots in soil in storage cellar	" "	" "	2 to 3 months
Onions	30.6	Any cool, dry place	" "	Dry	Through fall and winter
Parsnips	30.4	Where they grew, or in storage cellar.	" "	Moist	" , " , "
Peppers	30.7	Unheated basement or room	45° to 50°	Moderately moist	2 to 3 weeks
Potatoes	30.9	Pit or in storage cellar	35° to 40°	"	Through fall and winter,
Pumpkins and squashes	30.5	Home cellar or basement	55°	Moderately dry	" "
Root crops (miscellaneous)	---	Pit or in storage cellar	Near 32° as possible	Moist	" "
Sweet potatoes	29.7	Home cellar or basement	55° to 60°	Moderately dry	" "
Tomatoes (mature green)	31.0	" " "	55° to 70°	"	4 to 6 weeks
Fruits:					
Apples	29.0	Fruit storage cellar	Near 32° as possible	Moderately moist	Through fall and winter
Grapefruit	29.8	" "	" "	"	4 to 6 weeks
Grapes	28.1	" "	" "	"	1 to 2 months
Oranges	30.5	" "	" "	"	4 to 6 weeks
Pears	29.2	" "	" "	"	2 to 5 months

necessary for early potatoes. Decay is not likely to be a problem if you store them at 70° to 75°F. . If your summers are mild, just bank (or ridge) some soil around the potato plants in the late summer, thus protecting them from light (turns them green and inedible) and providing for drainage till you dig them in the fall—but don't leave potatoes undug if your region gets high temperatures and heavy rainfall.

Celery is best maintained by pulling the crop. Leave the tops dry: do not wash them. The roots should be placed in slightly moist sand or soil. To avoid odour contamination, do not store with cabbage or turnips.

Another method of storing celery is to dig a trench 10 to 12 inches wide, about 24 inches deep, and any desired length. Dig the plants when they are fully grown, taking a clump of soil with the roots. Then pack the plants in the trench, watering them as you do so, and leave the trench open long enough for the plant tops to dry off. You won't have to water them again, unless the soil is very dry at the time of storing or extended warm weather follows it. Make a sloping roof for the trench by setting a 12-inch board on edge beside the trench; bank soil against the board and then put boards, poles, corn-stalks (which have had the tops removed) across the trench, with one end resting on the upright board and the other end on the ground. Spread a light covering of straw or other material that will pack closely over the roof. As the weather becomes colder, add more covering.

· FIGURE 1 ·

You can also store celery in a hotbed. First remove surplus soil from the hotbed and substitute a covering of boards for the sash. Then pack the celery in the hotbed in the same way you would pack them in a trench.

Yet another method of celery storage is to bank a few inches of soil around the base of the plants in the garden at the end of the growing season. Build the bank up to the top of the plants before severe freezing occurs and, as weather becomes colder, cover the banking with straw or corn fodder held in place with boards.

Cabbage and *Chinese cabbage* may be stored in outdoor storage cellars, in cone-shaped pits, or in long pits (fig. 2). Pits seem preferable, because of odour contamination to other produce from cabbage. The advantage of long pits over cone-shaped pits is that you can remove a few heads of cabbage from a long pit without disturbing the rest of the pit. To store cabbages in a long pit, pull the plants out by the roots, place them head down in the pit, and cover them with soil.

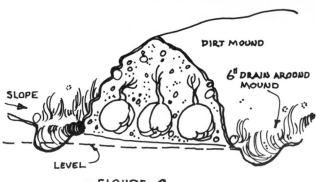

· FIGURE 2 ·

You can also store cabbage as illustrated in figure 3. Pull the plants out by the roots and set them side by side with their roots in the trench. Pack soil around the roots and then build a frame about two feet high around the trench. The frame may be made of boards, poles, or stakes driven in the ground. Next, bank soil around the frame. Finally, place poles across the tip of the frame to hold a covering of straw, hay, or corn fodder.

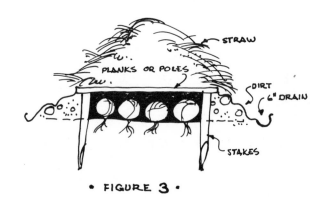

· FIGURE 3 ·

For cellar storage, first remove the outer loose leaves. Remove the roots and stem, and wrap the cabbages. Put them in boxes and bins and place them in your storage cellar.

Many people store root crops right in the ground where they grew. To do this, mulch the roots in early fall to prevent alternate freezing and thawing. When the weather is always cold, pull back the mulch and allow the roots to become thoroughly frozen. Then mulch them heavily. The roots are dug as needed. This is especially handy in light snow districts.

Root crops keep best between 32° and 40°F. Continued storage above 40°F. causes them to sprout new tops and to become woody. Watch out for turnips and rutabagas, as they give off odours; the best place for them is an outdoor cellar or pit. A cone-shaped pit (fig. 4) is a good place for root crops but only in areas where they are protected from freezing.

Pumpkins and *squashes* should be harvested before frost and left with a small piece of stem on them when they are cut from the plants. If possible, cure them for 10 days at 80° to 85°F., and if these temperatures are impossible to maintain, just leave them beside your furnace for at least two weeks. Curing will harden the rinds and heal surface cuts, but won't help bruised areas and pickleworm injuries. Don't store pumpkins or squashes below 50°F. (except for acorn squashes, which shouldn't be cured and are best stored between 45° to 50°F.).

Tomatoes should be picked from healthy vines late in the fall, which means planting in the spring. Harvest tomatoes before the first frost (when the temperatures start to range between 32° and 50°F.) or if the frost gets them first, pick the ones not damaged by freezing. After picking and stemming the tomatoes, wash and dry them before storing. Wiping them isn't a good idea, as it causes scarring which leads to decay. Store tomatoes that show red separately from green tomatoes, as this will reduce bruising and separate the tomatoes that will be used first. Pack the green tomatoes one or two layers deep in shallow boxes or trays for ripening. At 55°F. mature green tomatoes will take about 25 to 28 days to ripen, and should be wrapped (use paper or cellophane) if your storage area is dry. Do not put them in an area with temperatures below 50°F. Sort the tomatoes every 7 to 10 days, separating the reds from the greens, and removing any that show decay.

With *sunflowers,* cut off the heads with a foot of stalk attached when the birds are beginning to eat ripe outer rows of seeds. Hang them in a cool, dry place to dry; the seeds in the centre rows, which are still green, will ripen. When all the seeds are ripe and dry, remove seeds by rubbing lightly. Store your seeds in dry, airtight containers.

Garlic should be stored by braiding the stems together and hanging in a shed, garage, or basement.

Apples should be picked when they are mature, but still hard. In picking, the apples should be lifted up and away from the branch so that the stem comes away with the apple. When the stem is jerked out, the centre of the apple starts to decay. If you pick them when they are still green, they are subject to scald and bitter-pit. Overmature apples will quickly ripen on you. Bruising and skin cuts not only make the fruit more subject to decay, but actually make it deteriorate faster in storage. Do not store apples that have glassy spots in the flesh. This is known as water core. Varieties that are highly subject to scald should be mixed with shredded oiled paper at the rate of one-half pound of paper per bushel, or else wrapped with oiled paper. Another method which might extend apple storage life is to dip them in a mixture of water and concentrated kelp juice.

Varieties that mature in September (i.e. Grimes Golden, Jonathan) cannot be kept long. Athan, McIntosh, Cortland, and Delicious (red and golden) last for two to five months. Stayman, Winesap, Northern Spy, York Imperial, Arkansas Black Twig, Baldwin, Ben-Davis, and Rome Beauty will store four to six months. The Winesap and Yellow frequently last from five to

*Yellow Newton, Rhode Island Greening and McIntosh are better when stored at 36° to 38°F.

eight months. You can store apples many ways, as long as you don't allow them to freeze (see table 1 for freezing points). When the days and nights are cold, apples should be stored in insulated boxes in outbuildings, in hay in a barn, in straw-lined pits, or in soil and straw-covered barrels. These methods *won't* protect apples against freezing if the temperatures are below 10°F.

Pears should be harvested when they still seem to be immature. If allowed to begin to yellow on the tree, they develop hard gritty cells in the flesh. They are best picked in the same manner as apples. Winter Nelis, Anjou, and Easter Buerre store the best (up to seven months). You'll have to allow them to ripen at room temperature after you take them out of storage.

Growing organic *grain* is a satisfying operation, but improper storage can lose all the advantages inherent in the process. The old-time farmer used to cut and bind grain in sheaves, where it stood and cured gradually in the fields before being threshed. Today's mechanized methods save time, but have certain disadvantages. When grain is harvested by combine, it is cut, hulled, and poured into 100-pound bags, but it is still "green" and must be treated with care to prevent mold. It may seem dry, but it will continue to give off moisture for over a month. Furthermore, wild garlic, ragweed, and other seeds will be included in each bag. The grain must be cleaned with a fan seed cleaner, or winnowed outdoors by throwing it up in a breeze, or dropping it past a fan to blow away chaff. Once cleaned, bags should be placed on end on slats in a dry place (not on a dirt or concrete floor), and separated by several inches to allow air circulation. The presence of a good cat will prevent mouse damage; otherwise, use a metal, screened enclosure.

After a few days, invert the bags and disturb the grain to permit air to reach all kernels. Invert again each week for about a month, after which time the grain should be cured. The most logical method for storage after curing is a metal drum in a dry place. Temperatures between 40° and 50°F. with little moisture (50 per cent humidity) seem to be the best. Small quantities can be stored in glass jars, and, if you have a freezer, you can keep wheat indefinitely.

If your grain becomes mouldy from accidental exposure to moisture, it may not be a complete loss. Just wash it in plain lukewarm water several times and dry over a hot-air furnace grate or similar source of warmth. You can tell from the smell whether it is still musty or not.

Seeds should be stored where there are fairly cool temperatures maintained, as well as low moisture (humidity).

Pit-type Methods of Storage

If you have neither the energy nor the money to build a permanent storage room, mound or pit storage is the cheapest and easiest alternative. They are mainly used to store potatoes, carrots, beets, turnips, salsify, parsnips, cabbage, and even fruits such as apples and pears. The pit may be built on the ground, or in a hole six to eight inches deep in a well-drained location. After picking a spot, cover it with a layer of straw, leaves, or other bedding material. Next, stack the vegetables or fruits on the bedding in a cone-shaped pile. Cover the produce with more bedding, and then cover the entire pile with three or four inches of soil. Firm the soil with the back of a shovel to make the pit waterproof and dig a shallow drainage ditch around and away from the pit to a lower level.

Small pits containing only a few bushels of vegetables or fruits will get sufficient ventilation if the bedding material over the vegetables extends through the soil at the top of the pile.

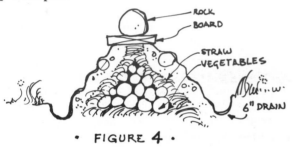

· FIGURE 4 ·

Cover the top of the pile with a board or piece of sheet metal to protect the stored produce from rain; a stone will hold the cover in place. To ventilate large pits, place two or three boards or stakes up through the centre of the pile of vegetables or fruits to form a flue. Cap the flue with two pieces of board nailed together at right angles. It's troublesome removing produce in the wintertime from these pits, and once opened, everything in the pit should be removed. A number of small pits are handier than a few larger ones. If you put a variety of vegetables in a number of small pits, it's a simple task to dig up one a week; but if you do it this way, separate the different types of vegetables with a layer of straw and *don't* put fruits and vegetables in the same pit.

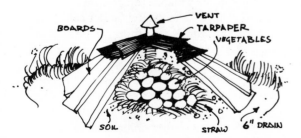

· FIGURE 5 ·

Here's another version of mound storage (fig. 5). A ventilating pipe can be included (to help stop decay), but must be capped in freezing weather. Drainage must be trenched around the mound.

Apples and cool vegetables (ones that require a storage temperatures close to 32°)may be stored in barrels sunk in the ground (fig. 5), preferably after packing in the early morning when it's cool. A pit is dug either in a well-drained level place or on a slope. It is lined with gravel or cinders for drainage and, after being put in place, lined with more gravel. The head of the barrel is covered with a burlap sack full of leaves and weighted down with boards and stones.

An open pit with hardware cloth screening and wooden lid works in a well-drained location. Store the root crops in sand until the pit is full. Cover with baled hay and a plastic cover.

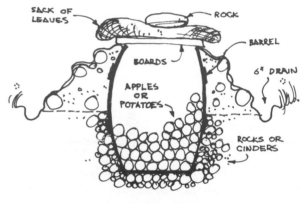

· FIGURE 6 ·

Hay bale storage can be done on top of the ground, which will be suitable for most crops. Make a rectangle of hay bales, with the centre partially hay-filled, and final bales for a lid. A stone can be placed under the top bales for ventilation, then removed when freezing weather prevails.

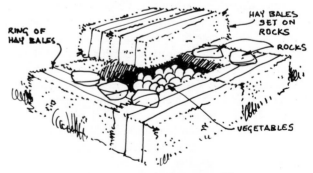

· FIGURE 7 ·

Large (18″ x 30″, or 24″ x 24″) tiles can be placed in a pit on well drained soil. Positioning should be near the kitchen and shaded from sun. As many as three to four baskets, boxes or other containers can be held in each pit. A simpler version of the tile pit consists of a 20-gallon garbage pail inserted into a hole. Produce can be placed directly into the pail, but there is some danger of rusting after several years of usage.

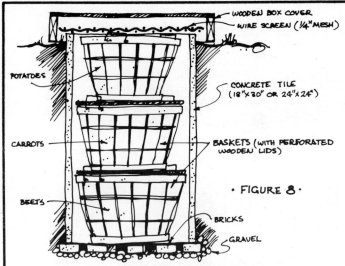

WOODEN BOX COVER
WIRE SCREEN (1/4" MESH)
POTATOES
CONCRETE TILE (18"×30" OR 24"×24")
CARROTS
BASKETS (WITH PERFORATED WOODEN LIDS)
BEETS
BRICKS
GRAVEL

• FIGURE 8 •

A box pit is another version which permits removal of small units at a time. Fruits or vegetables are stored in small boxes or baskets (one to two weeks' supply to a box). Remove them as you need them.

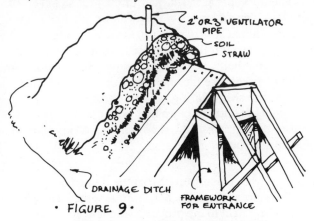

2" OR 3" VENTILATOR PIPE
SOIL
STRAW
DRAINAGE DITCH
FRAMEWORK FOR ENTRANCE

• FIGURE 9 •

Permanent Outside Storage

When you want something big, and permanent, you may as well build an outside storage shelter — in a bank, between two closely adjacent rises of ground, beside the foundation of an already erected building, or as a separate cellar.

If you have a farm which has a barn on it, here's a design which you might want to use or adapt for your own personal situation. This cellar was built next to the barn wall, beneath the barn approach (fig. 10). A section of the approach measuring 12 feet by 54 feet was removed and the earth wall was straightened in preparation for placing the forms to hold concrete.

Rough used lumber was utilized to build the forms, and cut lengths of 6-inch saplings (small logs) were used as supporting timbers. The earth wall on the north side and the stone wall of the barn (south side) eliminated several forms. After the concrete set overnight the forms were removed and used to support the roof slab. Thus the amount of form material was cut down. The walls and footings were poured of a lean mixture (cement one part; bank-run gravel, six). The roof slab was made of a one to three mixture. Some used brick and stones were thrown in with the concrete. A thin layer of heated road tar was brushed on the finished roof slab as waterproofing. This was reinforced with construction steel, since truck loads of five tons or more were passing over the barn approach. Plans of reinforcement can be obtained from construction steel manufacturers or their outlets.

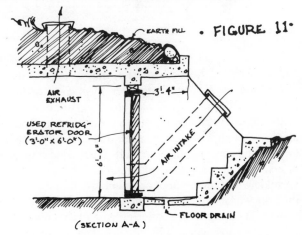

EARTH FILL
• FIGURE 11 •
AIR EXHAUST
3'-4"
USED REFRIGERATOR DOOR (3'-0" × 6'-0")
AIR INTAKE
6'-6"
FLOOR DRAIN

(SECTION A-A)

One door opening was placed in each end of the storage-cellar, one square foot of door area for each 117 cubic feet of storage volume. Commercial cold storage doors were installed. You can probably find a set of these quite easily by keeping a lookout for a small butcher shop being demolished or selling out. Seven inlet and three outlet ducts were installed as ventilators. "Seconds" of 18 inch vitrified sewer tile were used for this purpose. Their location and number should be used to suit your individual conditions. The number used in this storage may have been excessive, though they will insure adequate ventilation under any condition and will prevent dead air pockets forming in the corners and elsewhere.

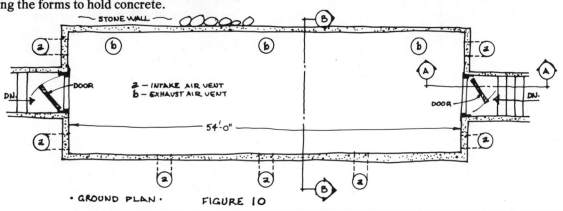

STONE WALL
DOOR
DN.
a — INTAKE AIR VENT
b — EXHAUST AIR VENT
54'-0"
DOOR
DN.

• GROUND PLAN • FIGURE 10

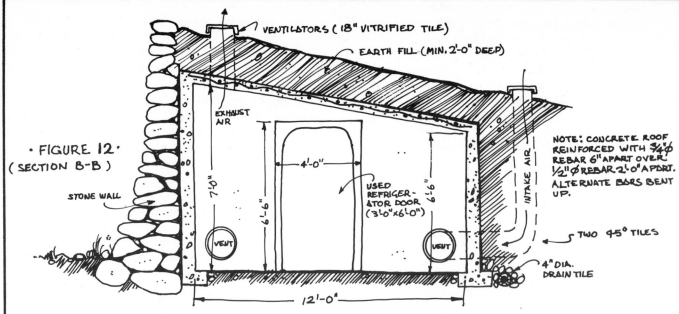

· FIGURE 12 ·
(SECTION B-B)

VENTILATORS (18" VITRIFIED TILE)

EARTH FILL (MIN. 2'-0" DEEP)

EXHAUST AIR

STONE WALL

4'-0"

7'-0"

6'-6"

6'-6"

USED REFRIGERATOR DOOR
(3'-0"x6'-0")

VENT

VENT

INTAKE AIR

NOTE: CONCRETE ROOF REINFORCED WITH ¾"∅ REBAR 6" APART OVER ½"∅ REBAR 2'-0" APART. ALTERNATE BARS BENT UP.

TWO 45° TILES

4" DIA. DRAIN TILE

12'-0"

The air-intake area equals one square foot for each 340 cubic feet of storage capacity; the out-takes, one to 794 cubic feet. A 1/20 horsepower, airplane-propeller-type exhaust fan with 105-watt electrical in-put was installed to aid ventilation, but it isn't a necessity, merely an aid. The earth maintains a relative humidity satisfactory for the cool vegetable or fruit. If dry conditions are prevalent and you wish to maintain a high humidity, sprinkle water on the floor occasionally. A line of four-inch tile was laid just below the ground level inside the cellar at its periphery, connected with drain openings at each door and covered with cinders. The completed storage cellar has a minimum of two feet of earth fill, covered with sod on the roof and ends. This will prevent the entrance of frost through the roof slab, and the sod will help to maintain proper temperatures.

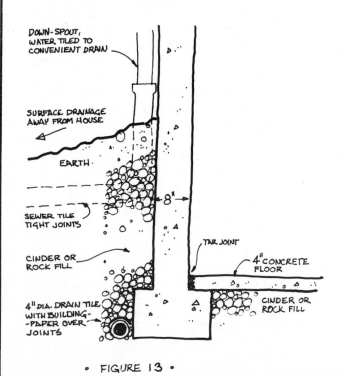

DOWN-SPOUT, WATER TILED TO CONVENIENT DRAIN

SURFACE DRAINAGE AWAY FROM HOUSE

EARTH

SEWER TILE TIGHT JOINTS

8"

TAR JOINT

4" CONCRETE FLOOR

CINDER OR ROCK FILL

CINDER OR ROCK FILL

4" DIA. DRAIN TILE WITH BUILDING-PAPER OVER JOINTS

· FIGURE 13 ·

The tile vents at the surface of the ground have strong wooden and metal covers which cannot be injured by either animal or machine. Coarse mesh screens in all openings prevent rodents and trash from entering while the storage is being ventilated at night. Home made padded plugs fit into the tile openings from the inside and prevent air leakage during sub-zero weather.

If you are bothered by a high water table at certain times of the year, fig. 13 is a design for making watertight joints inside your storage cellar.

A Basement Storage Room

The storage room is a place where temperature and humidity are held to the proper level for keeping fruits and produce. This means lower than usual household or basement temperatures, ranging from 30° to 40° F. After deciding on the size and location (where low temperatures can be most easily maintained), the area must be insulated from temperatures prevailing in the rest of the house.

At least one wall having outside exposure should be used. A wall on the north side with a window that is easily reached is preferable. The other walls can be made of wood.

The walls to close off a corner of the basement are easily constructed with a two by four-inch framework, sheathing on both sides, and three-inch insulation batts between the studding. Leave an opening in one wall for a door. This may be framed with two by two-inch studs, faced on each side with quarter-inch plywood, and the centre filled with insulation. Fit the door tightly and secure it with a type of latch that holds it firmly closed. To insulate the ceiling of the storage space, sheath underneath the ceiling joists and apply three inches or more of insulation between the joists, extending the insulation out over the walls of the storage space.

It's advisable, when constructing the walls, to lay the floor plate on bricks (on edge) so that the finished walls are four inches off the floor. A form board on the outside will retain a straight line. With this arrangement, the wooden wall is away from water that is poured on the storage floor for the purpose of increasing the humidity.

Two types of insulating material can be used: *board* or *loose fill*. It is important to keep them dry or their insulating properties will be reduced. Moisture vapour barriers are used, inside and out, such as damp-proof paper, tar, or asphalt.

Board insulation (i.e., cork board) can be nailed to the walls and ceiling. Two thicknesses should be used to prevent leakage through joints.

Loose fill insulation includes planer shavings, cork dust, and minerals. The sheathing and damp-proofing should be done at the same time as you fill the wall space with insulation. Planer shavings work well for insulating the walls and ceiling, as they are dry and do not tend to settle. Add hydrated lime to the shavings (20 to 40 pounds per cubic yard) to help keep them dry. It also acts as a repellant to vermin and rodents. Tamp the shaves as they are filled between studs, until a density of seven to nine pounds per cubic foot is obtained.

For floor insulation, where it's required, use board-type insulation. The insulating board is laid and then mopped with hot tar. Cement or other flooring is laid on top. Where chinks occur at rough wall or floor surfaces, caulking compound is used to fill the space and protect the exposed insulating material from dampness.

The temperature of the surrounding basement will determine the thickness of the walls. A prevailing temperature of 60°F. outside the storage room calls for the following thickness of insulating materials:

Three inches: wood-fibre insulating board, cork board, granular cork, fibrous rock, rock wool.
Four to five inches: planer shavings
Six inches: compressed peat.

Lower basement temperatures will require less insulation.

The simplest method to provide ventilation is to open and close the storage room door, but preferably two windows should be available for intake and outlet ventilators. The ventilators may be of wood or, when possible, of tile, built into the foundation wall. The intake opening should be near or through the floor.

If you have a cellar with a window, here's the best arrangement. Remove the window entirely. Divide the

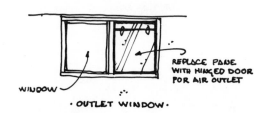

· OUTLET WINDOW ·

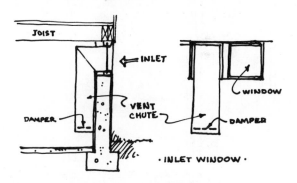

· INLET WINDOW ·

· FIGURE 15 ·

window frame either horizontally or vertically into two openings of equal size. Equip one opening with either a hinged or sliding door. Equip the other opening with an air duct that extends down to about one foot from floor level. Put a sliding door in this duct. If the window frame is divided horizontally, attach the cool air duct to the lower opening. Cover the outside of both openings with copper screening. When the doors are opened, cool air will come in via the air duct and warm storage air will go out the other opening. This arrangement provides better distribution and more effective cooling in the storage than merely opening a window. Take note: openings and ducts should be not less than one square foot in cross-sectional area. Light must be excluded from stored vegetables and fruits, so cover any excess window(s) with boards. If it gets extremely cold outside, you may have to open the door to let in a little warm air from the basement.

It's never advisable to have anything of wood permanently fixed to the floor; the dampness will rot it, and the extra surfaces and corners will form lodging places for molds, plant disease germs, and dirt. Portable slat floors in sections may be used to support barrels, boxes,

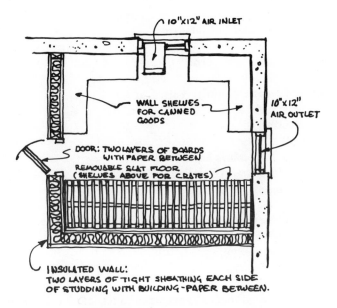

· FIGURE 14 ·

and crates. All shelves and bins should also be of slatted construction, to permit good air circulation. The bottom shelf or bin should be at least four inches above floor level, so that the floor can be cleaned underneath the shelf and water can be poured on the floor to maintain a high humidity.

Keep You Storage Area Clean

Give it a couple of coats of latex paint after it's finished. Wash it thoroughly after each storage season.

Stairwell Storage Room

If your house has a sloping cellar door and stairwell into the basement, this area can be adapted easily and cheaply.

· FIGURE 16 ·

The Sod and Log Root House

If you're high on energy and natural materials (logs and sod) and low on finances, here's an alternative to the standard type of construction.

Pick a spot (preferably a hillside or knoll, but a flat spot will work as well) and remove soil over a space a little bit larger than the ground plan of the root house and to the depth of two feet or more, providing there is no danger that the bottom will be wet. In the construction of the house, select poles or logs of two sizes, the larger ones being shortest; these are for the inside pen, as it is subjected to greater strain.

The ends of the logs are cut flat, so that they will fit down closely together, and make a pen that is nearly tight. At least two logs in each layer of the inner pen should be cut long enough to pass through and fit into the outer pen. These serve to fasten the two walls together. The space between the two is two feet on each side. Figure 14 shows the excavation and the beginning of the root house walls, with the method of "locking" them together. The doorway is built up by having short logs, which pass from one layer of poles to the other, and serve as supports to the ends of the wall poles.

The space between the two walls is filled with earth. Sods are used to fill in between the logs to block the earth. It's best to begin putting in the earth before the walls are completed, otherwise it will require an undue amount of hard lifting. When the walls are built up five to six feet on one side, and about two feet higher on the other (to give the necessary slope), the roof is put on. This is a good time to install a ventilation pipe. The roof should be of poles placed close together. Secure the poles to the logs and cover them with sod, 18 inches of earth, and sod again on the top. Two doors should be provided, one on the inner, and the other on the outer wall, both to fit closely. A filling of straw can be placed between the doors, if it is found necessary to do so to keep out the frost.

Bibliography

How to Grow Fruits by the Organic Method
Rodale
Rodale Books, Inc.

Encyclopedia of Organic Gardening
Rodale
Rodale Books, Inc.

Organic Gardening and Farming Magazine
Rodale
Rodale Books, Inc.

Five Acres and Independence
M.G. Kains
Greenburg, New York

Wood Heat Quarterly, Vols. 1 and 2
Lowther Press
Wolcoff, Vermont

Storing Vegetables and Fruits
U.S. Government Printing Office
Washington, D.C.

Home Storage of Vegetables,
Ontario Dept. of Agriculture
Parliament Buildings
Toronto, Ontario

A special thanks is extended to Rodale Publications for permission to use information from their books in this article.

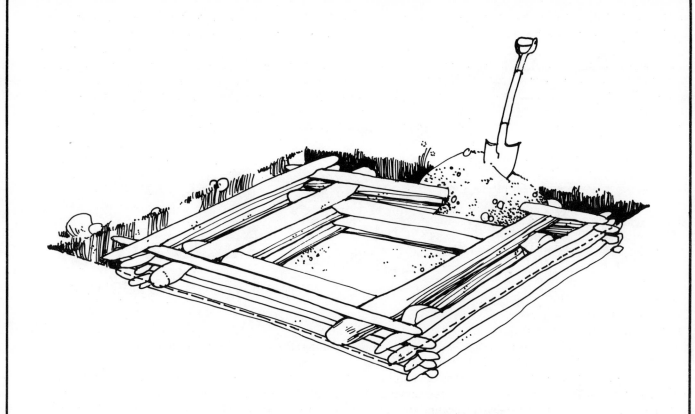

• DOUBLE WALLING OF SOD AND LOG ROOT HOUSE •

FIGURE 17
• THE SOD AND LOG ROOT HOUSE •

Poultry Housing

by Bus Hayden

Space

The most important principle in the housing of birds is that of space; available space determines the number and variety of fowl which can be kept. The recommended floor and roost space for the three main groups are as follows:

Breeds	Floor Space (per bird)	Roost Space (per bird)
Asiatics	4 sq. ft.	10 in.
Utility (American and English)	3 sq. ft.	8 in.
Mediterranean	2 to 3 sq. ft.	6 to 8 in.

Less than these amounts of space creates havoc: it promotes disease, cannibalism, and leaves the weaker birds no place to feed or roost adequately, making them unhappy "boarders."

Climate

The next most important item is climate. The climate of a chicken coop should, above all, be dry and free from draft. It requires adequate ventilation, but this can be obtained by having only one side of the house open, since a draft can only be created where there is both inlet and outlet for air currents. This open side should be facing away from the prevailing and storm winds: in our case, a western exposure is best. Where a western exposure isn't possible, either a roof vent, or vents around the windows (covered with cheesecloth or burlap) should suffice. When part of an existing building is being devoted to poultry, a draft-free roosting area can be achieved by placing the roosts in an adequate-sized box, which would consist of a floor or drop-board, three walls, and

ceiling: the size of the box is determined by the number of roosts needed.

Temperature

Birds can withstand several degrees of frost, but temperatures over 75°F. can cause problems. Fowl which are confined at higher temperatures or with no shade become irritable and begin to peck at one another, especially during the moulting seasons (of which the chicks have three). The erupting of new pin feathers leads the birds to picking: when blood is drawn, it easily leads to cannibalism.

Lighting

Poultry must have adequate light in order to see and feed, for it identifies its food entirely by sight. A dull, gloomy coop leads to lethargic, non-active, non-producing birds. Birds do best in a well-lighted and well-ventilated coop, where there is an abundance of natural light which does not raise the temperature of the coop. In addition, it is highly recommended that all coops be whitewashed inside. This will reflect light, so that most of the floor space can be used for activity. Windows can afford to be fairly high where they receive direct light from the cooler winter sun, but not from hot summer sun. For maximum winter productivity, artificial light supplementing the natural daylight to maintain a 12-(or at most 13-) hour day is preferable. Light in excess of 13 hours can produce a false moult, and hence a cessation of egg production: less than 12 hours reduces egg production, for it takes roughly a 12-hour day to produce an egg. Birds, like all animals, are regular in their habits, and extensive variation in the hours of light will have a detrimental effect on production. Unless one can maintain a very regular artificial light supplement, it is preferable to depend on natural light, though production will be somewhat less.

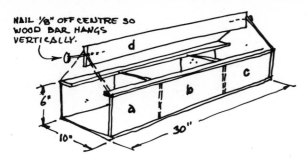

Feed Hopper—floor or stand

(a) grit box
(b) mash section
(c) oyster shell
(d) floating bar (1" x 4" with nails driven in ends; allows it to rotate)

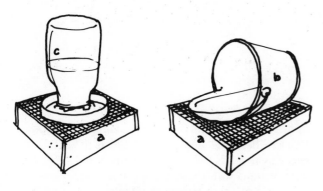

Water Stand

(a) box 2' square: tomato flat or frame covered with 1/2" mesh wire
(b) side pail
(c) glass fountain

Roosting

The bars on which the birds roost (approximately two-inch by two-inch stock is usual) are placed on the horizontal, above and parallel to a platform called a drop board. The first one is placed 8 to 10 inches out from the back wall, and subsequent ones at 16 to 20-inch intervals. The drop board should extend a further 16 inches in front of the front roost: this allows the birds to alight before seeking a spot on the roost. Drop boards should be a maximum of 30 inches from the floor of the coop. The roosts themselves should be six to eight inches above the drop boards for convenience in cleaning the latter. Fowl deposit over half their droppings at night; the use of the drop board thus helps to maintain a cleaner litter on the floor (bedding). It also makes available straight poultry droppings (manure), which when allowed to dry can be stored in empty feed sacks as an excellent fertilizer for plants requiring high nitrogen content. As for myself, I recommend the area under the drop board be used to house the community nest. As this space is visually dark, and therefore less effective for feeding activity, it makes an ideal nest site. I made a box using one-inch by eight-inch stock, three boards deep. This places the drop board at approximately 24 inches from the floor.

Exercise Yards

These are located by preference on the east or west side of the building, unless the southern exposure is fairly dense in plantings. Poultry enjoy morning and evening light; in the heat of the day, they are inactive and seek shade.

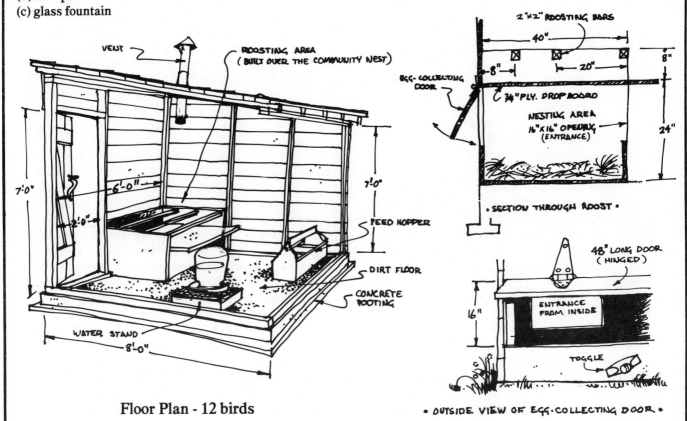

Floor Plan - 12 birds

· OUTSIDE VIEW OF EGG·COLLECTING DOOR ·

Sauna

by Steve Terkel

We built our sauna out of a natural need for cleanliness; a means to cleanse one's body as well as a place of mental relaxation and enjoyment. It seemed simple enough: nothing more than fire, air, water, and stone. The notion of the sauna as a communal affair — a group endeavor, something to be enjoyed with others — was added incentive. The healthful and remedial effects were more apparent as we better understood the design, construction, and maintenance of the sauna.

First was the task of choosing a good sauna site. Since we had a river crossing our land, it was a matter of selecting a spot deep enough for the "plunge," a ritual very much a part of the sauna. The plunge and the accompanying rush of cooling sensations is a stimulating exchange for the intense heat of the sauna bath.

The traditional sauna is a one-room structure, with a wood-burning stove as the heat source. The interior is constructed in a series of platform levels to allow the bathers to move higher as they desire hotter temperatures. The best material for sauna construction is seasoned rough wood, as it enables moisture to be absorbed and the necessary amount of air to pass through the walls. Our sauna was built using recycled barn lumber. It took lots of nail pulling, but by using recyclable materials we kept the cost way down and might have saved some trees too. Besides, green lumber is likely to warp, come apart at the seams, or develop cracks and openings. If new lumber is needed, make sure that only kiln-dried lumber is used for the interior of the sauna.

The sauna is designed to breathe; that is, allow some circulation of air. In order to insure a proper heat chamber, take care to seal any cracks in the upper part of the sauna. Since heat rises, a well-insulated, tight roof will retain heat the longest. Any leaks in the floor or lower walls should also be sealed, but don't worry if you can't get them all. Traditional sauna walls are built

loosely at the bottom to provide the necessary ventilation. The door should be low, as should any windows. Use a rather small door, so that too much heat does not escape when it is being opened and closed. We lined the interior walls with cedar shakes; it's a very porous wood and has a pleasant fragrance. Don't paint or oil the walls, as this will restrict the normal circulation of the air.

The sauna has withstood 2,000 years of almost consistent design and few will dispute that the wood-fueled sauna is still the best. Our sauna is heated by a medium-sized wood stove, with stones piled on top. Sauna heat is non-radiant; that is, the heat is absorbed by the stones, then circulated throughout. This is dry, indirect, penetrating heat. Choose the stones carefully; they should neither expand nor crumble. A good size is slightly bigger than a grapefruit. Dark-coloured river rock is a start; if in doubt, bang it with a hammer; if it breaks, keep looking.

The firing up of the sauna is a sort of ritual in itself. Much care is taken to fire it well in advance, to insure that it is completely heated before the bathers enter. Some maintain that the "ripening" of the sauna is like the tuning of an orchestra before a concert. Usually we burn a hard-wood like oak with some fir and heat it for two to three hours. It seems that the longer the sauna is heated the better and more efficiently it will function.

The sauna bath is essentially immersion in hot dry air; the temperature ranges from 170° to 220° F. The whole purpose is to perspire thoroughly, thereby cleaning the pores, toning the body, and inducing relaxation. The body perspires more in dry heat than in moist heat. The drier the air, the more heat the bather can stand. Some real sauna freaks take saunas as hot as 250° F. The heat is the difference between the sauna and the steam bath or the sweat lodge. It is easier to stand tempera-

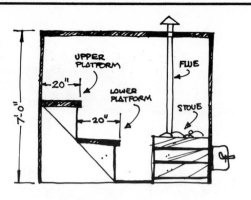

Side View

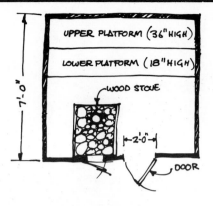

Top View

tures of 190° to 212°F. in dry air than one of 120°F. in water-saturated air. When water is sprinkled on the hot rocks in the sauna, the increased humidity is even dry, as the steam is quickly absorbed by the walls. This dry steam quickens perspiration from already open pores and cleanses more effectively.

Here are some thoughts on the "how to" aspects of taking a sauna:

(1) Take a 10 to 15 minute sauna at 180° to 200°F. A lower heat may be preferred by beginners.

(2) Sprinkle water on the rocks to increase humidity 10 per cent. Use water sparingly, so that steam is distributed evenly.

(3) Beating oneself with birch leaves loosens dirt and stimulates the cells. The whisk is usually birch, but oak works fine. It is a bundle of small leafy branches tied at one end, then soaked in hot water to soften it before use.

(4) Whisking is usually followed by washing and a quick dip in a lake or stream to cool off.

(5) Return to the sauna, take a position on highest and hottest platform, and repeat the procedure. This period of perspiration and whisking may be shorter than the initial one. A third time may be desired.

(6) Finish with a final plunge in a lake or stream, or in winter a roll in the snow. Movement should be calm and deliberate. It's quite a rush: the sharp contrast is pleasantly invigorating, and not the shock that some imagine.

(7) Let yourself dry naturally in fresh air, as cooling off is very important. Don't dress until body temperature has returned to normal.

(8) A 10 to 15 minute rest should always follow. The sauna is a very calming peaceful experience: don't rush it, you've got all the time in the world.

A really good sauna book (perhaps the only one) is:
Sauna, The Finnish Bath
by H.J. Viherjuuri
Stephen Green Press
Brattleboro, Vermont.

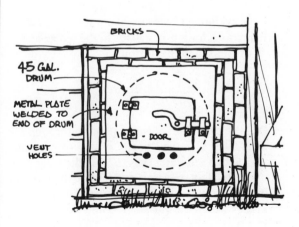

Front View of Stove

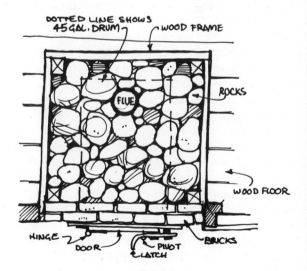

Top View of Stove

The stove should be totally enclosed by rocks. This is best done by building a wood frame around the stove, netting the frame in with wire mesh and then piling the enclosed area with rocks.

If possible, build the stove into a wall so that the door

faces outside. This will allow you to fire the stove without having to enter the sauna.

A stove can easily be made out of an old forty-five gallon oil drum; weld a door on one end and attach a stove pipe.

Harnessing the Small Stream

by C.D. Basset

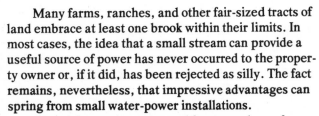

Many farms, ranches, and other fair-sized tracts of land embrace at least one brook within their limits. In most cases, the idea that a small stream can provide a useful source of power has never occurred to the property owner or, if it did, has been rejected as silly. The fact remains, nevertheless, that impressive advantages can spring from small water-power installations.

Electricity can be generated for general use, for pumping water, and for stand-by or emergency purposes; and the pond that is usually created can serve additionally as a means for watering livestock in dry times, for fire-fighting, as a swimming pool, as a place to raise fish for sport or as a "crop."

Power can be obtained from any flowing stream, no matter how small. Whether it is desirable to harness this power depends on two factors. First, does water flow all the year round, even in the late summer months? Second, does enough water flow to make the harnessing of it economically sound? The first factor is, of course, known to the property owner by observation; the second may be determined by simple measurements.

What's the least amount of power that is worth developing? There is in this country at least one water-wheel manufacturer who makes a line of small-capacity units, and this company's smallest hydroelectric unit develops 1/2 kilowatt. From this it can be inferred that, in this company's experience, it is not economically wise to harness a stream that will not develop at least 500 watts dependably at the switchboard. Half a kilowatt will light

10 fair-sized lamps or supply 2/3 hp. to operate, say, a deep-well pump. With this figure in mind as a criterion, the reader can make a preliminary reconnaissance of the water power available on his property. The chances are he will be surprised; even a seemingly insignificant stream can deliver many times this minimum.

The power available at the site of a water wheel (that is, before deductions for inefficiencies in the wheel and generator) is expressed in this formula:

$$H.P. = \frac{62.4 \times Q \times H}{33,000}$$

Here Q is the cubic feet of water passing through the wheel in one minute; H is the "head" or vertical distance in feet through which the water falls; 62.4 is the weight in pounds of one cubic foot of water; and 33,000 the number of foot-pounds per minute in 1 horsepower. A number of methods exist by which the variables Q and H can be determined, but before considering them, it's well to examine first the possible sites for the dam and wheel, since they will necessarily affect the amount of head secured.

The location of the dam, as suggested in Figure 1, should be governed by two principles. It should be placed where the greatest useful head is obtainable; that is, where the greatest fall occurs in the shortest length of stream. Such a site is often indicated by a natural waterfall, by a conspicuously steep slope, or by the swiftness of the current. The second locating principle is a simple matter of cost: a dam should be placed where it can be smallest and still impound the most water. This means, in general, that it should be placed where the stream valley or cut is narrowest.

The site of the water wheel (Fig. 2) may be either at the dam or some distance below it. The former location is the more common, being simpler to build and eliminating the need for a pipe or penstock to deliver water to the wheel. Disadvantages include the fact that the spillway must be of ample capacity to protect the powerhouse in time of high water, and the fact that only the "artificial head"—that created by the dam itself—is available. In cases where the ground falls away abruptly below the dam site, the "divided-flow" layout may be desirable, for it greatly increases the head.

Another preliminary calculation should be made as to the height of the proposed dam. This is restricted, as a rule, only by the height of the valley walls at the site, and by the materials, equipment, and money available for building it. The higher it is, the greater the head and the larger the pond that will be created. "Pondage"—water stored for use in times of peak demand — is an important factor in water power calculations. Power is rarely needed 24 hours a day, and construction of a dam of sufficient height to provide water storage will greatly increase the power available at the time of day required.

If, for example, a wheel is to be run for 16 hours a day, and if a dam is built that will impound all water

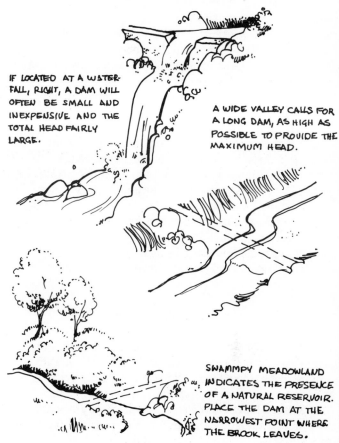

• FIGURE 1 LOCATING THE DAM •

IF LOCATED AT A WATER-FALL, RIGHT, A DAM WILL OFTEN BE SMALL AND INEXPENSIVE AND THE TOTAL HEAD FAIRLY LARGE.

A WIDE VALLEY CALLS FOR A LONG DAM, AS HIGH AS POSSIBLE TO PROVIDE THE MAXIMUM HEAD.

SWAMMPY MEADOWLAND INDICATES THE PRESENCE OF A NATURAL RESERVOIR. PLACE THE DAM AT THE NARROWEST POINT WHERE THE BROOK LEAVES.

• FIGURE 2 LOCATING THE WHEEL •

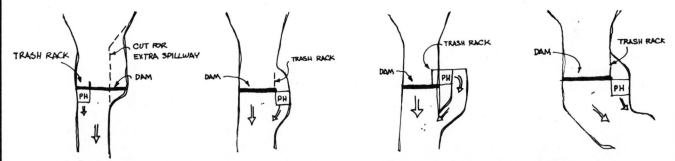

TRASH RACK — CUT FOR EXTRA SPILLWAY — DAM

DAM — TRASH RACK

TRASH RACK — DAM

DAM — TRASH RACK

TYPICAL LAYOUTS WITH THE POWERHOUSE AT THE DAM, A LOCATION THAT USES ONLY THE ARTIFICIAL HEAD.

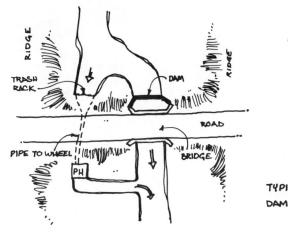

RIDGE — TRASH RACK — DAM — RIDGE — ROAD — PIPE TO WHEEL — BRIDGE — PH

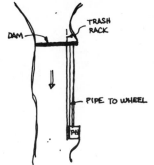

DAM — TRASH RACK — PIPE TO WHEEL — PH

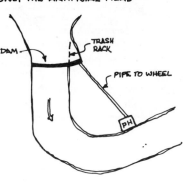

DAM — TRASH RACK — PIPE TO WHEEL — PH

TYPICAL "DIVIDED-FALL" LAYOUTS, WITH THE WHEEL BELOW THE DAM, WHICH ADD THE NATURAL TO THE ARTIFICIAL (DAM) HEAD.

flowing into the pond during the idle eight hours, the power capacity will be increased by 50 per cent. Don't neglect to distinguish between "live storage"—the volume of water represented by the difference in height of the spillway flash boards and the wheel intake — and "dead storage"—the volume of water below the level of the wheel intake. The former is power banked against a time of need; the latter is worthless, powerwise.

Once the dam and powerhouse are tentatively sited, and the height of the first is provisionally set, it is time to measure the power available. Assume that all water flowing in the stream can be made to flow through the wheel, which is a fair assumption on small installations. This flow (Q in the power formula) can be determined by the "weir method," which involves constructing a temporary dam of controlled proportions, or by the "float-method," which is theoretically a trifle less accurate, though still quite satisfactory.

The float method (Fig 3) involves the formula:

$$Q \text{ equals } A \times V \times 60$$

in which Q is the volume of water flowing in cubic feet per minute, A is the cross-sectional area of the stream in square feet at the site, and V is the average velocity of the stream at this point, expressed in feet per second.

Select a length of the stream that is fairly straight, with sides approximately parallel, and unobstructed by rocks or shoals for a distance of about 100'. Stretch a taut wire squarely across the stream near the middle of this length and measure the width of the stream here in inches. Mark this width off on the wire and divide it into 10 equal divisions. From the centre point of each division, measure the depth of the water in inches. Then average the depth figure by adding each value and dividing by 10. The cross-sectional area of the stream, A, is now sec-

ured by multiplying this average depth by the width, and dividing the result by 144 to obtain the answer in square feet.

Your next step in determining Q is to measure the rate of flow. Using a steel tape, mark off a course along the bank that is 100' long: the mid-point of this course should be at the line where the cross-section was measured. Stretch wires or rope tautly across the stream at each end of the course, and make a float by filling a bottle so that it rides awash. Provide it with a pennant so that you can follow it easily. Then set the float adrift in the middle of the stream, timing its progress over the course with a stop watch, beginning just when the pennant passes the first wire and stopping just as it passes the second.

Make a series of runs, averaging the results. The speed of the float in feet per second is then the length of the course divided by the average time. This result is not, however, suitable for immediate use in the flow formula, since not all the water in a stream flows as rapidly as that in the centre and near the top. If you multiply the float speed by the coefficient 0.83, the resultant value will serve as V in the flow formula.

Given an estimate of the amount of head to be present at the wheel, you can now make a rough determination of the horsepower your stream can provide. It's worth emphasizing, though, that this figure is necessarily only as accurate as the measurements that produced it, and that the power indicated is that present *at the time of measuring.* A single stream-flow value is not of itself particularly useful unless it is obtained at the time of lowest water, usually in the late summer months. Moreover, even if you have measured the flow at slack-water time, the figures should if possible be supplemented by others secured during maximum springtime flow, so that you can calculate the size of spillway needed to prevent damage to your installation in times of high wa-

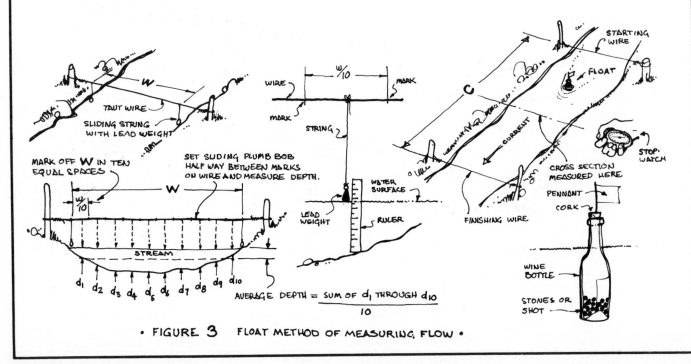

· FIGURE 3   FLOAT METHOD OF MEASURING FLOW ·

ter.

It's a good practice, for backyard engineers as well as for professionals, to refine, cross-check, and test your measurements by all means at your disposal. Such checks will not only reduce the chance of disappointment in the final result, but will also permit calculated economics in construction and greater efficiency in operation.

Before you begin even a preliminary reconnaissance of waterpower on your property, the writer suggests you secure a looseleaf notebook to be devoted solely to the project. Develop the habit of neatly entering all data as it is obtained, not forgetting to note dates and stream conditions at the time measurements are made. Such a record is a great help in performing sound calculations and producing excellent results.

Putting Water to Work

Measuring the flow of water in the stream or brook on your property is the logical first step in planning a small waterpower project. The float method of making this measurement is generally the easiest to perform and, if done carefully, is accurate enough for most purposes. If, however, a stream is so shallow at low-water time as to impede the progress of a weighted float, the weir method of measuring flow has advantages. Essentially a kind of water meter, a weir is a rectangular notch or spillway of carefully controlled proportions located in the centre of a small temporary dam. Two simple measurements permit the volume of flow to be accurately calculated.

Before constructing the dam, measure the depth of the stream at the site; the depth of the weir notch (M in Fig. 4) should equal this. Since the dam need not be permanent, a simple plank or tongue-and-groove lumber will serve adequately. No water must flow except through the weir, so care should be taken to seal the ends and bottom of the dam by extending planks into the banks and below the bed of the stream. Clay or loam puddling on the upstream side will stop minor seepage. Be sure the dam is perpendicular to the flow of the stream.

The weir should be located in the centre of the dam, with its lower edge not less than 1' above the surface of the water below the dam. This lower edge should be accurately leveled. Both this and the vertical edges of the weir should be beveled with the sharp edge upstream; a 1/8" flat on the bevel will keep the edge from breaking down. Proportion the weir so that its length L is not less than 3M, and larger if possible.

Drive a stake in the stream bed at least 5' upstream from the weir, pounding it down until its top is exactly level with the bottom edge of the weir. Allow the stream to reach its maximum flow through the weir and then measure with a ruler the depth in inches of water over the stake. Referring to the table on this page, you can now read the number of cubic feet per minute of water for each inch of L, the weir width. If you multiply the figure from the table by L, the result is the total amount of water flowing in cubic feet per minute, which is Q in the

horsepower formula.

If your stream is already dammed, there is no need to construct another dam just to measure flow. It is quite possible to employ the existing dam, using its spillway as a weir, provided that all water can be made to pass through the spillway. Construct a wooden or metal frame to fit the spillway and seal it in place snugly. The centre of this frame should incorporate a properly proportioned weir notch. As before, M should equal the depth of the water flowing through the spillway before the weir is installed, and L may in most cases be half the width of the spillway.

To get an accurate estimate of available horsepower, you will need a precise figure for H, the head of water that will be present. *Head* may be defined as the vertical distance in feet from the surface of water in the pond behind the dam to the surface of the stream below the dam at the site of the wheel. This figure may be obtained by any of several methods in cases where a dam is already present, and with scarcely greater difficulty at the site of an unbuilt dam.

Measuring a difference in elevation can be quickly and accurately done with an engineer's transit and leveling rod. But since not everyone has access to these instruments, and since thos who do would not need instructions on so simple a joo as running a level, we'll pass on to other methods.

Figure 5 illustrates a very simple way of measuring a vertical distance. The equipment required is a carpenter's level, a folding rule or steel tape, a 1" by 2" by 6' board with two edges planed parallel, two wooden pegs, a stake, and a C-clamp. These are items that can be found in almost any home, and certainly any farm.

Depth D Inches over stake	1/8''	1/4''	3/8''	1/2''	5/8''	3/4''	7/8''
1 inch	.40	.47	.55	.65	.74	.83	.93	1.03
2 ''	1.14	1.24	1.36	1.47	1.59	1.71	1.83	1.96
3 ''	2.09	2.23	2.36	2.50	2.63	2.78	2.92	3.07
4 ''	3.22	3.37	3.52	3.68	3.83	3.99	4.16	4.32
5 ''	4.50	4.67	4.84	5.01	5.18	5.36	5.54	5.72
6 ''	5.90	6.09	6.28	6.47	6.65	6.85	7.05	7.25
7 ''	7.44	7.64	7.84	8.05	8.25	8.45	8.66	8.86
8 ''	9.10	9.31	9.52	9.74	9.96	10.18	10.40	10.62
9 ''	10.86	11.08	11.31	11.54	11.77	12.00	12.23	12.47
10 ''	12.71	12.95	13.19	13.43	13.67	13.93	14.16	14.42
11 ''	14.67	14.92	15.18	15.43	15.67	15.96	16.20	16.46
12 ''	16.73	16.99	17.26	17.52	17.78	18.05	18.32	18.58
13 ''	18.87	19.14	19.42	19.69	19.97	20.24	20.52	20.80
14 ''	21.09	21.37	21.65	21.94	22.22	22.51	22.70	23.08
15 ''	23.38	23.67	23.97	24.26	24.56	24.86	25.16	25.46
16 ''	25.76	26.06	26.36	26.66	26.97	27.27	27.58	27.89
17 ''	28.20	28.51	28.82	29.14	29.45	29.76	30.08	30.39
18 ''	30.70	31.02	31.34	31.66	31.98	32.31	32.63	32.96
19 ''	33.29	33.61	33.94	34.27	34.60	34.94	35.27	35.60
20 ''	35.94	36.27	36.60	36.94	37.28	37.62	37.96	38.31
21 ''	38.65	39.00	39.34	39.69	40.04	40.39	40.73	41.09
22 ''	41.43	41.78	42.13	42.49	42.84	43.20	43.56	43.92
23 ''	44.28	44.64	45.00	45.38	45.71	46.08	46.43	46.81
24 ''	47.18	47.55	47.91	48.28	48.65	49.02	49.39	49.76

Table from James Leffel & Co.

This table shows the quantity of water passing over a rectangular weir in cubic feet per minute (cfm) for each inch of notch width. Depth D is read as a combination of the left-hand column and the top row. For example, if the depth over your stake is 5⅜'', follow over 5 (fifth row) to ⅜ (fourth column), and read the value as 5.01 cfm. Don't forget that this figure should now be multiplied by the width in inches of your notch.

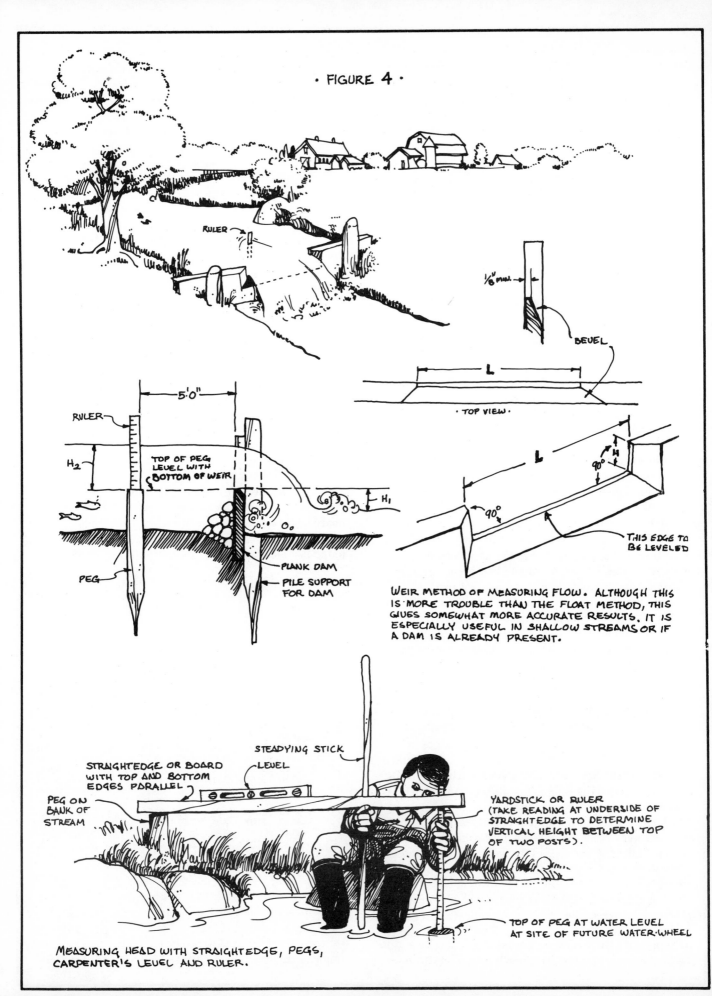

· FIGURE 4 ·

RULER

⅛" MIN.

BEVEL

· TOP VIEW ·

L

RULER

5'0"

TOP OF PEG
LEVEL WITH
BOTTOM OF WEIR

H₂

H₁

L

90°

90°

H

PEG

PLANK DAM

PILE SUPPORT
FOR DAM

THIS EDGE TO
BE LEVELED

WEIR METHOD OF MEASURING FLOW. ALTHOUGH THIS
IS MORE TROUBLE THAN THE FLOAT METHOD, THIS
GIVES SOMEWHAT MORE ACCURATE RESULTS. IT IS
ESPECIALLY USEFUL IN SHALLOW STREAMS OR IF
A DAM IS ALREADY PRESENT.

STEADYING STICK

LEVEL

STRAIGHTEDGE OR BOARD
WITH TOP AND BOTTOM
EDGES PARALLEL

PEG ON
BANK OF
STREAM

YARDSTICK OR RULER
(TAKE READING AT UNDERSIDE OF
STRAIGHTEDGE TO DETERMINE
VERTICAL HEIGHT BETWEEN TOP
OF TWO POSTS).

TOP OF PEG AT WATER LEVEL
AT SITE OF FUTURE WATER·WHEEL

MEASURING HEAD WITH STRAIGHTEDGE, PEGS,
CARPENTER'S LEVEL AND RULER.

Though the method can be somewhat tedious if the difference in elevation is large, the results will be quite accurate with ordinary care in leveling and measuring. Note in the drawing that in the case of a pre-existent dam, one or more measurements needed to carry around the edge of the dam are subtracted from, rather than added to the total.

Less practical in most cases, though still of occasional special value, are two other ways to determine head. Elevations can be measured quite readily by the techniques of photographic surveying. For those who are familiar with the procedure, it is a simple matter to take the required pictures in the field and then scale the required elevation at the desk from the developed photographs. Another method involves the use of a barometer, either mercury or aneroid, to indicate differences in height. However, this method is useful only where the head to be measured is considerable, say, more than 25', and calls for special techniques to hold the probable error down to acceptable proportions. Except in unusual circumstances, the writer recommends that the method in Figure 5 be employed, inasmuch as it requires little special equipment and with ordinary care gives good results.

With sound figures for both H and Q, you are now ready to calculate the available horsepower of your installation with the formula given previously. If the power is found to be sufficient to warrant continuing with the project, say 2/3 hp. at the least, your next step is to determine the nature of your power requirements. Here individual variations are so many as to make it difficult to outline a specific procedure. It's possible, however, to suggest factors you should consider in planning your power plant.

Some of the uses to which small-capacity installations are successfully put include directly powering pumps, mills, machine tools, or other small-demand machinery; and driving a generator to supply electricity for either lighting or power purposes. The latter type of installation is of course the more flexible and generally useful. Determine, then, the uses you propose for your water power, and tabulate the horsepower required after each item. In the case of electric motors or appliances rated in amperes or watts, remember that watts are volts times amperes, and that 746 watts are equal to one horsepower.

From this tabulation, the peak load can be determined. This is the sum of the power demands made by different pieces of equipment that may probably be in use at one time. Knowing power and load, you can now determine if the proposed installation will be on a sound basis.

Do not use your available horsepower figure directly, since deductions should first be made for losses in the water wheel and in the generator, if you intend to be using one. For small installations, assume wheel efficiency to be 75 per cent; many small wheels will better this, but the assumption will provide leeway for possible optimism in measuring H and Q. Generator efficiency can be assumed to be 80 per cent, a figure that will also be bettered in many cases, but is on the safe side. Thus switch-

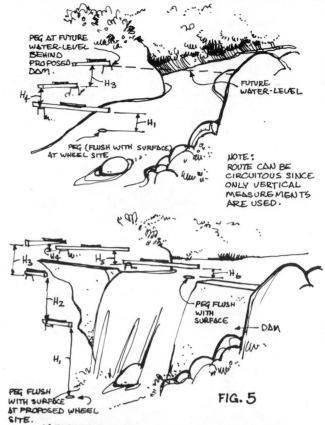

FIG. 5

MEASURING HEAD. WITH A CARPENTER'S LEVEL, STRAIGHT EDGE, AND PEGS, HEAD CAN BE MEASURED BEFORE OR AFTER DAM IS BUILT.

board power may be expressed at .75 x .8 x hp, or .6 of the available horsepower.

At this stage of the game, it's well to mull over the possible variations and combinations, rather than to proceed with specific construction plans. Consider for example the decision required if the indicated switchboard power will seemingly handle the peak load — whether to build a dam just large enough to do this job, or to build one substantially larger to handle possible future increases in power requirements. The former choice will be obviously cheaper at first, but may not be so in the long run, since power demands have a way of growing and since it is rarely satisfactory to increase the structure of an existing dam.

If the peak load is apparently too high, various possibilities should be considered. Will "pondage"—water stored behind the dam overnight or in slack periods — help out? Can the use of equipment be dispensed with? Is the project necessarily a year-round enterprise, or can the low-power characteristics of the dry season be ignored? A word of caution on these points may not be amiss: it's far better to plan an installation that will provide more power than you need than one which doesn't supply enough.

Whether, in the event that you decide to generate electricity, to use AC or DC is another decision to make. In circumstances where the generator must be located some distance from the load, AC is the only choice, for DC transmission losses would be too high, amounting in small installations to a prohibitive percentage of switch-

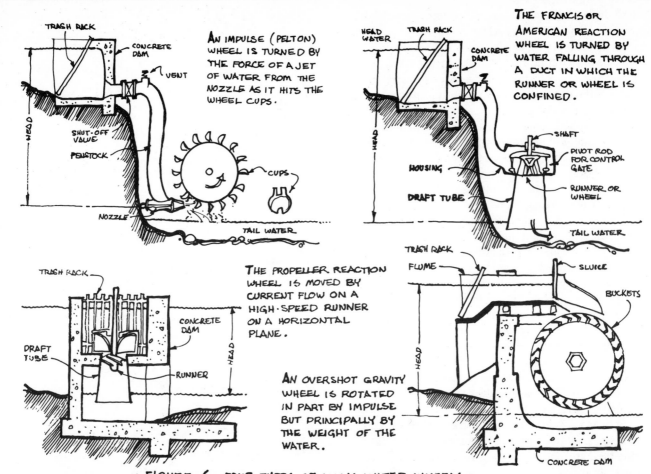

AN IMPULSE (PELTON) WHEEL IS TURNED BY THE FORCE OF A JET OF WATER FROM THE NOZZLE AS IT HITS THE WHEEL CUPS.

Labels: TRASH RACK, CONCRETE DAM, VENT, HEAD, SHUT-OFF VALVE, PENSTOCK, CUPS, NOZZLE, TAIL WATER

THE FRANCIS OR AMERICAN REACTION WHEEL IS TURNED BY WATER FALLING THROUGH A DUCT IN WHICH THE RUNNER OR WHEEL IS CONFINED.

Labels: HEAD WATER, TRASH RACK, CONCRETE DAM, HEAD, HOUSING, DRAFT TUBE, SHAFT, PIVOT ROD FOR CONTROL GATE, RUNNER OR WHEEL, TAIL WATER

THE PROPELLER REACTION WHEEL IS MOVED BY CURRENT FLOW ON A HIGH-SPEED RUNNER ON A HORIZONTAL PLANE.

Labels: TRASH RACK, CONCRETE DAM, HEAD, DRAFT TUBE, RUNNER

AN OVERSHOT GRAVITY WHEEL IS ROTATED IN PART BY IMPULSE BUT PRINCIPALLY BY THE WEIGHT OF THE WATER.

Labels: TRASH RACK, FLUME, SLUICE, BUCKETS, HEAD, CONCRETE DAM

· FIGURE 6   FOUR TYPES OF SMALL WATER WHEELS ·

board power. If your buildings and equipment are already wired to receive one type of current, it would obviously be sensible to fix on the same type of power; if for example your farm is already wired for a battery-type lighting system, there would be little reason to revamp the installation for AC. If, on the other hand, you are starting from scratch, I recommend the use of DC wherever possible. An AC generator must be closely regulated at or slightly above synchronous speed, and close regulation requires complicated governing equipment that is tricky to build or expensive to buy. A compound-wound DC generator, on the other hand, provides inherently close voltage regulation over a wide speed range; and even a shunt-wound DC generator with a direct-acting field-rheostat regulator would be satisfactory.

Selecting the right wheel for your plant is perhaps the final step in your preliminary planning. There are three general types of water wheel — impulse, reaction, and gravity — and several fairly common varieties of each type. However, for small plant purposes, it is possible to narrow the number down to those shown in Figure 6. Note that two types of reaction wheels, the Francis and the propeller, are shown, and but one variety of gravity wheel, the overshot one.

The impulse or Pelton wheel, operated exclusively by the force of the water from the jet, includes among its advantages very slight leakage and friction losses, good efficiency under varying flows, and a sufficiently high

shaft speed to drive a generator. It is more resistant to pitting by water containing sand, silt, or minerals than the reaction type. Its disadvantages include the fact that it cannot use all the available head, is larger than a reaction wheel developing the same power, and will wallow in high tail water. It must be mounted as close to the tail water as possible.

The reaction wheel, either the Francis or propeller type, is turned by the fall of water through a duct or pipe in which the wheel is confined. It is the most compact of all wheels for a given power, uses all of the available head, and operates at a satisfactory speed for direct coupling to a generator. It is an efficient wheel over a wide range of conditions, and it can be mounted at any convenient height above tail water. Disadvantages include rapid corrosion with silted water, and relatively high leakage and friction losses, especially in small units.

Finally, there is the overshot gravity wheel, which is turned largely by the weight of the water and partly by impulse. It has good efficiency under varying flow, and is unaffected by sand, silt, or minerals in the water. Gravity wheels turn at a low speed, which is undesirable for driving a generator or high-speed machinery, but suitable for some pumping and grinding applications. Such a wheel will wallow in high tail water, is the largest wheel for given power, and will be obstructed by ice in winter unless housed.

Dams Turn Water Into Kilowatts

Concrete, though desirable, isn't necessary for damming a small stream. Beavers have gotten by for years without it. Suitable materials can be found on almost any farm. Logs, rough-hewn timber, rock, masonry, planking, gravel, sand, and clay are all useful. Choose the materials most readily available on your property, or the least expensive if you must obtain them elsewhere.

You will have determined the height and width of the dam you will need to convert your stream to power. The summer months provide an ideal time for its construction, for then most brooks are at their lowest level and the water will not impede the progress of work.

Four basic types of small dams are shown in the accompanying drawings. All are adaptable in general to the kind of materials likely to be on hand and also to the head of power desired.

There are two basic principles of design to bear in mind no matter which you build. First, a dam should be sealed both above and below its foundation to prevent the seepage of water through or under it. Seepage through a dam, if permitted, weakens the structure and will eventually break it; that under a dam will undermine its foundation. Then, too, some means must be provided to prevent undermining of the dam by the water that flows or spills over it.

In addition, you should check with your local authorities and possibly file plans for your dam with them. General supervision comes under the Water Board.

Figure 7 illustrates the earth dam. Sealing this type of dam is most important, since seepage will literally carry it away if allowed to progress. The seal is put in first and the dam built around it. How far down it should go depends upon the kind of soil. A sand foundation, for instance, requires the seal to extend deeper than clay. If planking is used, it would be well to apply a protective coat such as tar or creosote.

A general pattern for depositing the earth fill is shown in the drawing, but it is not necessary to follow it unless different types of earth are available. Deposit the fill by layers, rolling and tamping each layer well. Then protect the waterside surface from erosion by covering it with a matting woven from brush. Plant turf on the top and downstream side to hold the earth.

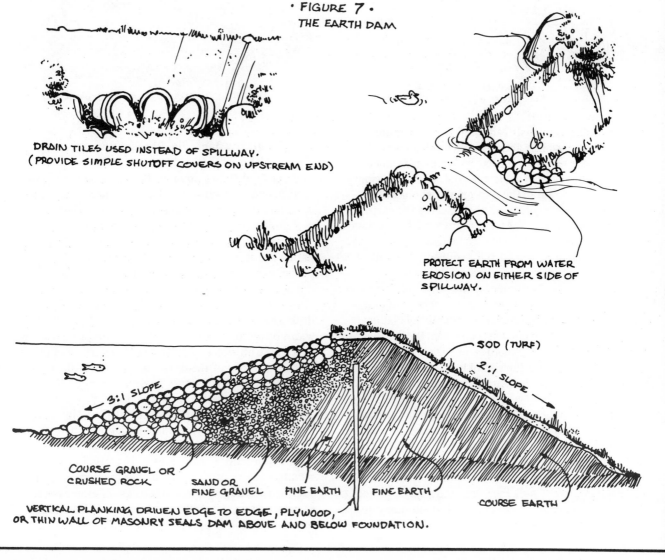

· FIGURE 7 ·
THE EARTH DAM

DRAIN TILES USED INSTEAD OF SPILLWAY.
(PROVIDE SIMPLE SHUTOFF COVERS ON UPSTREAM END)

PROTECT EARTH FROM WATER EROSION ON EITHER SIDE OF SPILLWAY.

SOD (TURF)

2:1 SLOPE

◄ 3:1 SLOPE

COURSE GRAVEL OR CRUSHED ROCK

SAND OR FINE GRAVEL

FINE EARTH

FINE EARTH

COURSE EARTH

VERTICAL PLANKING DRIVEN EDGE TO EDGE, PLYWOOD, OR THIN WALL OF MASONRY SEALS DAM ABOVE AND BELOW FOUNDATION.

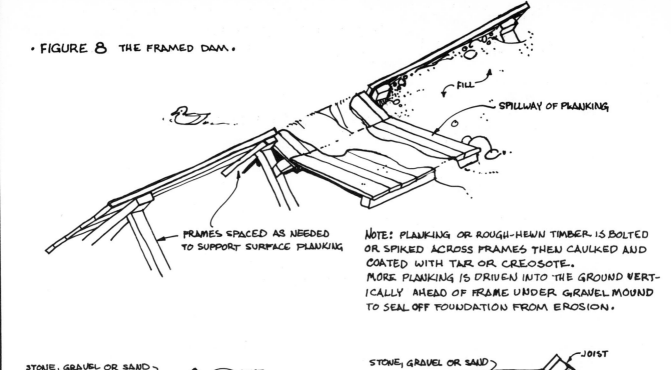

• FIGURE 8 THE FRAMED DAM •

FILL

SPILLWAY OF PLANKING

FRAMES SPACED AS NEEDED
TO SUPPORT SURFACE PLANKING

NOTE: PLANKING OR ROUGH-HEWN TIMBER IS BOLTED
OR SPIKED ACROSS FRAMES THEN CAULKED AND
COATED WITH TAR OR CREOSOTE.
MORE PLANKING IS DRIVEN INTO THE GROUND VERT-
ICALLY AHEAD OF FRAME UNDER GRAVEL MOUND
TO SEAL OFF FOUNDATION FROM EROSION.

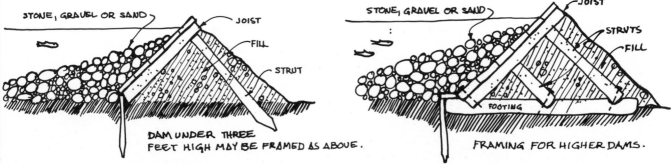

STONE, GRAVEL OR SAND
JOIST
FILL
STRUT

DAM UNDER THREE
FEET HIGH MAY BE FRAMED AS ABOVE.

STONE, GRAVEL OR SAND
JOIST
STRUTS
FILL
FOOTING

FRAMING FOR HIGHER DAMS.

Such a dam obviously cannot have water spilling over its crest, since this action would wash it away. Two suggestions for handling the excess water are shown. The spillway must be of some material, such as masonry or planking, resistant to the erosion of rushing water, and the sides must protect the open ends of the earth dam from spillage water. An alternative method of handling runoff water is with drain tiles instead of a spillway. Some means must be provided for shutting them off. A simple cover on the upstream end would serve.

Figure 8 shows the framed dam, which likewise can be easily built, particularly on a farm where lumber in any form from logs to planks is abundantly available. Each frame consists of one joist, on which the surface timber is laid, and one or more struts. Once the height of the dam is determined, the size of individual frames will vary depending on the contour of the gulley, those frames located at the lowest part being the largest. The frames are spaced according to the support the surface timber needs; that is, the thinner the surfacing, the more supports needed.

Lay the planking surface or rough-hewn timber horizontally and edge to edge across the frames, and bolt or spike each in place. Caulk the joints and apply a protective coating. Fill is put in behind the downstream side. Build the spillway entirely of planking or similar materi-al.

The gravity dam (Fig. 9) relies upon its weight for its stability. This dam would be most feasible where large rocks or field stones abound. Bricks, concrete or cinder blocks, and even chunks of broken concrete pavement are also excellent materials. The dam is strictly a masonry type, each block being laid with mortar.

Length is not a critical factor for any of these three dams, but it is important for the arch dam (Fig. 10). The placement of such a dam in a gulley is limited not only to the point of least width, but also to the point where the banks are highest. Otherwise, this dam would impound little water. It would seem unwise to build one to span a width of more than 10'. If the heavy timber is used only as a frame on which to spike or bolt a surface of planking, as shown in one of the drawings in Figure 10, the number of timber arches will depend on the strength of the planking and also on the height of the dam.

Only early foundations are considered in the drawings, but you may be fortunate enough to have a solid rock foundation on which to build. In that case a seal below the foundation will not be necessary, but some means must be provided to anchor the dam to the rock, such as with anchor bolts in the case of either the framed or gravity dam. Likewise the dam should be sealed at the rock foundation to prevent seepage under it.

ROCK, GRAVEL OR SAND.

BRICK, CONCRETE BLOCK, CINDER BLOCK, BROCKEN PAVEMENT, OR FIELDSTONE

• FIGURE 9 •
THE GRAVITY DAM

In most instances it will be found best to restrict the width of the spillway for excess water to some part of the total length of the dam. This will always be necessary in the case of an earth dam, to prevent washing. The spillage water may be allowed to pour over the entire length of framed, gravity, and arch dams, however, if the precautions shown in Figure 11 are taken.

If the downstream side of the dam, or of the spillway, is a curved hard surface of masonry or timber approximating the natural curvature of the water flowing over, it will guide the spillage water so it will be directed downstream without actually falling. Such a curved spillway surface is particularly satisfactory for an earth dam. Large rocks, bricks, or other hard objects placed on the downstream side of a spillway not having a curved surface will break the force of the free-falling water and prevent erosion.

The spillway in its simplest form takes the shape of a rectangular depression in the crest of the dam. It should usually be large enough to carry off sufficient excess water, so that impounded waters will not top the dam at any season of the year. This, of course, is quite a problem, since accurate determination of spillway capacity requires a knowledge of the total area drained by the creek being dammed, plus data on the amount of rainfall at all seasons.

However, most of us will know whether or not the creek we are damming stays within its banks during the year. If it does, then a safe rule to apply would be to make the area of the spillway equal to the cross-section area of the creek at the dam when it is brimful or just ready to flood. The formula is illustrated in Figure 11.

If the stream does flood, then either construct a dam that in an emergency can allow water to top its full length or build some sort of floodgate into the dam so it can be opened when necessary. One form such a floodgate could take is a group of drain tiles through the dam, as shown in Figure 7.

The height of the dam you build will be determined by the area of the land to be covered by the impounded water. In general, the higher the dam, the greater the area covered by water above it.

All vegetation, brush, floatage, and the like in the area to be flooded, and for about 15' around it, should be burned out or otherwise cleared before the dam is built. This keeps down the breeding of mosquitoes and helps retard pollution. It is required in the regulations of some states and is a wise precaution even when not covered by law. In addition, all trees in the area to be flooded should be cut reasonably close to the ground.

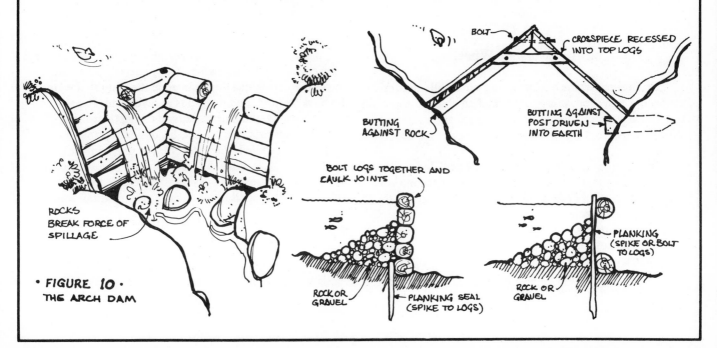

ROCKS BREAK FORCE OF SPILLAGE

• FIGURE 10 •
THE ARCH DAM

BOLT

CROSSPIECE RECESSED INTO TOP LOGS

BUTTING AGAINST ROCK

BUTTING AGAINST POST DRIVEN INTO EARTH

BOLT LOGS TOGETHER AND CAULK JOINTS

ROCK OR GRAVEL

PLANKING SEAL (SPIKE TO LOGS)

ROCK OR GRAVEL

PLANKING (SPIKE OR BOLT TO LOGS)

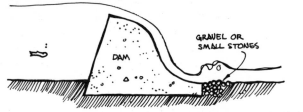

• CURVATURE OF SPILLAGE APPROXIMATED WITH MASONRY •

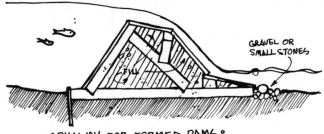

• SPILLWAY FOR FORMED DAMS •

• FIGURE 11 •

METHODS OF PREVENTING SPILLAGE FROM UNDERMINING DAM

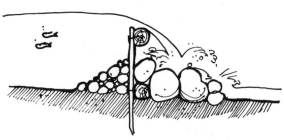

• ROCKS BREAK FORCE OF SPILLAGE •

$L \times H = W \times D$

L IS LENGTH OF SPILLWAY
H IS DEPTH OF SPILLWAY
W IS AVERAGE WIDTH OF BRIMFULL CREEK
D IS FULL DEPTH OF CREEK

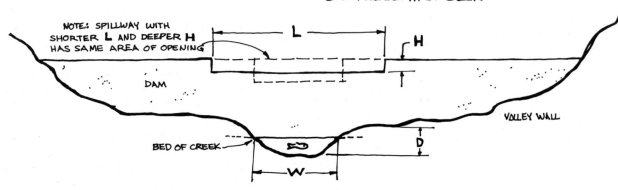

NOTE: SPILLWAY WITH SHORTER **L** AND DEEPER **H** HAS SAME AREA OF OPENING

Building An Overshot Wheel

Often seen beside a picturesque rural mill, an overshot water wheel possesses two excellent characteristics — considerable mechanical efficiency and easy maintenance. Many have remained in service for decades.

Operated by gravity, the overshot wheel derives its name from the manner in which water enters the buckets set around its periphery. Pouring from a flume above the wheel, the water shoots into buckets on the down-moving side, overbalancing the empty ones opposite and keeping the wheel in slow rotation.

Such a wheel may be located near, but not actually in a stream. If a site on dry ground is chosen, the foundation may be constructed dry and the water led to the wheel and a tailrace excavated.

It should be noted, however, that an overshot wheel is practical only for a small-capacity output. How much power it will produce depends upon the weight of water the buckets hold, and its radius or lever arm. Expressed in another way, the output depends upon the weight of water transported and the height, or head, through which it falls while in the buckets. For maximum efficiency, the wheel must use the weight of the water through as much of the head as possible. Therefore, the buckets should not spill or sling water until very near tail water.

Power Increases with Width

Although of simple construction, an overshot wheel is cumbersome in size. For this reason, before attempting to build one, be certain you have the facilities to move and lift it into place when completed. Also allow yourself plenty of working floor space. It must be under-

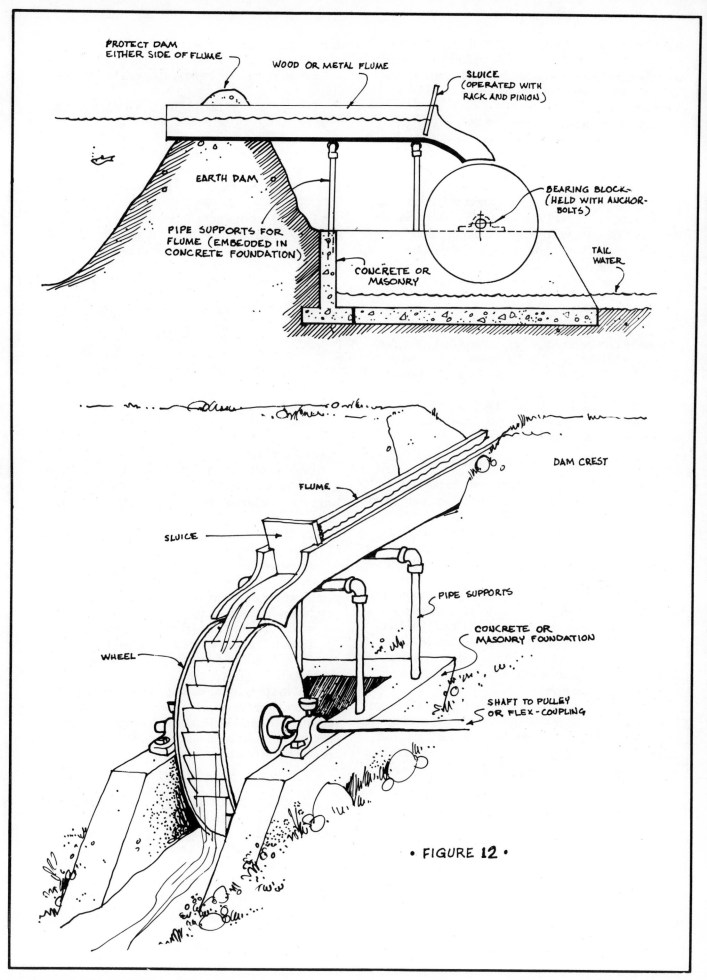

PROTECT DAM
EITHER SIDE OF FLUME

WOOD OR METAL FLUME

SLUICE
(OPERATED WITH
RACK AND PINION)

EARTH DAM

BEARING BLOCK
(HELD WITH ANCHOR
BOLTS)

PIPE SUPPORTS FOR
FLUME (EMBEDDED IN
CONCRETE FOUNDATION)

CONCRETE OR
MASONRY

TAIL
WATER

DAM CREST

FLUME

SLUICE

PIPE SUPPORTS

CONCRETE OR
MASONRY FOUNDATION

WHEEL

SHAFT TO PULLEY
OR FLEX-COUPLING

• FIGURE 12 •

stood, too, that such a wheel is a sizable project and requires a lot of material and time. Extreme care in cutting and assembling the parts is not essential, however, because the wheel, operating at slow speed, need not be accurately balanced.

Accompanying this article are drawings that illustrate the construction of a small wheel suitable for a water head of 6'3". The wheel itself has a diameter of 5', leaving a flume head of 15" to propel the water into the buckets. As shown in the table at the bottom of page 56, you may build the wheel to give a power output ranging from 1/2 hp. to 1 hp. at 10 r.p.m. All dimensions remain the same except the width, the horsepower increasing as this is increased. For 1/2 hp., the wheel should be 15-31/32" wide. For 1 hp., it should be 31-29/31." Before deciding on the wheel size, read Guy Immega's article on page 57.

Virtually all large wheels are built with wood or steel arms, as in the drawing above, and have a shroud plate only around the outer edge, but you may find it simpler and more satisfactory to build the drum-type wheel described here. In this case, each shroud plate is a disc of 1/8" sheet steel sole plate to which it is continuously welded by the buckets, by one of the two large diameter 1/4" steel hub flanges to which it is also continuously welded, and by the long hub itself.

Large Sheet Required

If preferred, the shroud plates may be made of wood. If so, care should be taken to bolt them securely to the hub flanges. Bushings pressed into the wood for bolts will give the wheel a longer life expectancy.

Sheet steel for the discs may be ordered direct from several large companies, in case your local supply house is unable to furnish it. Ordinarily, such steel comes in standard 48" widths, so you may have to weld together two or more sheets to get the required 5' diameter, using either a butt weld or a backing plate. This will produce some distortion or ripple, as will the welding on of the numerous clips required. So long as distortion is local, however, and the main lines of wheel and shaft remain true, this will do no harm.

After the sheet has been prepared, scribe a 5' circle on it and cut it with the cutting flame of a gas welding torch. With ordinary care, this method should give sufficient accuracy. Vent and drainage holes should be drilled as indicated around each disc to lessen corrosion with the drum.

Good Buckets Important

The buckets are the most important element of the wheel. To give maximum efficiency, they must be formed so that the water enters smoothly at the top of their travel and remains in them until just before they reach the bottom. For this reason, the bucket form indicated on page 55 should be followed faithfully. Either sheet metal or wood is an acceptable material, but metal is better suited to cold climates, since wood is damaged when ab-

sorbed water freezes. Because the buckets are subject to wear from the water and sediment that it carries along, you may want to install them so they can be easily replaced.

In laying out and making wooden buckets, follow these steps:

Using a common centre, strike off two arcs, one with a 21-1/2" radius and the other with a 2'6" radius. Then draw a radius line intersecting these arcs.

From the point where the radius crosses the outer arc, draw a chord 10-1/2" long and, from the new point where this intersects the outer arc, draw a line to point E. You now have the inner trace of the bucket.

Take a piece of the bucket stock and lay it along the upper edge of this inner trace, and you have a cross-section through the bucket. Cut your stock accordingly, making the length equal to B in the table of dimensions.

Steel Buckets Require Jig

Steel buckets are only slightly more difficult, if you follow these steps:

Using a common centre, strike off two arcs on a piece of plywood, one with a 21-1/2" radius and the other with a 2'6" radius.

Draw a radius line and then a tangent to the inner arc, making it vertical to the radius. From the point of tangency, measure 5" along the tangent. Mark this point.

Using this mark as a centre, strike off an arc with a 5" radius. This is part of the inner trace of the bucket.

At the point where the original radius line (step 2) crosses the outer arc, draw a chord 10-1/2" long, and at point F where this chord intersects the outer arc, draw a new radius line. Also at point F, measure off 15° of the new radius and draw line FG 11-1/2" long.

Then, using G as a centre, strike an arc with an 11-1/2" radius. This forms the rest of the inner trace of the bucket.

Cut the plywood along this line and along the lines that form a quarter ellipse. Using this as a pattern, cut several more quarter ellipses from scrap. Nail these to stretchers to make a bending jig around which the buckets may be formed.

Weld Wheel Parts

Welding of the various parts of the wheel produces an exceptionally strong construction. After getting together or making all the required parts, begin the assembly by welding four clips to each end of the hub sleeve. Then weld the required number of clips to the shroud plates for the sole plate, and weld the shroud plates to the clips on the hub sleeve. After welding both hub flanges to the shroud plates and the sleeve with a continuous weld, attach the sole plate to the clips on the shroud plates with No. 8 self-tapping screws. Also weld the sole plate to the shroud plates with a continuous weld, and the bucket-support angles to the sole plate.

Attach wooden buckets to the supports with 3/4" No. 10 roundhead wood screws. If you use steel buckets, rivet or screw 10 clips to each side of each bucket and attach the buckets to the angles with No. 8 self-tapping screws. Then drill holes through the shroud plates in the way of the clips for the same type of screws.

Lubricate Bearings Well

Using locknuts and washers, fasten the hub sleeve to the shaft with two 3/8" by 4-1/2" bolts, placed at right angles to each other. Two bearing mountings having 2-3/8" renewable liners with shoulders should be bolted to the foundation. Place shims about 1/4" thick under the bearings.

Standard bearing mountings, variously called pedestals or blocks, may be bought complete with wick oiler or cup oil reservoir and with built-in self-aligning features. Standard bronze-bearing metal liners or inserts likewise may be bought from any machine component supplier. Babbitt liners are equally satisfactory.

Although the wheel turns slowly, it is heavy and will be running almost constantly, so good lubrication of the bearings is essential. To this end, care should be taken to insure that the bearing liners are finished to the correct fit. Porous inserts or inserts containing graphite are ex-

cellent for this application, but may cost more than regular bearing inserts.

It is important that the foundation be carried deep enough so that water falling from the buckets will not undermine it. Avoid a long flume if possible, in order to keep the construction as simple as possible. Strengthen it along its entire length with an exterior frame and support it well from dam to wheel with pipe uprights.

Sluice Governs Wheel

The sluice gate may be located at any convenient place along the flume. Since it is the governing mechanism of the wheel, its installation should be anything but slipshod. If it is installed at an angle, as on the following page, water pressure will keep it at any desired position. If installed vertically, some mechanism, such as a rack and pinion, should be provided to keep it in place.

Adjust the sluice so that the buckets will run one-quarter full. This will give a wheel speed of 10 r.p.m. If the buckets are allowed to run more than one-quarter full, the efficiency of the wheel will drop for two reasons. Because of the increased speed, centrifugal force will throw water from the buckets. They also will begin to spill before approaching tail water. Although this practice does waste water, it may be profitably employed during freshet to increase the power output, for at such times the excess water would be wasted anyway.

· FIGURE 13 ·

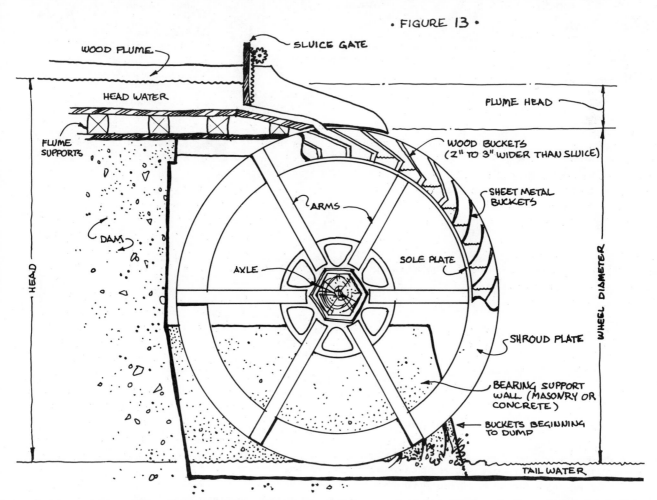

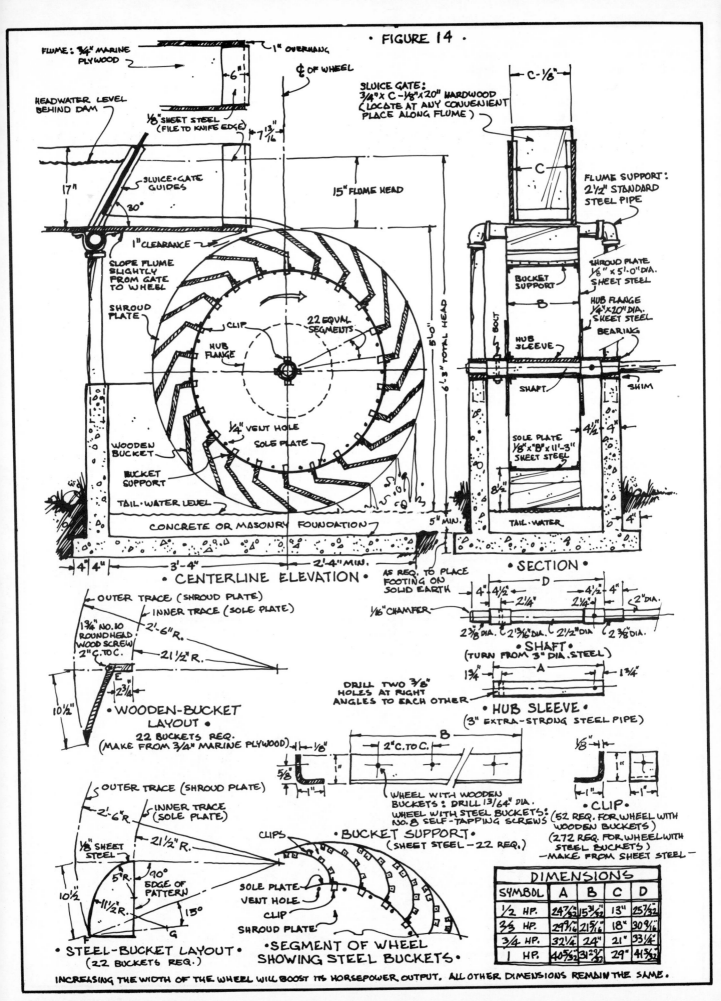

· FIGURE 14 ·

FLUME: 3/4" MARINE PLYWOOD

HEADWATER LEVEL BEHIND DAM

1" OVERHANG

6"

₵ OF WHEEL

SLUICE GATE: 3/4" x C -1/8" x 20" HARDWOOD (LOCATE AT ANY CONVENIENT PLACE ALONG FLUME)

C -1/8"

1/8" SHEET STEEL (FILE TO KNIFE EDGE)

7 13/16"

C

FLUME SUPPORT: 2 1/2" STANDARD STEEL PIPE

17"

SLUICE GATE GUIDES

15" FLUME HEAD

30°

1" CLEARANCE

SLOPE FLUME SLIGHTLY FROM GATE TO WHEEL

SHROUD PLATE

CLIP

22 EQUAL SEGMENTS

HUB FLANGE

SHROUD PLATE 1/8" x 5'-0" DIA. SHEET STEEL

BUCKET SUPPORT

B

HUB FLANGE 1/4" x 20" DIA. SHEET STEEL

HUB SLEEVE

BEARING

BOLT

6'-3" TOTAL HEAD

SHAFT

SHIM

WOODEN BUCKET

1/4" VENT HOLE

SOLE PLATE

SOLE PLATE 1/8" x "B" x 11'-3" SHEET STEEL

4 1/2" 4"

BUCKET SUPPORT

TAIL-WATER LEVEL

8 1/2"

CONCRETE OR MASONRY FOUNDATION

5" MIN.

TAIL· WATER

4"

· SECTION ·

4" 4"

3'-4"

2'-4" MIN.

· CENTERLINE ELEVATION ·

AS REQ. TO PLACE FOOTING ON SOLID EARTH

4" 4 1/2"

D

4 1/2" 4"

OUTER TRACE (SHROUD PLATE)

INNER TRACE (SOLE PLATE)

1/16" CHAMFER

2 1/4"

2 1/4"

2" DIA.

1 3/4" NO.10 ROUNDHEAD WOOD SCREW 2" C. TO C.

2'-6" R.

21 1/2" R.

2 3/8" DIA. 2 13/16" DIA. 2 1/2" DIA. 2 3/8" DIA.

· SHAFT · (TURN FROM 3" DIA. STEEL)

E

2 3/4"

10 1/2"

· WOODEN-BUCKET LAYOUT ·

DRILL TWO 3/8" HOLES AT RIGHT ANGLES TO EACH OTHER

1 3/4"

A

1 3/4"

· HUB SLEEVE · (3" EXTRA-STRONG STEEL PIPE)

22 BUCKETS REQ. (MAKE FROM 3/4" MARINE PLYWOOD)

1/8"

2" C. TO C.

B

1/8"

OUTER TRACE (SHROUD PLATE)

5/8"

1"

1"

2'-6" R.

INNER TRACE (SOLE PLATE)

21 1/2" R.

1/8" SHEET STEEL

5" R.

90° EDGE OF PATTERN

WHEEL WITH WOODEN BUCKETS: DRILL 13/64" DIA. WHEEL WITH STEEL BUCKETS: NO. 8 SELF-TAPPING SCREWS

· CLIP ·

(52 REQ. FOR WHEEL WITH WOODEN BUCKETS)

CLIPS

10 1/2"

11 1/2" R.

15°

SOLE PLATE

VENT HOLE

CLIP

· BUCKET SUPPORT · (SHEET STEEL - 22 REQ.)

(272 REQ. FOR WHEEL WITH STEEL BUCKETS) —MAKE FROM SHEET STEEL —

G

SHROUD PLATE

· STEEL-BUCKET LAYOUT · (22 BUCKETS REQ.)

· SEGMENT OF WHEEL SHOWING STEEL BUCKETS ·

DIMENSIONS				
SYMBOL	A	B	C	D
1/2 HP.	24 7/32	15 3/4"	13"	25 7/32
2/3 HP.	29 1/16	21 5/16	18"	30 9/16
3/4 HP.	32 1/4	24"	21"	33 1/4
1 HP.	40 5/32	31 29/32	29"	41 5/32

INCREASING THE WIDTH OF THE WHEEL WILL BOOST ITS HORSEPOWER OUTPUT. ALL OTHER DIMENSIONS REMAIN THE SAME.

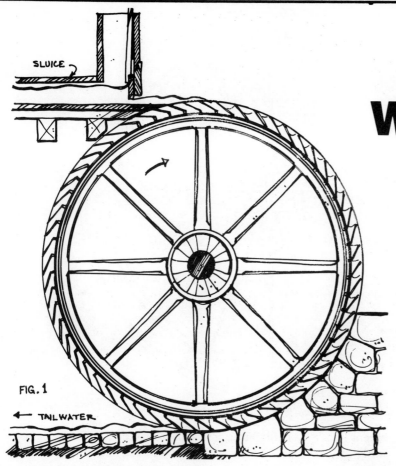

SLUICE

FIG. 1

← TAILWATER

Water Wheel Design

by Guy Immega

Choice of Wheel

There are three basic types of traditional water wheels. The overshot wheel takes water in at the top and discharges it at the bottom. The breast wheel takes water in somewhere in the middle of the wheel and discharges it at the bottom. The undershot wheel (Poncelet) both accepts and discharges water at the bottom.

The choice of wheel design depends largely upon its location. If you have a high head of water (20 feet or more), then an overshot wheel is a good choice, because a fairly narrow wheel (small volume) can be built and no complicated breastworks are required. A disadvantage of the overshot wheel is that it requires an elevated feed trough, and a power license (since the water is taken out of the stream bed).

A breast wheel is suitable for falls of between 5 and 15 feet. It is more difficult to build, because a breastwork (a shaped shoulder under the wheel designed to retain water on the wheel) is required, and the wheel must be wider to get the same power out.

A Poncelet undershot wheel is suitable for falls under seven feet. It must be very wide (for the same power), and requires a fitted race beneath the wheel.

For heads of 50 feet or more, a Pelton wheel is a good choice. Pelton wheels require very little water and a long feed pipe.

Overshot and High Breast Wheels

The simplest and most efficient of traditional water wheels are the overshot and highbreast wheels. Water enters at or near the top of the wheel, is carried down one side of the wheel in buckets, and is discharged at the bottom. The power of the wheel is not derived from the speed of the water entering the wheel, but from the force of gravity acting on the loaded side of the wheel — thus deriving the classification of "gravity wheels" (as opposed to impulse wheels and turbines). Gravity wheels in general are large in diameter, and operate at slow speed with high torque.

Overshot: An overshot wheel (fig. 1) is usually constructed with a nearly horizontal feed trough such that the water will enter the buckets with a velocity somewhat greater than the wheel, so as not to be struck by the back of the buckets and be thrown off the wheel. A sluice gate is generally provided at the end of the pentrough to regulate the amount of water in the feed trough. An important modification of the overshot wheel is the pitch-back wheel, in which the direction of waterflow is reversed in the pentrough so that water may smoothly enter the wheel, and exit so that the bottom is eight or nine inches above the tailrace (level of millpond); then the direction of the water will be reversed as the water falls out of the wheel into the tailrace, thus allowing a pitch-back wheel to rotate in the opposite direction, and use a straight pentrough feed.

A weakness in the design of overshot wheels is that water begins to be discharged at a point above the bottom of the wheel, and thus escapes before it has done all

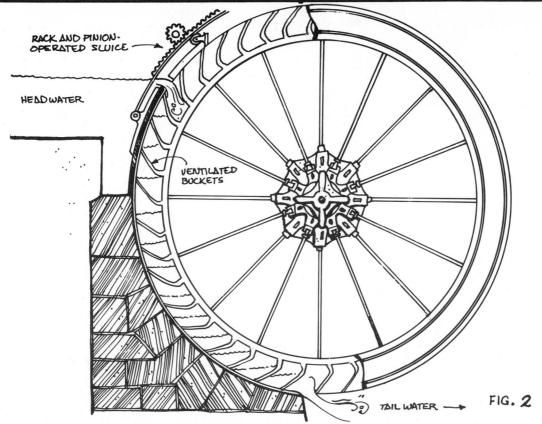

RACK AND PINION-
OPERATED SLUICE

HEADWATER

VENTILATED
BUCKETS

TAIL WATER →

FIG. 2

the work due to the fall. Three solutions to this problem are: (1) use a curvilinear form of bucket; (2) only partly fill the buckets (build a wider wheel); (3) build a close fitting-stationary breast to retain the water on the lower half of the wheel. Overshot wheels are from 60 to 75 per cent efficient, and require 12 to 10.8 cubic feet per second, to obtain one horsepower per foot of fall.

Breast Wheels: Breast wheels generally receive water below the top of the wheel, and have a close-fitting breast to keep water on the wheel. Some designs include a curved feed sluice gate which is lifted to obtain closure — rather than lowered — so that water entering the wheel will be at maximum possible elevation; this scheme allows the water to enter the wheel at variable levels, according to the height of the river. The design of this sluice gate is more complicated, as it usually is curving to fit the wheel, and must fit tightly at the bottom so as not to leak water to a lower portion of the wheel. After the sluice gate, there are often guide plates to divide the water into the wheel.

The design of the buckets on breast wheels is different from overshot wheels. The difference is that the buckets are ventilated, so as to allow air to escape as they are being filled. This obviates the problem of incomplete filling. There are two basic types of ventilated buckets: with and without a sole plate. The sole plate is a hoop of material as wide as the wheel, which isolates the back of the buckets from the inside of the wheel. Ventilated buckets without a sole plate allow air and excess water to vent to the interior of the wheel. Ventilated buckets with a sole plate allow air and excess water to vent to the next highest bucket. Obviously, the ventilated bucket with sole plate is the most efficient.

In high breast wheels of 25 feet in diameter or larger, the breast is not required as the buckets have narrower openings (as with an overshot wheel), and to retain water longer on the wheel. In this case, the loss due to spilling does not warrant the effort involved in building a high and close-fitting breast. Breasts can be constructed from wood and sheet metal, or from masonry. To be most efficient, they should be close-fitting. With a close-fitting breast, care must be taken to avoid having large foreign objects enter the wheel, as they will get caught between the wheel and the breast and cause damage. Breast wheels should always be mounted above the tail water, and the bottom of the breast itself should stop about 10 inches from the extremity of the vertical diameter of the wheel. Both precautions are designed to prevent wheel drag. The efficiency of breast wheels is about 60 per cent.

Wheel speed: The speed of the periphery (edge) of overshot and breast water wheels is usually between four and six feet per second. A minimum velocity of three feet six inches per second is standard for falls of 40 to 45 feet,

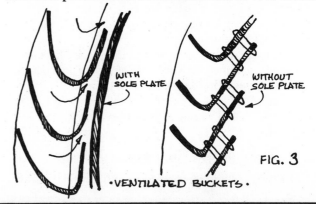

WITH
SOLE PLATE

WITHOUT
SOLE PLATE

FIG. 3

·VENTILATED BUCKETS·

and a maximum velocity of seven feet per second is standard for falls five or six feet. In general, the higher the fall, the slower the edge speed, and vice versa; the formula is s equals 7.44 h (.088) where s is speed in feet per second, and h is height of fall in feet.

Wheel Buckets: Bucket aperture is the narrowest distance between buckets measured perpendicularly to the direction in which the water enters the wheel. Bucket aperture varies according to how high up on the wheel the water enters. The aperture should be from five and a half to eight inches for high breast wheels, and from 9 to 12 inches for low breast wheels. Note: Bucket aperture is different from bucket spacing.

The area of opening of the buckets is the product of bucket aperture times the length between the shroud (inside width of wheel). For overshot and high breast wheels, one square foot area of opening per five cubic feet of bucket capacity is usual; for breast wheels which receive water at a height of not more than 10 degrees above the horizontal diameter, one square foot area of opening per three cubic feet of bucket capacity is usual. With these proportions, the depth of the shrouding (depth of bucket toward centre of the wheel) is assumed to be about two to two and a half times the bucket aperture.

The spacing of buckets, or their distance apart, should be from one to one and a half feet. The approximate formula is n equals 2.5d, where n is the number of buckets, and d is the diameter of the wheel.

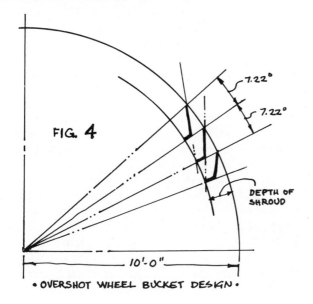

• OVERSHOT WHEEL BUCKET DESIGN •

The shape of buckets is important to the operation of the wheel. The ideal shape is a curvilinear one, but often it is more practical to approximate the ideal with straight sections. For overshot wheels (fig. 4), a convenient method for determining the bucket shape is to draw one radius inclined 34° from the horizontal, and a second radius exactly one bucket arc (determined from the computed number of buckets on the wheel) below it; if a vertical line is drawn through the point determined by outer edge

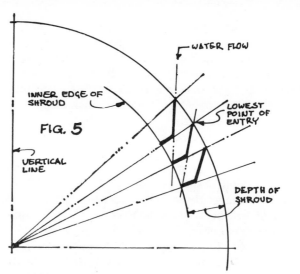

• BREAST WHEEL BUCKET DESIGN •

of the wheel and the first radius, then the bucket shape is defined by the vertical line and the second radius. The depth of the shrouds (the shrouds are the outer sides of the buckets — they determine the depth of the buckets, measured towards the centre of the wheel) is usually twice the bucket aperture (bucket aperture being the smallest dimension between buckets, and not bucket spacing).

The shape of the buckets for breast wheels is determined slightly differently. The wheel is planned so that the point and angle at which water enters the wheel is known; entry should be nearly tangential. Since the breast of a breast wheel is designed to keep the water on the wheel, the bucket shape need not be designed to hold water all the way to the bottom; therefore, the bucket shape (fig. 5) is planned to allow maximum ease of water entry, which means that the initial angle of entry of water determines the shape of the bucket. To be precise, a line is drawn from the bottom edge of the feed trough in the direction of water flow to the wheel. Through the point where this flow line intersects the outside edge of the wheel, draw a radius. Draw a second radius exactly one bucket arc (determined from the computed number of buckets on the wheel) below it. The bucket shape is then defined by the flow line and the second radius. The depth of the bucket is again two to two and a half times the bucket aperture.

Design Computations: The design of a water wheel is done according to the following steps. First the height of fall, and the volume of flow of the stream are determined. The amount of power available can then be computed. Next, the type of wheel should be selected: overshot wheels are easier to build, breast wheels can use lower falls. The selection of wheel will determine its diameter. The form of bucket is next determined. The computed edge speed of the wheel, and the volume flow of the stream, will determine the volume capacity of the bucket necessary. (Note: The buckets should never be more than 1/3 to 1/2 filled). The volume capacity of the buckets will fix the necessary breadth (width) of the wheel.

As an example, suppose you have a little stream (30 inches wide and 6-1/2 inches deep) with a flow of 200 cu. feet per min. which has a head of 20 feet. This makes 7.87 horsepower (for power calculations, see page 40) available. If you wish to build an overshot wheel on this creek (it's the simplest to build), the diameter of the wheel will be 20 feet.

The number of buckets is n equals 2.5 (20) equals 50 buckets; one bucket arc equals 360/50 equals 7.22 degrees. From the geometry of the wheel, it is determined that the depth of shroud is about 1.12 feet or 12-3/4 inches. The distance between buckets equals the circumference of the wheel divided by 50 equals 20 pi/50 equals 1.25 feet per bucket. The edge speed of the wheel is s equals 7.44 - 20(.088) equals 5.69 feet per second.

Therefore the number of buckets which pass the feed sluice per second is the edge speed divided by the bucket spacing: 5.69 feet per second divided by 1.25 feet per bucket equals 4.55 buckets per second. The volume flow of the stream is 200 cubic feet per minute, which equals 3.33 cubic feet per second. Therefore, the amount of water each bucket must hold is the volume flow of the stream divided by the number of buckets per second, which is 3.3 cubic feet per second divided by 4.55 buckets per second, equals .69 cubic feet per bucket. The sectional area of each bucket is the area of the wheel minus the area of the wheel to the bottom of the buckets, divided by 50 buckets: (pi x 10 squared minus pi x 8.98 squared) divided by 50 equals (314 - 254) divided by 50 equals 1.2 square feet. Therefore the breadth of the wheel must be volume of the bucket divided by the sectional area equals .69 cubic feet per bucket divided by 1.2 square feet per bucket equals .572 feet wheel width. Since each bucket must be only 1/2 to 1/3 full, the breadth of the wheel should really be about 1-1/2 feet.

Checking the geometry, the bucket aperture is about 5 inches (assuming 1/2 inch thickness of wood in the bucket). The aperture times the wheel breadth equals about .6 square feet opening per 2 cubic feet total bucket volume, which is the same as 1 square foot bucket opening per 3.3 cubic feet bucket volume. Therefore the area

of opening of the bucket is rather larger than the ideal, 1 square foot to 5 cubic feet volume. This means that the outer boards of the bucket should be larger and closer to back of the preceding bucket. This would both decrease the area of opening, and help retain the water on the wheel for a longer time.

Undershot Wheels

A well designed low breast wheel is, in effect, an undershot wheel. It is of course, a gravity wheel, because the weight of the water causes the wheel to turn. There is another class of undershot wheels which are called impulse wheels, because it is the velocity of the water striking the wheel which causes it to turn. The conceptual ideal of an impulse wheel is to extract all the kinetic energy from moving water, reducing the forward velocity of the water to zero, and afterward letting it drain vertically downward. For this to happen, the edge speed of the wheel must be one-half the velocity of the water.

Primitive impulse undershot wheels were very imperfect in this respect, as the speed of the tailrace was considerable. The Poncelet wheel (fig. 6), however, is quite effective, being as good or better than a low breast wheel, and giving efficiencies of better than 60 per cent.

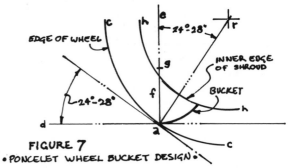

FIGURE 7
• PONCELET WHEEL BUCKET DESIGN •

The buckets on a Poncelet (fig. 7) wheel are curved, and open toward the interior of the wheel. To lay out the shape of the buckets, draw an arc cc as part of the external circumference of the wheel, and draw ar to be the radius of the wheel. Let ab equal 1/3 to 1/4 the height of fall, and draw hh as the inner circumference of the shrouding. Let the water first strike the bucket at the point a, from the direction da, so that the angle ear will be from 24 degrees to 28 degrees. On the line ae, draw fg equals 1/6 af. From the centre g, with a radius ga, draw an arc from point a to the inner edge of the shroud; this arc describes the shape of a Poncelet wheel bucket. With less efficiency, this shape may approximated with two or three straight boards.

The number of buckets on the wheel is determined by the formula n equals 8/5d plus 16, where n is the number of buckets, and d is the diameter of the wheel. The velocity of the water entering the wheel may be approximated by measuring the volume flow into the wheel (upstream) in cubic feet per minute and dividing this by the area of the opening to the wheel in feet squared, yielding an answer in feet per minute water speed. To obtain maximum power from the wheel, the edge speed of the wheel must be one-half the water velocity.

• PONCELET WHEEL •

FIG. 6

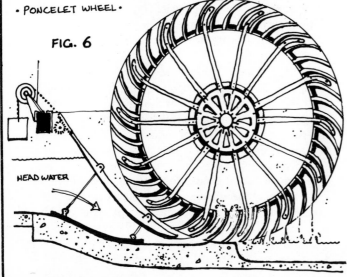

HEAD WATER

The bottom 18 to 20 inchedes of the wheel must be very carefully fitted to the race for efficient operation. Also, the tailrace should expand in width and depth to keep the wheel clear of backwater.

The wheel shown in the figure was 16 feet 8 inches in diameter, and 30 feet wide, and was driven by a fall 6 feet 6 inches high, yielding 20,000 cubic feet per minute. With an edge speed of 11 to 12 feet per second, the wheel produced 140 horsepower.

Construction of Wheels

Since the speed of water wheels is generally low, they tend to deliver power at high torque; therefore, the axle of the wheel must be very strong. The six-horse-power overshot wheel in the previous example will deliver five or six times the torque of an automobile engine. Therefore a large wooden beam (railroad tie) or tractor axle will be necessary. One method of avoiding torque problems and getting higher shaft speeds is to take power from the outer edge of the wheel; this was usually done with cogs, which are not common today. So it is tricky mechanically.

All gravity wheels must be very strongly built, as they must support the weight of the water on the wheel. Poncelet wheels may be lighter in construction, since they do not support any water weight.

There are two basic methods of wheel construction. The first is to have the spokes of the wheel support weight by compression. The second is to have the spokes support the wheel by tension; a wheel of this type was built with chains as spokes — but this is not recommended. Most wheels operate on a combination of these principles.

New Work: My researches in water wheels have led me to several new design ideas. The first is a valve ventilated overshot wheel. This would allow the bucket openings to be much smaller, while having the buckets fill more quickly and empty later, and thus keep the water on the wheel longer. Simple plastic flap valves might work well. A second design I've been working on is an impulse wheel, midway in head and volume flow between the Poncelet wheel and the Pelton wheel. This wheel would handle heads of about 20 to 50 feet in the form of waterfalls. This would allow small-diameter high-speed wheels to be used, without expensive feed pipes.

Finally, I have been working on an impulse wheel design which will accept water near the centre of the wheel, rather than tangentially. This would increase the speed of the wheel, making it more useful for electrical power generation.

Another device I have designed and built working models of is a "constant flow sluice." This sluice has a constant outflow of water, no matter how much the input changes (above a certain minimum). The sluice is useful in situations where only a small portion of a rather large flow is needed and under low head conditions (for instance, feeding a Michell turbine). The regulation of water flow is accomplished by a low dam with a very low

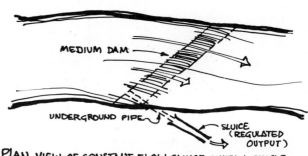

· PLAN VIEW OF CONSTANT FLOW SLUICE WITH A SINGLE STAGE OF REGULATION ·

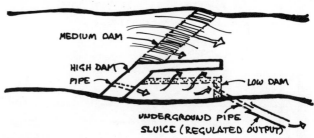

· PLAN VIEW OF CONSTANT FLOW SLUICE WITH TWO STAGES OF REGULATION ·

FIGURE 9

level to several inches above normal stream level. Most of the water flows over the dam, but the sluice later is taken from a pipe under the dam. This sluice water can be regulated again by a second small dam lower than the first. The advantages of the sluice are that it requires no adjustments, and that it is easy to build.

If anyone wishes to work on these or other new designs, please contact me at address below.

Assistance: If anyone needs help on the design or installation of a water wheel, I will be glad to assist. Contact by mail to:

Guy Immega
General Delivery
Lasquiti Island
British Columbia
Canada

Bibliography

Mills and Millwork
by Sir William Fairbairn
Longmans, Green and Co.
London, England
1888.

Power Development of
Small Streams
by Carl C. Harris and
Samuel O. Rice

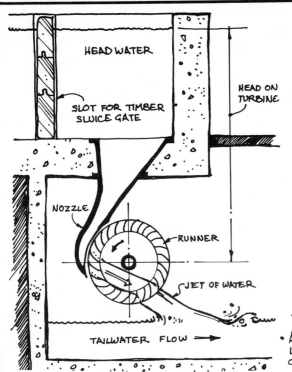

HEAD WATER

HEAD ON TURBINE

SLOT FOR TIMBER SLUICE GATE

NOZZLE

RUNNER

JET OF WATER

TAILWATER FLOW →

• FIGURE 1 •

• ARRANGEMENT FOR LOW HEAD USE WITHOUT CONTROL •

The Michell Turbine

The Michell (or Banki) turbine is simple in construction. Welding equipment and a small machine shop like those often used to repair farm machinery and automotive parts are all that is necessary.

The two main parts of the Michell turbine are the runner and the nozzle. Both are welded from plate steel and require some machining. Figures 1 and 2 show the arrangement of a turbine of this type for low-head use without control. This installation drives a direct-current generator with a belt drive. Because the construction can be a do-it-yourself project, formulas and design details are given for a runner of 12" outside diameter. This size is the smallest which is easy to fabricate and weld. It has a wide range of application for all small power developments with head and flow suitable for the Michell turbine. Different heads result in different rotational speeds. The proper belt drive ratio gives the correct generator speed. Various amounts of water determine the width of the nozzle (B1, figure 2) and the width of the runner (B2, figure 2). These widths may vary from 2" to 14". No other turbine is adaptable to as large a range of flow. The water passes through the runner twice in a narrow jet before discharge into the tailrace. The runner consists of two side plates, each 14" thick with hubs for the shaft attached by welding, and from 20 to 24 blades. Each blade is 0.237" thick and cut from 4" standard pipe. Steel pipe of this type is available virtually everywhere. A pipe of suitable length produces four blades. Each blade is a circular segment with a centre angle of 72 degrees. The runner design, with dimensions for a foot-long runner, is shown in figure 3; and figure 4 gives the nozzle design and dimensions. The dimensions can be altered proportionally for other size runners. Upstream from the nozzle discharge opening of 1-1/4," the shape of the nozzle can be made to suit penstock pipe conditions.

To calculate the principal turbine dimensions:

(B1) = Width of Nozzle (inches)

$$= \frac{210 \times \text{Flow (cubic feet per second)}}{\text{Runner outside diameter (inches} \times \sqrt{\text{Head (feet)}}}$$

(B2) = Width of Runner between Discs
= (B1) + 1.0"

Rotational Speed (rpm)

$$= \frac{862 \times \text{Head (feet)}}{\text{Runner outside diameter (in.)}}$$

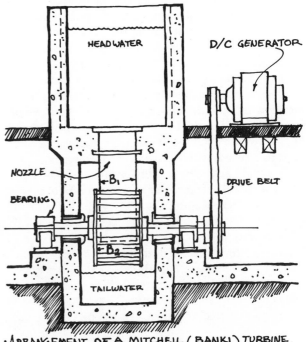

HEAD WATER

D/C GENERATOR

NOZZLE

B_1

BEARING

B_2

DRIVE BELT

TAILWATER

• ARRANGEMENT OF A MITCHELL (BANKI) TURBINE FOR LOW HEAD USE WITHOUT CONTROL (B) •

FIGURE 2

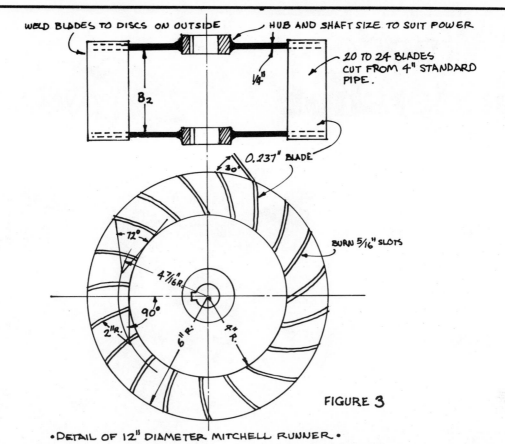

WELD BLADES TO DISCS ON OUTSIDE

HUB AND SHAFT SIZE TO SUIT POWER

B_2

¼"

20 TO 24 BLADES CUT FROM 4" STANDARD PIPE.

0.237" BLADE

30°

72°

BURN ⁵⁄₁₆" SLOTS

4 ⁷⁄₁₆" R.

90°

2" R.

6" R.

4" R.

FIGURE 3

• DETAIL OF 12" DIAMETER MITCHELL RUNNER •

The efficiency of the Michell turbine is 80 per cent or greater and, therefore, suitable for small power installations. Flow regulation and governor control of the flow can be effected by using a centre-body nozzle regulator (a closing mechanism in the shape of a gate in the nozzle). This is expensive because of governor costs. It is, however, needed for running an alternating-current generator.

The application of figures 1 and 2 is a typical example. For high heads the Michell turbine is connected to a penstock with a turbine inlet valve. This requires a different type of arrangement from the one shown here. As mentioned before, the Michell turbine is unique because its B1 and B2 widths can be altered to suit power-site traits of flow rate and head. This, besides simplicity and low cost, makes it the most suitable of all water turbines for small power developments.

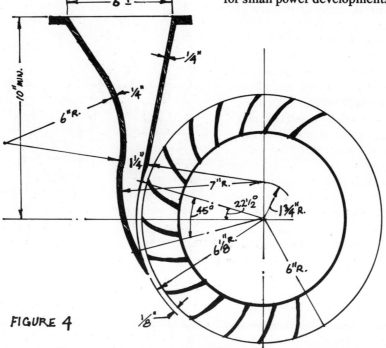

6" ±

10" MIN.

¼"

¼"

6" R.

1¼"

7" R.

22½°

1¾" R.

45°

6⅛" R.

6" R.

⅛"

FIGURE 4

• DETAIL OF NOZZLE FOR 12" DIAMETER MITCHELL RUNNER •

A Wooden Undershot Wheel

by Glen Bass

We divided the construction of the water wheel into three parts: the dam, the trough (or millrace), and the wheel.

The Dam

We used a beaver-type dam. Beavers are very experienced hydraulic engineers. You would be wise to invest some time in studying their methods, if you are going to mess around with a stream. You'll also have to get a power permit and water permit from the local water board.

The first thing we built was the *pier,* which is a log foundation that is embedded in one bank of the stream and lends support to the water wheel. The logs were all pre-cut, numbered, and notched, and then assembled to form the cubic structure which is illustrated in figure 1. In this structure, one side of the cube was left out, and the ends of the logs were embedded sideways into the stream bed with dirt and rocks. It was then filled with more rocks.

Next we built the *pylon.* That was assembled just like the pier, only it was a complete cube. Also, the pylon sits midstream. To install it in the stream, we laced heavy wire across the bottom of the cube to make a basket for the first layer of rocks. Then we floated the structure into position and sank it with rocks (see figure 1). In order to avoid some heavy lifting, it would be easier to assemble just the base of the pylon first, or as many layers as you can carry into the stream from the bank, then position it in the stream, and add the first layer of rocks, and so on. The top layer of the pylon was foreshortened slightly (see figure 2) to provide a base for the support

log, which extended from the pylon to the opposite bank of the stream (see figure 1). This is the backbone of the dam, so use good material. We chose a white pine log, very strong, not too heavy, and it was close to the site. To install the support log, we had to make sure that both ends of the log were secured; the end resting on the bank we secured with dirt and rock, and the end which rested on the pylon was secured with wire.

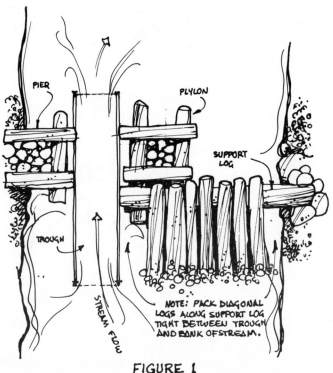

NOTE: PACK DIAGONAL LOGS ALONG SUPPORT LOG TIGHT BETWEEN TROUGH AND BANK OF STREAM.

FIGURE 1

Now we were ready to close the dam. This was actually the very last step in assembling the water wheel, but we did it at this point in order to test the structure before setting the wheel in place. Once the strength of the structure had been tested, the damming, which was composed of brush and support logs, was disassembled and then assembled again later. It was an extra day's work, but it saved us a lot of trouble later.

As in any project, certain steps *must* precede others. *Before closing the dam,* the trough had to be placed between the pier and the pylon, otherwise the rushing water would cut a huge hole in the stream bed, undercut the pier and the pylon, and mess up the whole thing. The trough served to channel the water over wood, rather than over the bottom of the stream, so there was no washing away of stream bottom.

Our next step was to cut a number of small logs. They had to be long enough so that one end of the small log leaned against the support log, while the other end of the small log was embedded in the stream bed and extended out against the current at an angle of 45 degrees relative to the bottom (see figure 2). The small logs were then placed as close together as possible, leaning in a line along the support log (see figure 1). They were not nailed in place. Their placement at a 45-degree angle in relation to the stream bottom distributed the pressure of the rushing water half onto the logs and half onto the stream bed itself. When all the logs were in place, the force of the water held them securely.

To complete the dam, we caulked the logs with lots of bark, brush, old hay, whatever was lying around. When doing this, however, we had to allow for the appropriate water level. We layered the packing to a level below the walls of the trough, so that when there's an overflow the water doesn't flow into the trough, but rather flows over the dam into the stream. We then placed a sheet of plastic over the packing, anchoring it at the bottom with rocks. It extended from the proposed water level down to the base of the dam and *out into the stream bed at least 2 ft.* (see figure 2). Again, the force of the

water holds the material. The packing supports the plastic so that it does not balloon out between the logs. The plastic on the stream bed in front of the dam prevents undercutting. Also, the plastic was placed so that when the dam filled, the excess water, if any, passed readily between the logs above the plastic thus forming a natural spillway.

The Trough

The construction of the wheel consists of two parts: the trough or millrace and the actual wheel. The trough is not absolutely necessary, but greatly increases the efficiency of the unit (by approximately 70 per cent).

Here I must try to explain a little about what you are trying to do, instead of how to do it. A stream may be viewed as matter (water) or as a *stream of energy.* The object is to convert some of this energy from linear motion to rotary motion. We describe the energy of the stream as either actual or potential. The actual energy is the tendency of elevated water to seek sea level, i.e. gravity. By constructing the dam, we accomplished two things: we ''backed up'' the stream or elevated it, and we channelled the motion into a place that would serve our purposes (the trough).

In constructing the trough, we had to plan it so that the wheel would fit closely inside it, allowing at least 1 in. clearance on each side. We decided to build the trough 4 ft. wide, based on equations from a textbook on hydraulics. Similar equations can be found on page 59. The trough had to be long enough to accommodate the wheel and also a gate at the front (see figures 3 and 4). The purpose of the gate was to control the flow of water through the trough in order to regulate the speed of the turning wheel. Also, the tail end of the trough had to be long enough to release the water smoothly and prevent undercutting of the stream bed in that area.

The floor of the trough has a *dish* into which the wheel fits. The size of the dish was determined as follows. We did all our plans to full scale with nails and

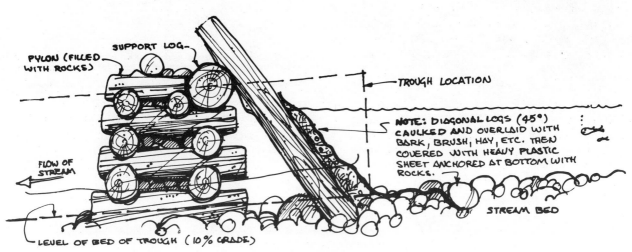

FIGURE 2

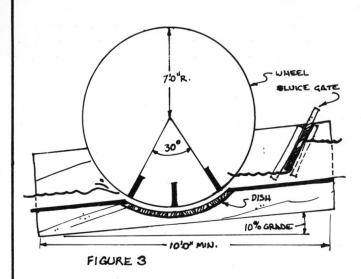

FIGURE 3

Before we installed the trough between the pier and pylon, we had to erect a structure to support the shaft of the wheel. We used two 18-ft. 2 x 6's on each side and installed them so that they were flush with the sides of the pier and pylon (see figure 4). The 2 x 6's extended well above the wheel and were tied together by a platform above the wheel. The cross support for the wheel shaft was made with a piece of 8-in. x 2 1/2-in. stock (see figure 4).

After this was completed, we nailed the trough in place between the pier and pylon. The floor of the trough was set at a 10 per cent grade relative to the level of water behind the dam. For example, a 10-ft. trough would be set at the same level as the water level behind the dam (see figure 3).

Remember that the shaft must be above the centre line of the "dish." Since the trough is placed on a grade, the actual centre line A-C will be slightly behind the apparent centre line A-B.

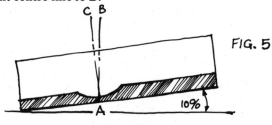

FIG. 5

string on the floor to avoid math errors. Draw an arc using the radius of the wheel (7 ft. in our case). Next draw a 30-degree angle, with the apex at the centre point. Where the legs of the angle cross the arc, draw a line. This line is in alignment with the flow of the trough, and the arc is the dish. In our trough, the dish was 4 in. deep. The 30-degree angle is important, because the paddles of the wheel will be spaced 15 degrees apart. This means that as one paddle is entering the dish, another is at mid-point in the dish, and a third is at the exit point. This provides a smooth motion to the wheel.

We used 3/4-in. marine grade plywood, leaving space for the dish, of course. The floor of the dish was constructed of 2 x 4's nailed crossways in between the plywood walls (also 3/4-in. marine grade) of the trough.

The Wheel

We started with an 8-in. x 8-in. x 7-ft. beam. For bearings, we used two large ball-bearings salvaged from the scrap bin of a heavy equipment repair shop, about 9 in. in diameter (see figure 6). The ends of the shaft were rounded to accept the bearings.

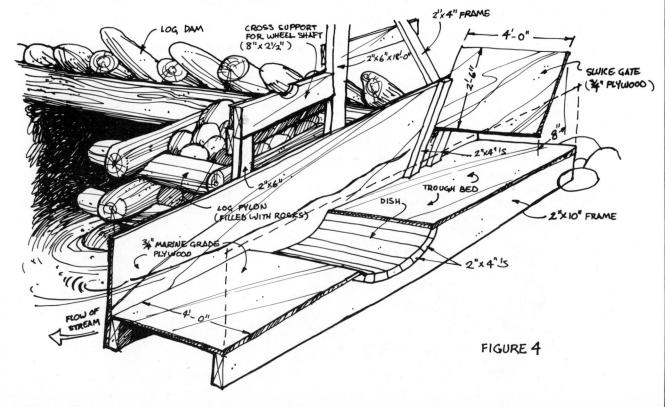

FIGURE 4

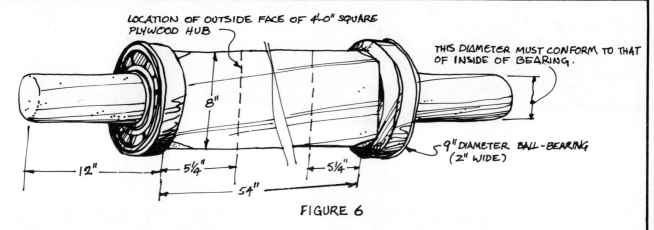

LOCATION OF OUTSIDE FACE OF 4'-0" SQUARE PLYWOOD HUB

THIS DIAMETER MUST CONFORM TO THAT OF INSIDE OF BEARING.

8"

9" DIAMETER BALL-BEARING (2" WIDE)

12"   5¼"   5¼"

54"

FIGURE 6

In order to fix the spokes of the wheel to the shaft, we bought a 4-ft. x 8-ft. x 3/4-in. sheet of marine grade plywood and cut it into 4-ft. x 4-ft. squares. Then we cut an 8-in. square hole in the centre of each piece. Before cutting the 8-in. hole, we found the centre point and drew a large circle on the plywood, and then we divided the circle into 30-degree segments (see figure 8). These 30-degree lines were the centre lines for the spokes. Next we fixed the plywood to the shaft. Figure 7 illustrates how we did this. First, we inserted the rounded end of the shaft through the hole in the plywood, so that the square edges in both parts were lined up, and then we fastened the plywood square onto the square part of the shaft end, using four 2 x 4's (refer to figure 6 for detail of the shaft end(. We used waterproof glue and ardox twist nails for all joints.

After this, we mounted the shaft on the cross support and aligned it to make sure it was true. Then we attached 12 6-ft. 2 x 4's to each plywood plate, using glue and bolts (see figure 9). By building the wheel in place, we were able to check the alignment constantly as we worked.

To join the ends of the spokes around the circumference of the wheel, we used 1-in. x 12-in. stock. On our wheel, the distance between the spokes at the circumference was 44 in.. After the stock was attached, we rounded the outer edges.

Next we added the paddles. There were 12 paddles that were affixed to the 12 spokes, and another 12 paddles that were affixed between the spokes. The paddles

affixed to the spokes consisted of two boards spanning the width of the wheel. Board 1 (see figure 9) was advanced 2 in. into the flow of the water by means of a small wedge attached to the end of each spoke, and board 2 was attached above board 1, but flush with the spoke. This created a scooping kind of paddle. The paddle affixed between the spokes was just one board and was attached to the 1-in. x 12-in. stock that was used to join the ends of the spokes around the circumference of the wheel (see board 2, fig. 9). Board 3 had to be aligned at the same angle as board 1, i.e., in relation to an imaginary spoke drawn from the centre of the wheel to the 1'' x 12'' piece of stock adjoining the spokes. If the water flows over board 3 rather than being cupped by it, another board similar to board 2 may be attached above it to make another scooping paddle (board 4, fig. 9). Ideally the paddles would be made of curved sheet metal (with a radius of 1 ft.), but because they would have cost $3.00 for each blade, we used wood.

Our wheel turns at 20 r.p.m. and generates an estimated 3 hp. Now we are looking for a water pump to complete the system. Our future plan is to build a long workshop parallel to the shaft of the wheel, with a high-speed metal shaft running the length of the shop. Attached to the shaft we plan a deep-freeze (with motor removed), a wringer washer, a 12-volt generator, a small wood lathe, and a flour mill.

We face two problems in operating this system: (a) ice in winter; (b) high water. Removing some logs from the dam should take care of the spring flood. The ice

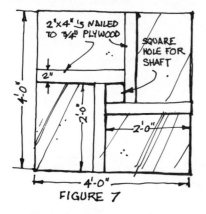

2"x4"'s NAILED TO 3/4" PLYWOOD

SQUARE HOLE FOR SHAFT

2"

4'-0"

2'-0"

2'-0"

4'-0"

FIGURE 7

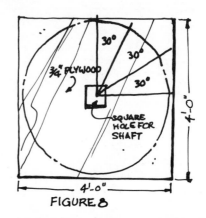

30°

30°

30°

3/4" PLYWOOD

SQUARE HOLE FOR SHAFT

4'-0"

4'-0"

FIGURE 8

problem we will work out when it comes. Perhaps enclosing the entire structure in a shed will solve this.

Generally we used good material throughout and spent $130.00 on lumber, nails, glue, etc.

Aside from the fact that we feel the wheel will be a dependable (and cheap) power source, the project has given us all a new sense of what energy is and how it is related to our lives.

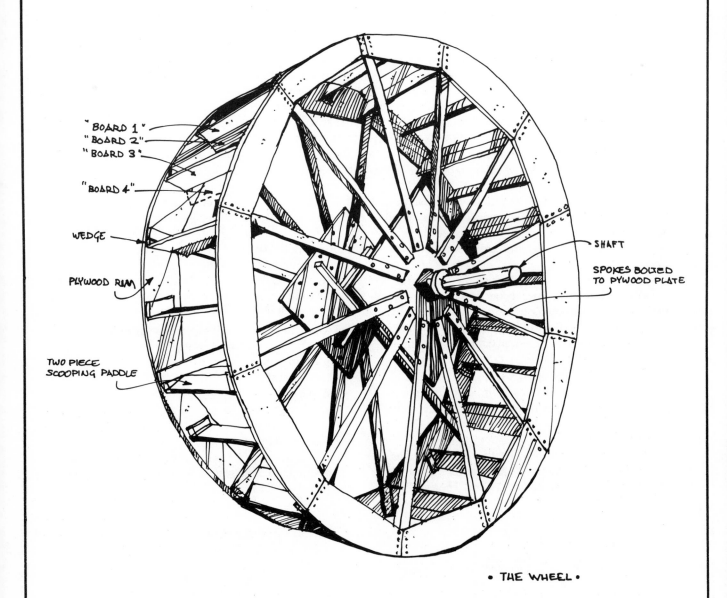

"BOARD 1"
"BOARD 2"
"BOARD 3"
"BOARD 4"
WEDGE
PLYWOOD RIM
TWO PIECE SCOOPING PADDLE
SHAFT
SPOKES BOLTED TO PLYWOOD PLATE

• THE WHEEL •

FIGURE 9

by Don Gilmour

A Wooden Overshot Wheel

If you wish to build an overshot wheel, the first thing would be to measure the available power by the amount of water flowing and the distance of fall. The directions for this can be found from pages 42 to 51.

My wheel has been running continuously for two years without added lubrication or trouble. It's simply designed and easily constructed with a minimal outlay of money. With a bit of hunting for used materials, you should be able to build it for very little money.

After measuring your available power, refer to page 56 for the best dimensions to construct your wheel. The construction requires the manufacture of five basic parts: the disc, the shrouds, the buckets, the mounting framework, and the pulleys.

The Disc

To make the disc, saw out of 5/8'' plywood a circle 44'' in diameter, and mark the centre. Now nail small sections of 1'' x 2'' on the sides, all around the rim. These pieces should be cut to the same radius or curvature as the rim of the disc. Do this on both sides. The object is to thicken the rim. Now cut a 4' x 8' sheet of 1/4'' plywood into strips 15'' wide. Bend the strips to that they overhang on the disc equally. Nail all around the rim like a wide tire. Nail a second layer over this, staggering the joints from the first layer to give added strength and tightness.

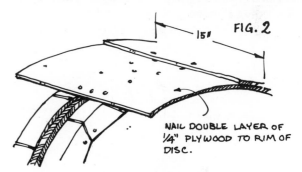

NAIL DOUBLE LAYER OF 1/4" PLYWOOD TO RIM OF DISC.

FIG. 2

15"

The Shroud

The shrouds close in the sides of the bucket (see figure 3). Attaching the shrouds increases the wheel diameter to approximately 5'.

To construct them, cut pieces of cedar lumber into sections to match the cardboard pattern, which is designed as follows:

Take a yardstick or equivalent size piece of wood and drive a nail through one end of it and into the floor. Measure 22-1/2'' from this nail and drive another nail through the yardstick only. Use this ''compass'' to scribe the two curved lines (figure 3) for the shroud pattern. Make the shroud pattern long enough to efficiently utilize the wood you have available. My lumber was 11'' x 7/8'' cedar stock.

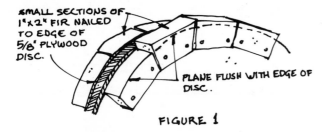

SMALL SECTIONS OF 1"x2" FIR NAILED TO EDGE OF 5/8" PLYWOOD DISC.

PLANE FLUSH WITH EDGE OF DISC.

FIGURE 1

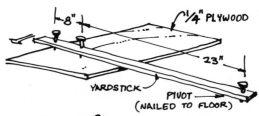

8"

1/4" PLYWOOD

23"

YARDSTICK

PIVOT (NAILED TO FLOOR)

FIGURE 3

Nails are driven through the double plywood rim into the edge of the shrouds to fasten them in place. A second set of shrouds made from the same pattern is constructed of 1/4'' plywood. They are nailed on the outside of the original shroud, in such a way as to cover the seam between shrouds; it also adds strength and increases water tightness. The neater and tighter the better.

The wheel should look something like a giant spool. You can butter up the cracks with any suitable asphalt roof patching compound or waterproof crack sealer.

The Buckets

The 12 buckets are made from fir. They are assembled and the two parts of each are nailed together on a bench, before installing between the shrouds. Measure the distance between the shrouds and make the buckets to fit neatly between, so they will stay reasonably watertight. The water inlet trough should be narrower than the wheel, with up to 10'' high sides.

Mark the location of each bucket on the wheel, so they come out similarly spaced. Use your judging faculties and divide up the spacing.

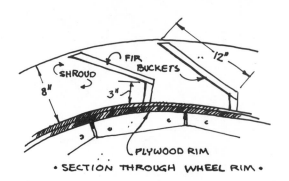

· SECTION THROUGH WHEEL RIM ·

FIGURE 4

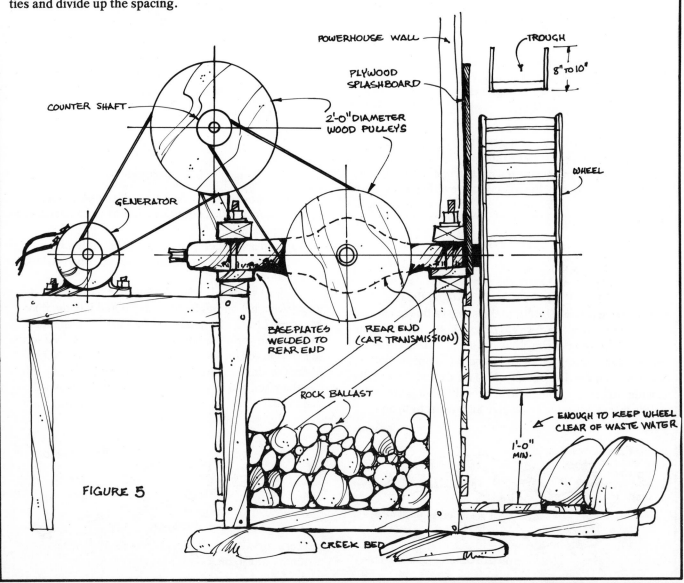

FIGURE 5

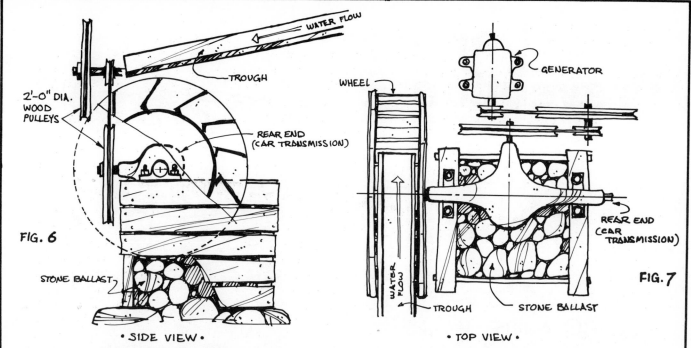

· SIDE VIEW ·

· TOP VIEW ·

Mounting the Wheel

Take a rear end from a full-sized car and fix the differential gears, so the two axles turn as one unit. You can
jam these gears by welding or otherwise, so they don't
operate. Cut off one axle and the axle housing to get rid
of the brake assembly, if you wish. The other axle should
be cleaned of brake parts to expose the hub and flange.
You may have to knock the bolts out and get rid of the
brake drum. The wooden disc of the water wheel needs
to have a hole made in its centre to closely fit the car
wheel hub. Also it should be drilled to match the old bolt
holes, and bolts installed with washers under the nuts.

Before mounting the wheel in place, have a base
plate welded to the axle housing. It should be on what is
to be the underside, with two holes for 1/2'' lagscrews,
or do it your own way. Make some kind of anchor to hold
the opposite housing from moving around.

If you want to do it pioneer style, then hew poles
square or use 4 x 4's for the framework, as in the illustration. Install the rear end in place, using lagscrews or
bolts to hold it. Install the wheel.

Pulleys

Make two pulleys from 5/8'' plywood and nail sections of 1'' cedar or fir lumber on one side of the rim to
widen it. These are for belt pulleys. Bolt one of them centrally onto the flange from which you removed the car
drive (torque) shaft. The second pulley goes on the countershaft with a 6'' x 5/8'' V-pulley alongside it. See what
you can scrounge up. The important thing is to get the 2'
and 6'' pulleys turning as a unit and on some kind of
bearings such as auto front wheels. If you make your
counter shaft of grease-sealed ball or roller-type bearings, you should have a more efficient or carefree plant.

There should be a gate to stop the water from flowing in the trough, thereby controlling the speed or shutting the wheel off. It can be made to slide over the end of

the trough, if the butts of planks are nice and square. It
operates in the manner of a gate valve.

At first run, the wood pulley can be turned true and
the rim given a slight crown (rounded groove) which
helps the belt stay on. Install the countershaft, fitting the
V-belt from the 2' pulley to the 6'' V-pulley on the countershaft. When the countershaft is running O K. turn the
rim of its pulley and crown a little. The turning operation
needs care to avoid accidents. Use a long-handled chisel
or scraper. One needs a firm support under the tool to
operate in a manner similar to a wood lathe. A V-groove
in these pulleys will wear the belt away. The slightly-
crowned wood face works for years without noticeable
wear.

The second belt goes from countershaft wooden pulley to the generator metal V-pulley or whatever you wish
to drive. A 4'' pulley will be easy on the belt and give you
about 1800 r.p.m. The wood pulley on countershaft can
be larger diameter for greater speed.

A car generator will give you a fine lighting system,
if you put the battery at the house end of the line. Use
No. 8 wire for a distance of 50' to 100' and beyond that,
No. 6 wire. The generator will build up extra voltage to
overcome the normal voltage drop in the line. Fifty-watt
bulbs are still available in 6 and 12 volts. You may still be
able to find 100-watt bulbs for 6 or 12-volt systems. The
bases are the same standard screw as the 110-volt bulbs,
so they fit standard light fixtures. A 32-volt battery system is still better than a 12-volt system.

You can get up to 500 watts of 110 volt A.C. from
this wheel with an efficient, self-regulating, four-pole al-
ternator, but it will be difficult to keep close to 60 cycles
unless the load is unchanging. You won't be able to store
power as you can on a battery system.

Log dams and all the woodwork which keeps wet will
last for years. Parts of the wheel that are exposed to the
elements should be coated with a preservative.

Frost Damage Prevention

by M.G. Kains

The killing of plants and plant parts by frost may often be prevented by simple, inexpensive, easily applied means.

Frost is the term which indicates the conversion of a liquid into a solid by the reduction of temperature. Though this definition covers all cases, such as the solidification of molten iron and other metals, it is popularly understood to mean the formation of ice from water at the temperature of 32°F.

As air cools, its power to hold water in vapour form decreases, until it is deposited in tiny drops (dew) on objects cooler than itself, such as foliage. The temperatures at which this deposition occurs depend upon the proportion of water vapour in the air at the time. This varies as the cooling proceeds. During summer, the dew point, as the deposition or saturation temperature is called, is often above 60°F.; in winter, often below 0°F.

When the dew point is below the freezing point, the water vapour condenses on still cooler surfaces in the form of fine particles of ice, which, because they reflect the sunlight and appear white, we call hoar or white frost. Often a similar appearance of "false hoar frost" occurs when the temperature is several degrees above freezing point. Usually this is due to the way the light is reflected from the dew.

The condensation of water vapour tends to check the fall of temperature, because what is called "latent heat" in this vapour is returned to the air, which becomes measurably warmer. Thus, within variable limits, the position of dew protects plants from frost damage as the temperature approaches or in some cases even goes below the freezing point. This accounts for many escapes of plants that would have been killed by frost, had the dew point been below instead of above the freezing point. You can often take advantage of this phenomenon and save your plants.

Plants vary in their resistance to frost damage, according to their origin and their condition. Those which originate in a cold climate (apple, cabbage) naturally are strongly resistant; those from a warm climate (orange, tomato) are weak and easily destroyed. Between these extremes are many intermediate grades. Those plants that, in a given locality, live through the northern or alpine winter in spite of deep freezing of the soil, are called hardy in that locality; those that succumb to the slightest frost are tender, and those between are variously classed as half-hardy, semi-hardy, half-tender, and semi-tender (e.g., French artichoke).

Tender plants are usually injured when the temperature continues at 32°F., 31°F., or 30°F. for several hours, especially when bright sunshine or quickly warming air strikes them in early morning. Few if any of them can stand lower degrees than these for even a short time; half-hardy plants often survive temperatures of 20°F., but seldom lower degrees.

In all these cases, plant condition plays an important part; for plants that have made rapid growth have soft, immature tissues and are full of water, are far less resistant than those which have developed slowly, have denser, stockier growth, and are less full (perhaps even in need of) water. This statement applies to hardy as well as tender plants; even trees normally hardy in a given locality may be winter-killed because they made a late, sappy growth which did not ripen or which was full of water when cold weather arrived.

The mere deposition of frost on the surface of foliage does not necessarily indicate that the plants have been killed or even damaged. But when the air is too dry for dew to be deposited, they may be frozen by a dry wind, or on a clear night without the deposition of either dew or hoar frost. In such cases damage is due to freezing of the water inside the plant and the consequent rupture of the

tissues. When the sun shines on tissues thus injured, the internal ice melts; the leaves have no chance to mend the broken cells, so the leaves droop, wilt, and turn back; hence the term "black frost."

Anything that will prevent the fall of temperature to or below the freezing point and anything that will shield the plants from direct sunshine while they are still frozen, covered with hoar frost, or severely chilled, will help ward off damage or even save plants that would otherwise die or be seriously checked in their development. A wind that springs up in the evening, clouds that appear during the night or early morning, or a rain that follows a frost will often either prevent the freezing or check the thawing process and thus save the plants. All these phenomena of nature are, of course, beyond your control, but you may imitate them, as outlined further on.

You can largely control the development and therefore the hardiness of your plants in several ways. For instance, during spring you can avoid over-feeding your young plants with stimulant fertilizer, such as manure, and also avoid giving them excess of water. Both these tend to make sappy growth easily killed by frost. On the other hand, by keeping the plants cool, almost cold ("hardening them off") as they approach the time for transplanting to the open ground, you can increase the hardiness of hardy, semi-hardy, and even tender plants. Plants so prepared will stand cold snaps, whereas those of the same species not so inured would probalby be killed or so chilled that they would "sulk" for several weeks before recovering or renewing a normal rate of growth.

Similarly we may prevent winter injury of hardy trees, shrubs and vines, by supplying ample water during summer and early autumn, witholding it later; avoid application of manures from midsummer forward; counteracting any excess of these by liberal dressings of potash (woodashes and flyash are good sources) during early fall; or by sowing buckwheat in July or rye in September, or both these together in July. As these crops grow, they remove excess water and nitrogenous plant food from the soil and develop plants which, when plowed or

dug into the ground in spring, return the plant food and their own bodies to form humus.

Fortunately you can predict accurately enough for practical purposes when to expect frost. The daily forecasts by the weather bureau give suggestions as to the general weather to expect, but you can make your own observations and predictions. Local conditions influence temperature. For instance, a nearby body of water, such as a lake, the sea, a wide or a deep river, or even a large pond affects the rate at which air temperature changes. In spring, because the water is cold, it keeps the air also cold and thus more or less retards plant development. In autumn the reverse effect occurs; the water, being warm, not only warms the air, but fills it with water vapour, thus warding off frost.

Open and flat country and small villages are more likely to suffer from late spring and early autumn frosts than are large cities and their nearby suburbs because, in the former, heat loss by radiation into space is more rapid in clear, clean air and under cloudless skies than in the latter, where the air is filled with smoke and dust and where the fires in countless houses, factories, and other buildings directly raise the temperature.

Dark-coloured, sandy, and well-drained soils absorb and hold more sun heat than do light-coloured, clayey, and poorly-drained ones, so are less likely to be frosty. Other conditions being equal, southern and eastern slopes are also warmer than western ones, because they more quickly absorb the sun's rays. Though this favours earliness of plant development, it often makes the growing of certain fruits (apricot, peach, Japanese plum) precarious or impossible, because the flowers are encouraged to open so early that spring frost kills them and thus prevents fruit production, though not usually killing the trees.

You can discover for yourselves that cold air, being heavier than warm air, flows like water from high to low ground and "settles" in hollows or "pockets" unless it can drain to still lower levels or be driven out by wind; that frosts are much more likely to occur when the air is still, the sky clear, and the stars brilliant, than when there is wind or clouds, especially when the former is strong and the latter cover the whole sky. The direction and force of the wind also help in making a local forecast. One that blows strongly from the north is far more likely to bring cool or cold weather than one from the south, just as one from the east is likely to bring clouds and rain, and one from the west clear skies and colder weather. The rate at which the barometer rises also helps, because it indicates the approach of clear weather and, if rapid, also of cold weather.

An unusually warm spell is almost sure to be followed by a cooler or cold one, because the general weather moves in prodigious waves from southwest to northeast across the country. Hence a light frost following a warm spell is likely to do more damage than an even more severe one following cool weather. For this reason, you should be on your guard when one of these warm spells occurs in spring: be ready to protect your seedlings, newly transplanted plants, and the flowers on your fruit trees and bushes.

When the sky is cloudy, when there is fog, or even when a haze occurs during or toward evening, frost is less likely to occur than when the night is clear, because these conditions of moisture in the air prevent loss of heat from the earth.

A reliable sign of approaching frost is the rate at which the temperature falls during the late afternoon and early evening. Starting with 50°F. or less, clear skies, and no wind, a fall of 2°F. or more an hour between four and eight o'clock usually indicates that freezing temperatures will be reached before morning, unless clouds or winds develop or unless you do something to prevent frost.

In a small way, individual plants may be protected by inverted flower pots, peach baskets, and other receptacles placed over them, by newspapers spread and held in place by stones or clods of earth. A more convenient adaptation of this way is to use a light screen of burlap, mounted on a frame, placed over the plants or beds. These all tend to hold the heat around the plants.

Smouldering fires, which produce abundant smoke and steam, form artificial clouds which check radiation in the same way as do true clouds. When the air is still, the smoke spreads out evenly and proves effective as a protection nearly as far as the clouds extend. This method is not feasible where the smoke would prove objectionable to neighbours. Numerous small, bright fires of wood, coal, or (preferably) oil are used extensively by commercial growers of fruit and vegetables to heat the air. They are less useful in small areas than the methods already presented and those that follow.

The most generally feasible method is to fill the air with water vapour in one of the following ways: stirring the soil with the wheelhoe or the cultivator toward evening, to expose an increased surface of damp earth; sprinkling the plants, the ground, and the adjacent area with a hose nozzle that breaks up the water into small drops, or using an overhead irrigation system for this purpose. The water evaporates and, as the vapour condenses, it liberates latent heat and thus checks the cooling process.

Freezing of the ground may injure even established trees, shrubs, and vines of some kind, so anything that will reduce the depth of frost penetration or prevent alternate freezing and thawing will tend to prevent such injury.

Experiment has proved that under sod, freezing reached a depth of 8 inches, whereas in an adjacent sodless area it reached 18 inches. Peach trees on the sod ground made healthy, uniform growth, whereas in the sodless soil they were slow to start, had many dead branches, and made poor development.

In another experiment, just before winter a few forkfuls of manure or shovelfuls of soil or peat were banked around the trunks of exceptionally vigorous peach trees, with the result that every tree so treated came through the winter without injury, whereas a few not banked all died.

When water freezes, it swells and lifts the crust of frozen earth above the unfrozen ground below. As it does so in autumn and early winter, it also lifts shallow rooted plants, roots and all. When it thaws, the soil settles back, but the plants do not. They are left with exposed roots. Each succeeding freeze lifts them some more and each thaw leaves them farther out of the ground, with the result that they dry and die. Hence the importance of applying a mulch in the fall.

In the spring equally fatal results may affect unmulched plants. When the surface thaws above a lower layer of still frozen earth, the thawed layer settles; and when it later freezes and lifts, it breaks the roots of small plants by pulling them. Hence, again, the importance of mulch; for beneath a sufficient layer of such loose material, heaving and settling are reduced to minimum and thawing of the ground proceeds from below upward, until the mulched soil has thawed out and thus eliminated danger of root breakage.

In order to have extra early beans, corn, melons, and cucumbers, I have often sown seed much earlier than was locally popular, thus risking frost damage. When no frost occured, I was ahead of competitors; and when it did come, I usually saved the plants by one of these methods. I have never thus risked transplanting eggplants, tomato, or pepper plants, because, even though not frozen, they "sulk" if chilled and start fruiting late.

In case you have not protected your plants and a frost has occurred during the night, you may be able to save them, even those covered with frost or whose tissues have been ruptured by freezing of their sap. Spray them with cold water as soon as possible after dawn or before sunrise and also shield them from direct sunlight after the sun appears, until they have thawed out and apparently resumed normal activity. Better keep them so shielded until between ten o'clock and noon. The most conveniently applied shield is the screen mounted on a frame with short legs.

Planting by the Signs & Phases of the Moon

by Dave Dawson

Gardening according to the phases and the zodiacal positions of the moon goes back to very ancient times. During the early stages of recorded history, mankind was very aware of the apparent passage of the sun, moon, planets, and stars around the earth, and held the phenomena of the celestial spheres in great awe and respect. Due to the tremendous magnitude of the heavens, and the stately order of their predictable patterned movement across the sky, early man probably formed many superstitions regarding their origin and purpose. But early historic man was also extremely aware of and in tune with his environment through sheer necessity of survival. Soon he began to notice a correlation between certain types of phenomena and the positions of the planets in the heavens. He noticed that people born at any given time of the year had certain general character traits held in common, for the most part, only with other people born around that time of year. He noticed that most maritime disasters happened during certain planetary configurations. But where this early man was most aware of the planetary influences was in the area most important to his continued preservation and well-being, which was the cultivation of plants to feed himself and his animals. Driven by a vital necessity for better crops, he became keenly aware of the moon's effect on the lives of the plants he cultivated. He also noticed that its effect was two-fold, as it affected growth according to its position in the Zodiac, and also according to its phases (from full moon to new and back to full). Through the centuries, man continued to plant according to the moon's position and phases, constantly adding to his knowledge of its effects on plant growth. Even today, a very large number of the world's farmers still plant according to the moon.

Although the idea of the moon having an effect on the growth and development of life on the earth has been under attack for several centuries now, it is just being learned through scientific research that the moon definitely does affect most living things on earth. Psychologists have discovered that the phases of the moon have a definite effect on the behaviour patterns of human beings. Scientists have discovered that clams do not open and close their shells according to the tide, as previously believed, but directly feel the position of the moon in the sky, although they are deep beneath the sea.

It is well known that the tides are controlled by the position of the moon in the sky, but what is not so well known is that as the moon grows from new to full, the tides get higher and the water table in the earth rises, while the opposite occurs when the moon progresses from full to new. Therefore, at the full moon, the ground would be expanded with moisture. If you were to sink a post into the ground, it would become quite loose as the moon waned, since the earth around it would contract with the loss of moisture. If you plant something which grows above ground, on the increase of the moon, the plant will find it increasingly easy to rush those vital liquids up the stem during the crucial early stages of growth, while if you plant it at the decrease of the moon, it will become increasingly more difficult, resulting in a stunted plant. Although through good fertilization, irrigation, and careful tending, much of the need to closely follow the moon is offset, it is still a useful aid to gardening; if you do all that and also plant by the moon you are that much more assured of a good crop.

First, I would like to outline a simple guide to enable you to figure out where the moon is at any given time, and then I shall give you the run-down on the best conditions for planting each crop.

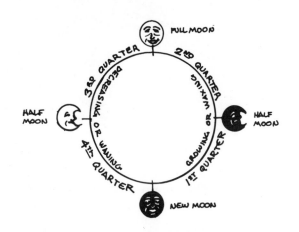

As you can see from the previous diagram, when the moon is growing from new to a half-moon, it is the first quarter; as it progresses from a half to a full moon, it is the second quarter; as it wanes from full to half, it is in the third quarter; and as it moves from half to new, it is in the fourth quarter.

If you know which sign and which degree of that sign the sun is in (in the Zodiac), you can also find the approximate zodiacal position of the moon by observing its phases. When the moon is new, it is in the same zodiacal position as the sun; when it is full, it is in the opposite sign, but the same degree. If it is a quarter moon waxing, then it is 45 degrees in advance of the sun; and if it is a quarter moon waning, it is 45 degrees behind the sun. Below is a diagrammatic example of this situation. Also given is the approximate time of year the sun enters each sign.

Each sign of the Zodiac contains 30 degrees, and as you can see from the diagram below, the sun is in each sign for about 30 days; therefore, you can approximately equate each day of the sun's progression into a sign with one degree of progression. The sun moves counter-clockwise around the Zodiac. When the moon is half full and growing, it is 90 degrees in advance of the sun; when it is half full but waning, it is 90 degrees behind the sun; when it is full, it is 180 degrees from, or opposite the sun; and when it is new, it is 0 degrees or in the same position as the sun.

Planting by the Phases of the Moon

Generally all crops which produce avove the ground and mature in one growing season should be planted during the increase of the moon. All crops which produce below the ground and crops which take more than one year to produce should be planted at the decrease or waning of the moon.

More specifically you should plant leafy plants of one-season duration such as lettuce, cabbage, brussel sprouts, cauliflower, broccoli, asparagus, spinach, etc. during the first quarter. Also grains do well, if planted in the first quarter. All these may be planted in the second quarter, if you are unable to plant them during the first.

All-in-one-season plants, which contain their seed within the fruit of the plant and grow on vines, should be planted in the second quarter. Examples are melons, pumpkins, squash, tomatoes, beans, and peas. All these may be planted during the first quarter, if you are unable to plant them during the second. Grains may also be planted during the second quarter.

During the third quarter, plant all crops which take more than one growing season to mature, including all trees, shrubs, berries, winter wheat; also all bulb and root crops such as onions, potatoes, turnips, radishes, parsnips, carrots, onions, and rhubarb.

The fourth quarter can be used for the same crops as the third quarter, but it is best for killing pests, pulling weeds, and preparing the soil.

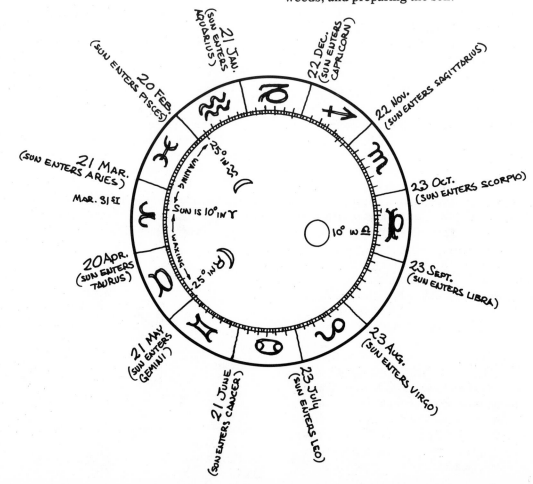

Planting According to the Sign of the Moon

Moon in Aries — this is a barren, dry sign and is good for killing weeds and pests. It is not good for planting, but it is good for cultivation.

Moon in Taurus — this sign is moist and productive. It is an earthly sign and is very good for root crops, and also good for leafy vegetables. Makes plants hardy.

Moon in Gemini — this sign is barren and dry. Good for destroying weeds and pests, but not good for planting. Cultivate,

Moon in Cancer — this sign is moist and is the most fruitful of all signs. It is the best sign for planting all crops, especially above ground; also good for irrigation.

Moon in Leo — this is the most barren and dry of all the signs of the Zodiac. It is the worst sign for planting, but is the best for destroying weeds and pests. Good for cultivation.

Moon in Virgo — this sign, although moist and earthy, is barren and is not good for planting. Good for destroying weeds and cultivation.

Moon in Libra — this sign is somewhat moist and semi-fruitful. Very good for flowers, if beauty is desired. Good for the growth of roots and the pulp of the plant.

Moon in Scorpio — a very fruitful and moist sign. Good for all crops. Very good for vines.

Moon in Sagittarius — barren and dry. Good for cultivation.

Moon in Capricorn—fruitful, somewhat moist, and earthy. Good for root crops.

Moon in Aquarius—This is a dry barren sign and is good for destroying weeds, pests and for cultivation.

Moon in Pisces — very fruitful and moist. This sign is the second best for all crops, especially for root crops. Good for irrigation.

For the best results, you should try to get a situation where the moon is in the best quarter and best sign simultaneously. This is not always possible, of course, and you should not hesitate to use one of the secondary signs or quarters. Remember also that you should not depend too heavily on the moon, for there are many other important factors in proper gardening, such as getting the crop in as soon after the last frost as possible (especially here in the northern latitudes, where the growing season is so short), good fertile soil, irrigation, and loving care. All these factors combine in order to bring you a healthy crop with a high yield.

Other Useful Hints

Harvest crops when the moon is waning or decreasing; this is especially important for fruits, as they tend to spoil easily otherwise; also when the moon is a dry sign. Cut timber when the moon is waning, to prevent rot and worm infestation. Set posts in the ground when the moon is waning, to prevent loosening. Harvest root crops for seed at or shortly after the full moon.

Irrigate when the moon is in a watery sign. Can vegetables, jelly, preserves, and pickles when the moon is in Sagittarius or Gemini and also in the fourth quarter.

Prune during the third quarter and when the moon is in Scorpio. Graft just before the sap begins to flow, when the moon is in the first or second quarter and in a watery sign.

For hatching eggs, Cancer or Pisces will be best for quck maturation and good layers.

For a complete and easy to follow guide to planting by the moon, with the position of the moon by sign and quarter for every day of the year given, I recommend you get *Llewellyn's Moon Sign Book and Daily Planetay Guide;* if you cannot find it in a book store, order it direct from:

Llewellyn Publications
Box 3383 - MSB
St. Paul, Minn. 55165
USA

Gravity Feed Water Supply

by Hugh Eliot

How Much Water?

After access to a homesite, a water supply is next in importance. Electric power and telephone are relative luxuries. Just as we assume access by means of a motor vehicle, in these days a water supply means a piped supply. In B.C. in particular there is often a supply of good water at a higher level than a house site. To help those who want to install their own gravity supply, I will try to deal with some of the problems involved and state in a simple way the laws of hydraulics involved. I assume the problem is to obtain water from a stream and that plastic pipe will be used.

How much of a supply do you need? To run a sprinkler with a 30-ft. radius and still be able to fill a bath without interfering with either operation — 10 gallons per minute at 20 pounds per square in. (p.s.i.). Is it available? What size pipe should be used? How deeply should it be buried?

The Survey

To get any answer to these problems, you have to find out the distance from the source to the site and what the difference in level or head is. First, go over the route. Determine its direction and mark it out with stakes. Where it goes through bush, slash a line of sight. To measure the distance, use a steel tape or a piece of wire 200 to 300 ft. long. Put in pegs each time the wire is moved along a length, marking the pegs with the distance.

On a preliminary survey, the relative heights of the source and the site might be taken off a map, if a large one is available. The best map is one which is scaled one-half in. to the mile with 50 ft. contours. It will help to check with your own survey. This can be done with an 18-in. carpenter's level and a 15 to 20 ft. pole. The pole should be marked at 1 ft. increments, as well as a high-lighted marker every 5 ft. The process involves setting up the level on a box or table. Make it level and then sight along to the pole at a 100, 200, or 300 ft. distance. The person holding the pole can help by pointing to the bars with another stick, clearly identifying the bar sighted. The level can then be set up at the foot of the pole and the pole moved farther down the slope. The process can be used to find the relative level of the site below the source, adding all the steps together. In the preliminary survey, it will be sufficient to determine the gradient in per cent of each stretch of the route where it is seen to change. Multiply the distance on the ground by this percentage and then add up these drops. Check them against altitudes on a map. For example, if the level is 2-1/2 ft. off the ground and sights to the 14-ft. bar, the difference in level between the two points is minus 2-1/2, or 11-1/2 ft. If the distance between the level and the pole is 120 ft., the gradient is 11.5/120 x 100, or 9 per cent. With care, this kind of survey could yield all the data necessary to know if the system would work and what it would cost. The length of the route is the sum of the sections. The drop or head available is the drops in each section. The average total gradient as a per cent is the total drop over the total distance times 100.

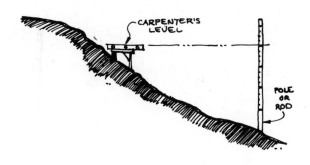

Necessary Pressure

What will the pressure be at the house? What should it be? It should be at least 20 p.s.i. to come out of domestic fittings, so that you don't have to wait a minute to fill a kettle and half an hour to get a bath. Each pound per sq. in. is the result of 2.6 ft. of head or drop in the supply line. To produce 20 p.s.i., you will need 52 ft. of head *but* that will only be the static head. As soon as you turn a tap on and start drawing water, the pressure drops. How much? It depends on the size of the pipe and rate of flow. It is stated in tables as the loss of head in ft. per 100 ft. of lengths of pipe for different rates of flow. A table (available from the manufacturers of plastic pipe) would show that for a flow of 10 gallons per minute, there is a loss of 2 ft. of head or .8 of p.s.i. If the drop in your line is only 5 ft. per 100 ft. of run, 40 per cent of your pressure will be lost in friction. If your line is coming down a mountain on a 25 per cent gradient, the loss will be only 2 ft. in 25 ft., or 8 per cent of the head.

Choosing Your Pipe

It's said lightly that the way to choose the size of pipe is to decide on the largest pipe you can afford, borrow some more money, and get the next largest size — then you'll have the proper pipe. Pipe cannot be too big, except for its cost; and the fact that, for a given wall thickness, as a pipe gets larger, the pressure it will withstand gets smaller. As a rule of thumb figure for a preliminary survey, I would suggest that for a line to a single homestead with some garden and a lawn, if the overall gradient of the line is around 5 per cent, the pipe should be 1-½ in. inside diameter; around 10 per cent gradient, 1-¼ in. i.d.; over 20 per cent gradient, 1 in. pipe, if it will withstand the pressure involved.

There can be two regrets after laying a water line, both quite futile — the pipe is not large enough and, in the colder climates, the pipe is not buried deeply enough for winter temperatures. Skimp on burying a pipe, and you'd better build an out-house. Nothing goes out of commission quicker than indoor plumbing when the water freezes. Listen to the more conservative estimates of necessary depth. Relative savings can be made where a pipe is in bush; but where pipe is under a road or footpath, or wherever snow might be removed or packed, bury it the maximum depth for the area. Keeping water running to prevent a line from freezing is not very practical. Too many accidents may happen. It's also wasteful and illegal to use water this way.

Other common practical problems are: (a) assuring enough water over the end of the pipe at the intake to fill it at all levels of the creek; (b) getting rid of dirt in the water. The theory of getting rid of dirt is very simple — much theory is. Fast-moving water can carry dirt. Standing water will drop it. So water should stand nearly still for a time, before entering the pipe. That means storing a hundred gallons in a tank, pool, or ditch with a very slight drop. Whatever the arrangement is, it must not freeze, and there must be some arrangement for flushing out the material that has settled out. None of these things are easy to arrange when obtaining water from a creek at the bottom of a narrow, steep ravine. That is the kind of a creek that will be heavy with silt when it's in flood. The common approach to such a creek is a trail, sloping uphill very slightly, bulldozed into the hillside. Bulldozing is expensive; $10 to $15 per hour. Sometimes this much of a capital cost can be shared, as well as parts of pipe trenches to different homes. That begs the question why not a communal water supply — which gets into social, legal, and economic engineering. The behaviour of people over water is a far more complicated business than the behaviour of water itself.

Air in a pipe obstructs flow of water. There should be valves all along the line to release air, especially if the route is a series of humps and dips. It is best that a route should slope uniformly downhill, but where the terrain is irregular, the line will work if there is an air bleeder at the bottom of each dip or at least at every splice between 300 ft. lengths of pipe. A bleeder in its simplest from is a

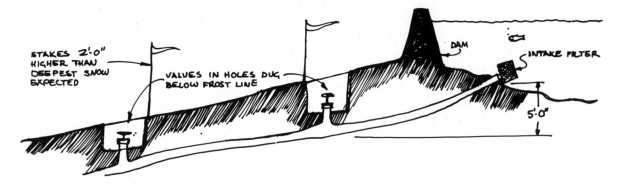

STAKES 2'-0" HIGHER THAN DEEPEST SNOW EXPECTED

VALUES IN HOLES DUG BELOW FROST LINE

DAM

INTAKE FILTER

5'-0"

T instead of a sleeve joining two lengths of pipe and a hose valve on the branch line; this is installed in a frost-proof hand hole and marked with a stake higher than the deepest snow expected.

Another simple but important point: where a pipe leaves a creek along an almost level trail cut in the hillside, try to arrange that there are a few feet of head immediately after the water enters the pipe. Locate your intake works 5 ft. vertically or 50 ft. of pipe on a 10 per cent grade from the beginning of the level stretch. Put a bleeder there and at the next splice down the level stretch.

Remember that your bleeder points are test points. When there is trouble with frost, dirt, or air, you may be able to recover your shortcomings as a hydraulic engineer with the bleeders. Put durable markers to show the location of the pipe and/or splices. It may be years before you or someone else wants to know where it is. I suggest that you bury a number of one gallon cans of concrete flush with the ground. Inscribe in the wet cement pertinent information about the pipe.

2" pipe splice 12" ← 8" deep

Some considerations *before* spending money on a water supply:

(1) See the government department concerned with water. How much will they allow you to take from the creek? What are the requirements to obtain a licence? In my experience, Water Rights engineers are very helpful even beyond information about official requirements.

(2) Find out the history of the creek from old inhabitants. Does it ever dry up? Does it flood badly?

(3) Is the creek water fit for drinking? Is it likely to become polluted? Is there building land for sale upstream?

(4) Laying a pipe line: legal, personal, engineering, financial. What are your rights? Are your neighbours agreeable? Are they interested in sharing the cost of a

ditch and intake works? My experience is that people are able to share these items. but not the pipe itself. Everyone lays their own pipe. As the neighbourhood develops and the land gets sub-divided, it becomes a plastic spider web — one reason for putting in precise durable markers showing where *your* pipe is.

(5) Digging the ditch: Get estimates from the back-hoe operators and consider with them the possibilities of hitting rock, other pipes, and buried cables. Get permission and the requirements for crossing a public highway. It generally requires an outer steel pipe to be buried at a depth specified by the highway department.

Chuck Valentine, a neighbour of Hugh Eliot, has also hassled with homestead water problems. Here he comments upon Hugh's article and relates a few of his own experiences.

v. m.

I feel 20 p.s.i. static pressure is minimal. Try for 60 to 80 pounds if you can. Once you start gardening a homestead, demands for water will grow from year to year and a dry spell brings all the demands at once. Every valve you turn on drops the pressure, due to friction losses in the pipe. Modern faucets are designed for higher city pressures and let little water through.

While Hugh's survey will work well, I find it cumbersome. It almost takes two people to sight a carpenter's level in the bush, and someone must carry the rod too. A method I always use is quite accurate enough for a home water supply:

Buy a small, cheap hand level. Measure the height of your own eye while standing erect on the ground. Start at your house-site and follow any route that will take you to your intended intake point at the stream. You don't have to follow the route of your pipe, which may be inaccessible at this planning stage. Sight horizontally through the level to any object on the ground that you can identify and sight on: a rock, stick, tuft of grass, child's hand, or foot. Then walk and stand there and sight again. Each sighting will take you one eye-height higher. When you reach your intake point, multiply number of sightings by eye height and voila! you will have the height of your intake above your house. Then lend the hand level to anyone else who needs it. My $4.00 hand level has been used for 18 years in our community this way. These levels have a bubble, a little mirror set at 45 degrees to see the bubble, a small peep hole, and a cross hair. To use them, just line up the bubble and the cross-hair (which appear side by side) and see what you're looking at. Certainly accurate within 5 per cent, probably better. Also good for levelling post and beam buildings, irrigation ditches, and drainage ditches.

The figure for head or drop to produce each pound per square inch pressure is 2.31 ft.

Hugh's figures (at the end of paragraph "Necessary Pressure"), as he says, are dependent on size of pipe, but he doesn't say what size pipe he refers to. Take them as a general idea of losses to be encountered, not to calculate from.

Without specifically checking his figures I agree from practice here that 1-1/4-in. and 1-1/2-in. plastic pipes are suitable sizes for 10 per cent and 5 per cent gradients. Never go smaller than 1-in. for most purposes, and even that is questionable.

Don't miss that important point about arranging some drop in the pipe first, if you have to go near-horizontally out of the creek canyon. It's very hard to start water through a near-horizontal pipe. Regarding bleeder valves along the pipe route, I've never seen this done, but would think they should be at the high points if they are to let air out, not at low points. Air rises and it's hard to get it out of the low points.

Do check the pressure range of your pipe before you buy it. If you have to have high pressure, over 80 pounds, buy heavier strength pipe for that portion of the line, not a smaller size. Avoid having the larger sizes of plastic pipe (1-in. and over) lying on the ground in the hot sun with water pressure in them and no water flowing. Then they can heat up, weaken, expand, and perhaps burst.

By the way, don't take that lightly about borrowing money to buy the next larger pipe than you can afford. I wish I had followed that advice myself.

When burying plastic pipe, cover it first with fine material, and be careful not to have large rocks over it: they could collapse it later. Best also to fill the pipe with water before backfilling, for strength and pre-shrinking.

Intake Filters

My intake is quite makeshift, but seldom requires a trip to the creek. I formed a 5-in. cylinder about 16-in. long out of a piece of very heavy brass screening I found on this place. I bolted one end to an extremely heavy brass casting I found (using brass bolts) and plugged the other end with a circle of cedar board, nailed on. The casting, probably a packing gland for an inboard propeller shaft, had a hole the right size to take a plastic pipe fitting! Then I wrapped the whole thing with a brass mosquito-size screening, clamped on with stainless-steel clamps meant for 5-in. plastic pipe. I simply dropped the heavy thing to the creek bottom and kept it from washing downstream by driving a piece of drill steel into the creek bed.

Some sand and sediment leaked through this and it was always a nuisance, so for the main house I ran the entire supply through an old hot-water tank (or "range boiler," the type that connects to a waterfront on a wood-coal stove) 12-in. in diameter and 60-in. high. Plugging the side holes, I cut off the filler pipe, so that it extends only half-way down the inside of the tank from the top. This throws the dirt to the bottom of the tank at rather high speed, but the water rises slowly through the 12-in. tank to the outlet at the top, leaving the sediment behind. Works quite well. Needs cleaning about twice a year.

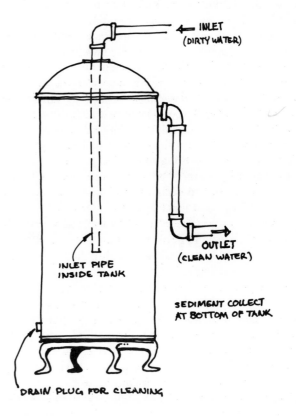

INLET (DIRTY WATER)

INLET PIPE INSIDE TANK

OUTLET (CLEAN WATER)

SEDIMENT COLLECT AT BOTTOM OF TANK

DRAIN PLUG FOR CLEANING

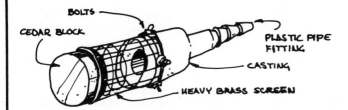

BOLTS

CEDAR BLOCK

PLASTIC PIPE FITTING

CASTING

HEAVY BRASS SCREEN

Beehive Defense

by Eric Anderson

My main purpose in writing this article is not so much to gather and list in one place the natural predators of the honey bee and preventative measures, but to focus attention on a problem. When it comes to protecting the hive from ants and moths, there are plenty of poisons that work very well. Too well sometimes. If you have problems with mice, there are poisons for them as well. A couple of grains of strychnine on an egg will stop the skunks, and all the raccoons, weasels, coyotes, and other animals that happen to like eggs. Then there is the bear. He's a little bigger problem, but with a little patience, lots of ammunition, and a 30.06, he won't cause any trouble. When I was doing my research for this article, I came up with nearly the same solution everytime: traps, guns, and poisons. After seeing my own hives destroyed by a black bear, not once, but twice in one week, I have sympathy with persons who still stick with those guaranteed but destructive methods. What else is there that really works? I don't have a lot of new and useful information, but I hope this will represent a core to work from, a core to test experiment with and improve upon.

A little care in storing combs will prevent a lot of trouble at a later date. The best storage area is a building that is dry, ventilated, well lighted, and bee or mouseproof. The first condition is essential. Most sheds, especially the older ones, seem to be naturally well ventilated. The last two conditions: well, sometime you'll get around to building a new shed, but until them there are a few things you can do.

First of all, before storing the empty supers away, put them back on the hive for a week or two. This will give the bees a chance to clean them up for you and greatly reduce the attraction to any pest. When storing the supers, they should be in piles five or six high, with a queen excluder on the top and bottom to keep out any rodents. Between each super, lay a couple of sheets of newspaper; the ink will act as a repellent to the wax moth and seals the ants out. Water will keep ants away. A friend of mine, while doing her extracting, found that ants

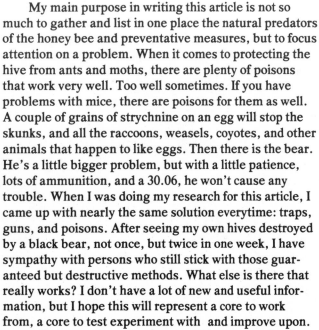

entered her porch by the space under the door. She kept a water sprinkler running there day and night until she was finished. If the supers are elevated on a stand or table, and the legs put in cans of oil, you can cut off the ants' access routes. This is probably the best solution, allowing you to forget the newspaper which blocks out light and ventilation, two conditions which are essential when dealing with the wax moth. In the north, the wax moth can't survive the cold temperatures (45°F. and below), so insulating the storage area is not necessary. When temperatures rise above 60°F., check for signs of tunnelling and boring, as well as webs and debris. To destroy these pests once the frames have been infected, you can heat the equipment at a temperature of 116° to 120°F. for 80 minutes.

Out in the yard, the hive can suffer damage from bears, skunks, ground hogs, woodchucks, and wasps, as well as from ants, wax moths, and mice. The important thing about these latter three is that they cannot do much damage unless the colony is weak, diseased, or starved. Other than keeping the hive dry by checking and placing the supers directly in line with the previous ones, there is not much that can be done to safeguard against the wax moth.

Ants attack the bees and the stores. Very often they are found between the top and the inner cover. By removing the inner cover for a week, the ants will be limited in their attack to the front entrance, which the bees are capable of defending. You can put the legs of the stand in cans and then put the can-covered legs in larger cans filled with oil. By keeping vegetation around the hive to a minimum and spreading small amounts of ash on the ground, you will further restrict the ants' access to the hive.

Mice enter the hive during the winter and build nests in the comb. The cluster supplies them with warmth. They will eat the bees and stores, leaving the hive occasionally for water. Besides destroying the comb, they urinate on the bees and constantly irritate

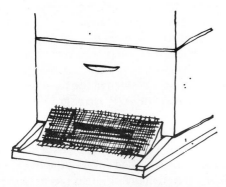

them, often causing the cluster to break up in cold weather. Signs of their presence are bits of chewed wax or feces at the hive entrance, and a heavy odour when the hive top is lifted. In winter when the flights of bees are few, a wire screen (1/4'' to 3/8'' mesh) on triangular blocks is placed across the entrance way.

The skunk attacks the hive at night. He scratches at the entrance of the hive and, as the bees come out to investigate, he gobbles them up. As more bees come out, he is forced to squash them and at the same time roll them into a ball, which he then eats. The beekeeper can always be sure when this pest is present by the scratches and mud on the front of the hive. Also there will be a small area that is polished smooth — the vegetation worn away from the mashing and rolling action. To prevent the skunk from using this area and thus defeat his attack, a screen with one-inch mesh should be securely placed three or four inches off the ground and level with the entrance. Another method of defence is to put a wire mesh fence around the hive. To discourage the skunk from digging underneath the fence, the wire mesh should be extended at least two feet out from the base and buried.

Bears, mainly because of their size, are probably the most difficult problem to overcome. Their power enables them to smash and completely destroy a hive in one raid. They don't often have trouble getting past defence structures. Once they have had the taste of honey (the adults actually prefer the brood), you can be sure they will return until the last is gone. It seems the answer is to convince the bear that he shouldn't bother, and that whatever is there he won't like. If you are lucky, you can quite often pull it off, but there is always one bear that is a little more persistent than the others. As one beekeeper told me: ''Every bear is different and their method of attack is often unique.'' They have been known to lift up a hive, carry it off a considerable distance, put it down, calmly start batting supers off in all directions. With the hive seriously divided into groups around the original location and the scattered supers, the bear has easy pickings. He pulls out a few frames and heads off a short distance from all the confusion to eat his dinner in peace.

Until now, the main concept in bear protection has been to build a defence perimeter around the yard. This has been done with crosscut saws, boards with spikes in them, barb wire — just about anything you can think of. The most sophisticated and successful method is the electric fence. They can be purchased through farmer and dairy co-ops for about $25. To make the electrical ground more effective, two feet of No. 16 chicken wire should be laid flat around the outside of the fenced-off area and connected to the controller output.

½" MESH SCREEN ON WIRE FRAME

SCREEN BURIED MIN. 8"

2'-0" MIN.

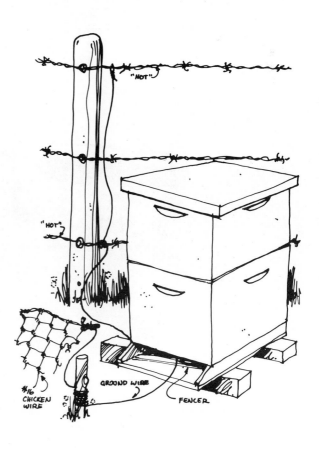

"HOT"

"HOT"

#16 CHICKEN WIRE

GROUND WIRE

FENCER

Strips of bacon can be placed on the barb wire to guarantee a surprising shock. Considering the price of the unit, it's a good idea to house it in an empty hive just inside the fence. The only problem with the electric fence is that it is not completely bear proof. Understandably there are laws that limit the voltage, so the main element becomes surprise. If for some reason things haven't gone well for the bear that day, it is possible he will feel an urge to destroy the thing that bothers him. With a couple of blows, he can easily knock the fence down.

The raised platform is also quite common, especially with the keeper who has only a few hives. Although severely limited in space and manoeuvreability, the stand can be very successful. The first requirement is soft ground, to allow you to securely place four 3'' pipes, 8' to 10' long, in a 4' square. Welded at the top of each pipe, you should have a plate (4'' x 4'') to bolt the wooden frame and platform to. It is possible to substitute trees for the pipe, which would give you the extra stability, but they must be covered well with very smooth tin. This is a mistake I made last year. I had covered the trees, but it was a patch job. I used many different pieces, some of it very bent and crumpled, so the surface wasn't smooth enough. The bear had no trouble climbing up and pushing a couple of hives over. Some people claim they can't climb at all, but are excellent pole vaulters. As I didn't see any marks on the tree that definitely proved he had climbed up, I can only suppose that he had little trouble holding on to the tin. Although quite exposed to the weather, the top of a shed also makes a very sturdy and unclimbable platform.

Another method which is more costly, but very handy if you move your bees out to the field in the spring and back to the wintering yard in the fall, is the caged trailer. The cage should be built with a wooden frame covered by heavy link fencing.

The trailer will eliminate time spent setting up fences and handling hives. Cost is the big drawback but often enough you can find heavy gauge link fencing second hand from old baseball diamonds, tennis courts, etc.

The newest concept in dealing with bears is to protect the target rather than the perimeter. The hives are placed back to back on top of a roll of 16-gauge (4'') netted wire. The wire is taken over the ends and top, then cinched tightly together. A second roll is wrapped around the sides and ends. It is also tightly cinched together. The hives are then covered with a light layer of mesh, the ends having a double layer. Along the top edges, the first wrap is connected to the second. This is repeated with a loose covering held down with four posts sunk into the ground and joined with straps. When the bees are attacked, they unite to fight the bear. There is no way that the bear can divide the colonies or the hive.

The major problem with this system concerns the temperament of the bees. If disturbed often by a persistent bear, the bees become angry and consume large amounts of the honey stores. The time-consuming problem of working with the wrappings is remedied with good spring management and extra supers early in the season. You shouldn't have to check the hives more than once or twice during the honey flow.

There are a few other pests that harm the hive or the bees in one way or another. Birds will catch bees in the field. Woodchucks chew on the supers, apparently looking for salt. They can be stopped with fences. Wasps will eat stray bees and often enter the hive to rob the stores. Dragonflies and robber flies will also prey on the bees away from the hive. Most of these pests are minor characters and their damage is insignificant.

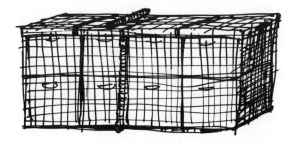

If you are just beginning with bees, then give some special attention to location. Bears are attracted to orchards in late summer and fall. A blueberry crop will also bring them around. Ants thrive in pest areas. In Germany, wasps living in areas where a lot of ash had been dumped, forced beekeepers out of business. Remember, most of the larger animals are afraid of man, so the closer to the house and lights the better.

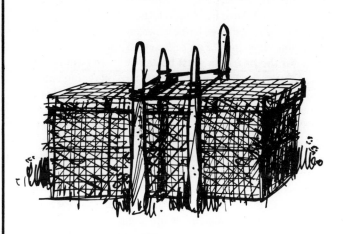

Bibliography

Beekeeping in the U.S.
Agricultural Handbook 335

Controlling the Greater Wax Moth
Farmers Bulletin 2217

Both are available from:
The Superintendent of Documents
U.S. Government Printing Office
Washington, D.C. 20402

Bee Diseases and Pest of the Apiary
Ontario Department of Agriculture
Parliament Buildings
Toronto, Ontario

A Treadle Driven Wood Turning Lathe

by W.C. Lecky

With the exception of turned wooden pulleys and the form to cast a flywheel, you can build this efficient treadle lathe with a few hand tools. Distance between centres can be increased to accommodate turnings more than 30 in. long, but in doing so, the treadle, which must be correspondingly lengthened, is apt to twist when pedaling is done at the tailstock end. Spindle height is such to enable one to pedal the lathe from either a standing or sitting position. Approximately 100 downward strokes of the treadle per minute will give a spindle speed recommended for turning. Common 2 by 4-in. fir stock is satisfactory for the stand. Side and front views in figure 8 give the correct length to cut each member. Note how the headstock is incorporated in the twin front legs. Except for fastening the bed pieces, the type of assembly shown to the right of figure 3 is used throughout, which permits tightening joints that may become loose. The small pin indicated is provided to keep the members in line when drawing up the bolts. Endless V-belting or round leather belting, joined, will do to rig the countershaft. As no tension adjustment is provided, it will be necessary, if an endless belt is used to drive the headstock spindle, to

vary the position of the rear countershaft pulley to be able to stretch the belt snugly over it. Belt dressing can be used if slipping develops.

Ball bearings in both the headstock and countershaft make the lathe exceptionally smooth running and are preferred to bronze bearings, although Ford model-T spindle body bushings can be used if you are unable to secure ball bearings. Figure 9 details the headstock. The holes for the bearings must be centered an equal distance above the bed and counterboard on facing sides to provide a press fit for the bearings. An auto-generator bearing will do for the inner bearing, but the outer one should be of the type to take end thrust when pressure is applied by the tailstock. The 3-in. pulleys, beside the drive and tail centres, are standard and come fitted with setscrews for attaching them to a 1/2-in. shaft. A 6 or 8-in. grinding wheel fitted to the outer end of the spindle serves a double purpose in providing a means for sharpening your lathe tools and at the same time contributing to the momentum. Collars are used against each bearing to take up end play.

The flywheel detailed in figures 5 and 6 provides the

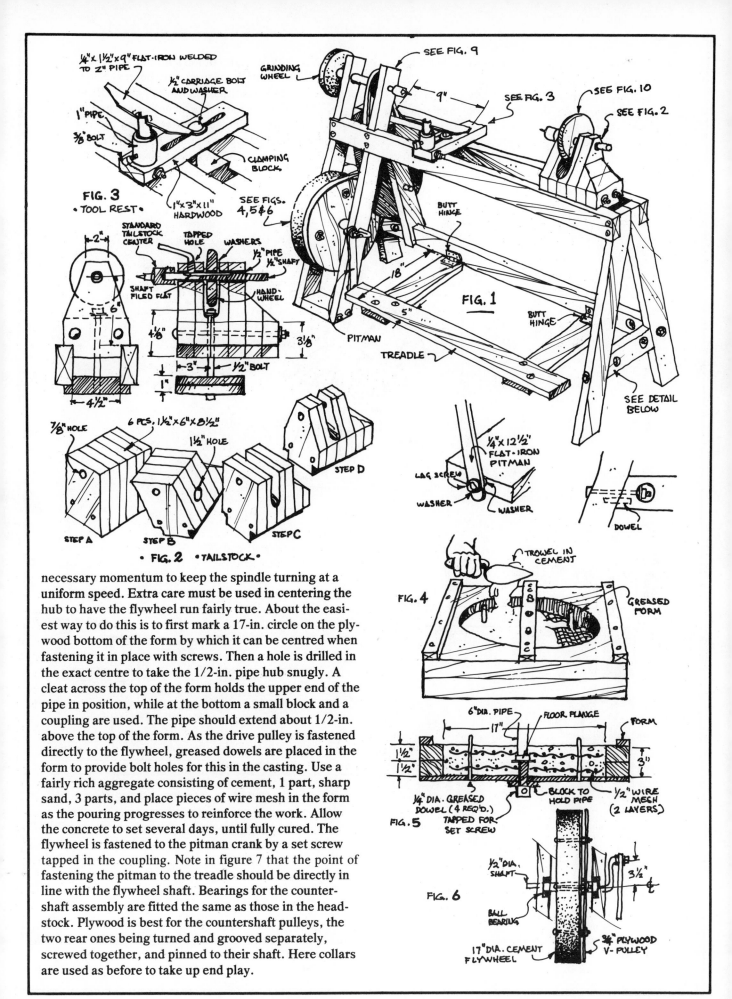

¼" x 1½" x 9" FLAT-IRON WELDED TO 2" PIPE

½" CARRIAGE BOLT AND WASHER

1" PIPE

⅜" BOLT

FIG. 3
• TOOL REST •

1" x 3" x 11" HARDWOOD

CLAMPING BLOCK

SEE FIGS. 4, 5 & 6

SEE FIG. 9

GRINDING WHEEL

9"

SEE FIG. 3

SEE FIG. 10

SEE FIG. 2

BUTT HINGE

18"

FIG. 1

BUTT HINGE

5"

PITMAN

TREADLE

SEE DETAIL BELOW

STANDARD TAILSTOCK CENTER

TAPPED HOLE

WASHERS

½" PIPE

½" SHAFT

SHAFT FILED FLAT

HAND WHEEL

2"

6"

4⅛"

3⅛"

3"

½" BOLT

1"

4½"

⅞" HOLE

6 PCS. 1½" x 6" x 8½"

1½" HOLE

STEP D

STEP A

STEP B

STEP C

• FIG. 2 • TAILSTOCK •

¼" x 12½" FLAT-IRON PITMAN

LAG SCREW

WASHER

WASHER

DOWEL

TROWEL IN CEMENT

FIG. 4

GREASED FORM

6" DIA. PIPE

FLOOR FLANGE

FORM

17"

1½"

1½"

3"

¼" DIA. GREASED DOWEL (4 REQ'D.)

FIG. 5

TAPPED FOR SET SCREW

BLOCK TO HOLD PIPE

½" WIRE MESH (2 LAYERS)

½" DIA. SHAFT

3½"

FIG. 6

BALL BEARING

17" DIA. CEMENT FLYWHEEL

¾" PLYWOOD V-PULLEY

necessary momentum to keep the spindle turning at a uniform speed. Extra care must be used in centering the hub to have the flywheel run fairly true. About the easiest way to do this is to first mark a 17-in. circle on the plywood bottom of the form by which it can be centred when fastening it in place with screws. Then a hole is drilled in the exact centre to take the 1/2-in. pipe hub snugly. A cleat across the top of the form holds the upper end of the pipe in position, while at the bottom a small block and a coupling are used. The pipe should extend about 1/2-in. above the top of the form. As the drive pulley is fastened directly to the flywheel, greased dowels are placed in the form to provide bolt holes for this in the casting. Use a fairly rich aggregate consisting of cement, 1 part, sharp sand, 3 parts, and place pieces of wire mesh in the form as the pouring progresses to reinforce the work. Allow the concrete to set several days, until fully cured. The flywheel is fastened to the pitman crank by a set screw tapped in the coupling. Note in figure 7 that the point of fastening the pitman to the treadle should be directly in line with the flywheel shaft. Bearings for the counter-shaft assembly are fitted the same as those in the head-stock. Plywood is best for the countershaft pulleys, the two rear ones being turned and grooved separately, screwed together, and pinned to their shaft. Here collars are used as before to take up end play.

Figure 2 details the tailstock and shows the progressive steps to follow in shaping the glued-up block. The spindle hole, which is bored while the block is still square, is bushed on each side of the handwheel opening with a 1/2-in. pipe nipple to receive a 1/2-in. threaded shaft. Note that one side of the shaft is filed flat for the end of the lock lever, which keeps the spindle from turning when being advanced or withdrawn by the handwheel. The latter is of wood and has a threaded bushing imbedded in its centre to fit the spindle. Washers centre it in the opening. Both tailstock and tool rest clamp in place by handwheels fitted below the bed, as shown in figures 7 and 8. The tool rest and holder are made according to figure 3. The post socket, which consists of a 1-in. pipe nipple inside a coupling, is anchored to the base by boring a hole in the latter to take the coupling snugly and then drilling crosswise through both for a 3-1/2-in. carriage bolt.

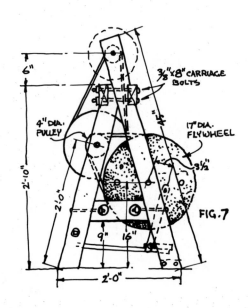

FIG. 7

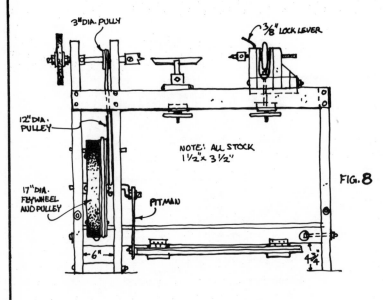

FIG. 8

NOTE: ALL STOCK 1½" x 3½"

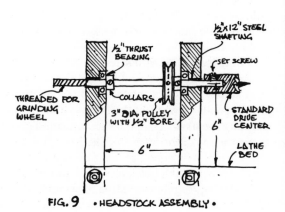

FIG. 9 · HEADSTOCK ASSEMBLY ·

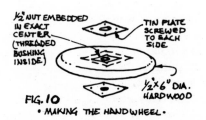

FIG. 10
· MAKING THE HANDWHEEL ·

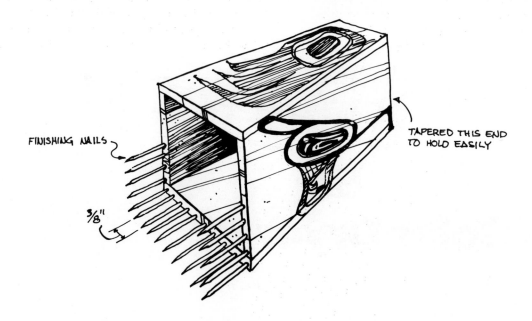

FINISHING NAILS

3/8"

TAPERED THIS END
TO HOLD EASILY

How to Build an Indian Berry Picker

Gathering the large, soft berries from blackberry, raspberry, thimbleberry, and salmonberry bushes presents no special problem except for the battle-of-the-thorn. But if you've ever spent the day popping huckleberries or any small berries from the bush, you must have wondered if there wasn't a better way of picking the small, round fruits. Well, folks, there is an answer, and it was the Indians who first came up with it. If you need lots of berries for those jellies, jams, and wines, have a large tribe to feed, or want to freeze or dry berries for winter use—and maybe sell some too—the Indian berry picker is the most efficient device to use. The original berry picker was usually whittled from wood in the shape of a scoop with a series of long V-shaped teeth at the mouth. The whittlers among us may want to carve their berry pickers Indian fashion. The rest of us can make our pickers from empty tin cans or nail together some lightweight wood to make the container.

If you use the tin can, solder pieces of steel or hard copper wire about 1/8" in diameter and 1-1/2" long in a semi-circle around the open end of the can. Space the wire

(long finishing nails from the hardware store will also work) about 3/8" apart, and sharpen the ends of the wires to reasonably sharp points.

If you make your berry picker from wood, nail and glue together an open-ended box that you can hold comfortably in your hand. Tap long finishing nails into the end of the bottom and half-way up the sides, spacing the nails about 3/8" apart. Sharpen the nails with a file.

To use your Indian berry picker, simply run the points through the berry-laden plant limbs. The berries will fall into your picker along with a few leaves and twigs.

To separate the leaves from the berries, empty your day's collection of berries on a stretched and slanting blanket. The berries will roll and bounce to the bottom of the blanket to be caught in containers, and the few twigs and leaves will stay on the blanket and can be shaken away. Also you can separate the debris from the berries by placing everything in a pail of water. Any leaves that have been picked with the berries will float to the top and can be skimmed off.

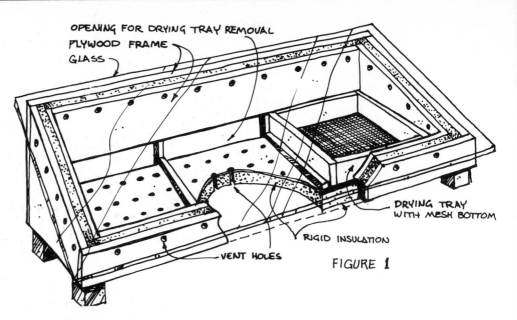

OPENING FOR DRYING TRAY REMOVAL
PLYWOOD FRAME
GLASS

DRYING TRAY
WITH MESH BOTTOM

RIGID INSULATION

VENT HOLES

FIGURE 1

A Solar Dryer

by T.A. Laward

The usual method of drying fruits is to lay them out in the sun for a few days until they seem to have dried out enough to be stored. It's cheap, but it does have its drawbacks; mainly bug and dust infestation. (Sun-dried apricots are nice, but I sure get tired of picking dust out from between my teeth.) To overcome the bugs and dust, as well as improve the quality of your produce (even reduction of the moisture to the low levels required makes a longer storage time possible), you might want to build a solar dryer.

Essentially, the dryer is a solar hot box. It consists of a rectangular container insulated at its base and preferably at the sides, and covered with a double-layered transparent roof. Solar radiation is transmitted through the roof and absorbed on the blackened interior surfaces. Owing to the insulation, the inside temperature is raised. Holes are drilled through the base to induce fresh ventilating air into the cabinet. Outlet ports are drilled on the upper parts of the cabinet side and rear panels. As the temperature increases, warm air passes out of the upper holes by natural convection, creating a partial vacuum and drawing fresh air up through the base. As a result there is a constant flow of air over your fruits (or vegetables), which are placed on perforated trays inside the cabinet.

Method of construction is limited only by your imagination, available materials, and a few general rules.

The length of the cabinet should be at least three times the width, so as to minimize the shading effect of the side panels.

Build the slope of the roof covering the angle designated in figure 2. This will give you the best angle for your latitude.

The transparent cover is best made of glass (1/8'' or 3 mm.), although a polyester plastic film (about 0.005'' thick) will also work.

You can build the framework out of most any building material. For the portable models, use wood, metal, hardboard, plywood, or even wicker or bamboo. If you wish to build something permanent, build it out of brick, stone, concrete, or maybe even adobe. When insulating,

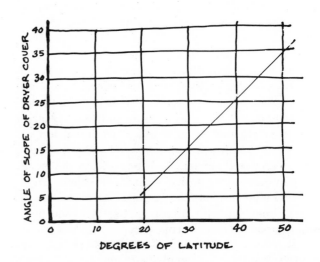

FIGURE 2

(Graph axes: vertical axis labeled "ANGLE OF SLOPE OF DRYER COVER" from 0 to 40; horizontal axis labeled "DEGREES OF LATITUDE" from 0 to 50)

try to use cheap local materials such as wood shavings, sawdust, reject wool, or goat's hair.

Construct the hot box along lines similar to those outlined in figure 1. Make the insulation about 2'' thick, both for the base and the side sections. Drill holes in the insulated base and fit them with short lengths of plastic or rubberized garden hose. If there are bugs around, cover these insulation holes with fine mosquito netting or gauze. Usually, the high heat inside the cabinet discourages insects, rodents, etc. from entering and feeding on the drying produce.

Attach the transparent (glass or plastic) covers to a frame and fit the frame onto the chassis of the cabinet, making sure that the cover is completely watertight so as to avoid deterioration of the interior and wetting of the insulation. Paint the framework black in order to absorb the maximum solar radiation.

Now is the time to drill a couple of holes in the rear and side panels to provide ventilation ports to remove the warm, moist air. The number of holes is dependent on your climate and whatever it is you wish to dry. A good method is to initiate the drying in the springtime, with a minimum of side holes, and to continue drilling them so as just to prevent inside moisture condensation. This prevents drilling too many ventilation holes.

Fit the rear panel with access doors to give entry into the cabinet. Construct the trays of galvanized chicken-wire or some similar material. Place them on runners about 1/2'' high, so as to ensure a reasonable level of air circulation under and around the drying material.

Paint the inside of the cabinet black. The outside of the side, rear, and base panels should be painted with aluminum paint. If you wish to, cover the inside of the side and rear panels with a layer of aluminum foil (recycled of course) or if you have none, paint them black.

The dryer will handle about 1-1/2 pounds of produce per square foot of drying area. A small thermometer inserted into one of the ventilation holes will prove handy. Shield the thermometer bulb from direct sunlight. Temperature can be controlled by opening and closing the rear door, if necessary. Practice will allow you to determine the optimal termperatures.

Your produce should be perfect for drying. Use the blemished stuff for canning. Blemished or bruised fruits will not keep as well and may turn a whole tray of drying fruit bad. The smaller the pieces to be dried, the shorter the drying time. The layer of fruit should be no more than one piece deep.

Your fruit is dried when it feels dry on the outside, but slightly soft inside. It should not be brittle, nor should it be possible to squeeze out any juice. After the drying is finished, store the fruit in glass or cardboard containers. For four successive days, stir the contents thoroughly each day to bring the drier particles in contact with some that are more moist. If, at the end of 4 days, the fruit seems too moist, return it to the dryer for further treatment. Afterwards, store it in a cool place. It's a good idea to check it occasionally for molds.

FRUIT OR VEGETABLE	PREPARATION FOR DRYING AND DRYING METHOD
Beans (pod): String, Green, Snap, Wax	Wash and dry, cut or break off ends and pull strings, cut or break into one inch pieces, spread on frames or string on heavy thread, dry.
Beans (shelled): Lima, Pinto, Great Northern, Black, Soy, Kidney, Lentils, Pea (navy), Cranberry, Blackeyed peas, Cow-peas	Shell, grade if desired, spread on frames, stir daily until completely dry.
Peas: All types	Prepare and dry as for beans.
Cereal and bread grains: Barley, Corn, Oats, Rye, Buckwheat, Rice	Spread on frames, stir daily until completely dry. Allow corn to stand on the stalks until fully mature, pick and husk, leave on cobs until grains are hard, strip from cob.
Herbaceous plants	If the plants have thick, juicy stems such as celery or rhubarb, slice thinly and spread on frames or string on heavy thread. Dry all other herbs whole, crumble when dry and separate large stems from leaves, store in air-tight containers.
Peppers: Bell, Green, Red, Cherry, Banana, Tabasco	Small peppers (Tabasco, Red) may be dried whole. Slice others in rings and spread on frames or string on heavy thread.
Tuberous root vegetables: Beets, Carrots, Parsnips, Potatoes, Salsify, Sweet potatoes, Yams, Turnips, Rutabagas	Peel or scrape skins, slice thinly and spread on frames, or cube and string on heavy thread. NOTE: When these vegetables dry, they may change colour due to oxidation, but the colour change will in no way harm the flavour.
Bulbous root vegetables: Onions, Leeks, Kohlrabi	Peel and slice into thin rings (no more than ⅛ inch thick), spread on frames or string on heavy thread.
Apples: All types	Wash, peel, slice into rings (no need to core), spread on frames or string on heavy thread. NOTE: Apples turn brown when dried due to oxidation, but the colour change does not affect the flavour.
Apricots: All types	Wash, cut in half and remove pit, spread skin side down on frames until dry. DO NOT TURN.
Berries: Blackberries, Blueberries, Loganberries, Gooseberries, Huckleberries, Raspberries, (black, red) Strawberries, Serviceberries, Mulberries, Juneberries, Shadberries, etc.	Wash, spread on frames until dry.
Cherries: All types	Wash, spread on frames until dry.
Currants: All types	Pull from bunches (grapes), wash, spread on frames until dry.
Figs: All types	
Grapes: All types	
Peaches: All types	Wash, halve or quarter if fruit is large, remove pit (peaches), spread skin side down on frames until dry. DO NOT TURN.
Pears: All types	
Plums: All types	Most plums do not dry well; the prune plum is best. Wash and spread on frames until dry.

How to Build a Juice Press

by F.E. Atkinson and C.C. Strachan

This fruit press design allows anyone who is handy with a few tools to construct a press for home use. The fruit press is primarily designed for apples, but it can be used for pressing any pulped fruit. The grater can be used for any fruits free of large stones. With apples, the fruit press will handle from one to five boxes, yielding 2 to 10 gallons at one pressing.

The essential parts consist of the frame, drainboard, rack, trays, platform, grater, and hopper. It has been found advisable to construct the parts of the press in the order they are listed.

Frame

The four corner posts are made of dressed 4'' x 4'', 47'' long. The dressed size will vary from 3-1/2'' to 3-3/4''. These posts are joined together with 2'' x 4'' braces, placed 12'' from the bottom, and across the top. These are set into the corner posts sufficiently so that their outer surface will be flush with the piece of 3/4'' x 2-1/2'' nailed on to the posts immediately above the lower braces. The 2'' x 4'' braces and the 3/4'' x 2-1/2'' are cut at a 45 degree angle at the corners. The length of these pieces is 28''.

The top 2'' x 4'' braces on both sides of the press are strengthened by 1-1/2'' angle iron 28'' long. Holes large enough for 1/2'' rods are drilled 9-3/8'' (measured to the centre of the hole) from each end. Two pieces of 1-1/2'' angle iron 19-3/4'' long, with similar holes 5-3/8'' from each end, reinforce the lower side braces. Holes are bored in the 2'' x 4'' braces to correspond with the holes in the angle iron. The 1/2'' x 37'' rods are put in place and the nuts tightened until the rods are firm.

The same 2'' x 4'' in the lower group that are drill-ed to accommodate the 1/2'' rods are also notched in four places to take care of the reinforcements on the rack These are illustrated in figure 3. These notches are 1-1/2'' wide, 1-3/4'' deep, and 3/4'' into the 2'' x 4''. Two of these notches are situated 1/8'' from the corner post, while the near side of the other two is 6'' from the corner post.

3-Ply Drainboard

A piece of 3-ply is tightly fitted into the square space developed by the lower 2'' x 4''. This 3-ply is located so that the high side opposite the drain hole is 2'' below the top of the 2'' x 4'' brace, while the side near the outlet hole is 2-1/2'' below the top of the 2'' x 4'' brace. Any rough stripping can be used below the 3-ply to form a ledge, while small right-angled triangles of 3/4'' material can be nailed in the corners for reinforcement. The length of the sides of these triangles on each side of the right angle is the distance from the corner formed by the brace and the corner post to the inside corner of the post. This will be in the neighbourhood of 2-1/2''. A suitable moulding for the top side to seal the joint between the 3-ply, the braces, and corner post may be made by planing 1/2'' x 3/8'' strips to almost a triangle in cross section. The 3-ply catches the juice and delivers it to the 1'' hole in the 2'' x 4'' brace in the front of the press.

Any easily worked metal can be used instead of the 3-ply, provided it is painted with a good paint and thoroughly dried. Four-hour white enamel is suitable.

Rack

The rack is made of 19 pieces of 1'' x 1'' nailed on to four stringers of 1-1/4'' x 1-7/8''. The stringers are spaced so that they will fit into the notches previously de-

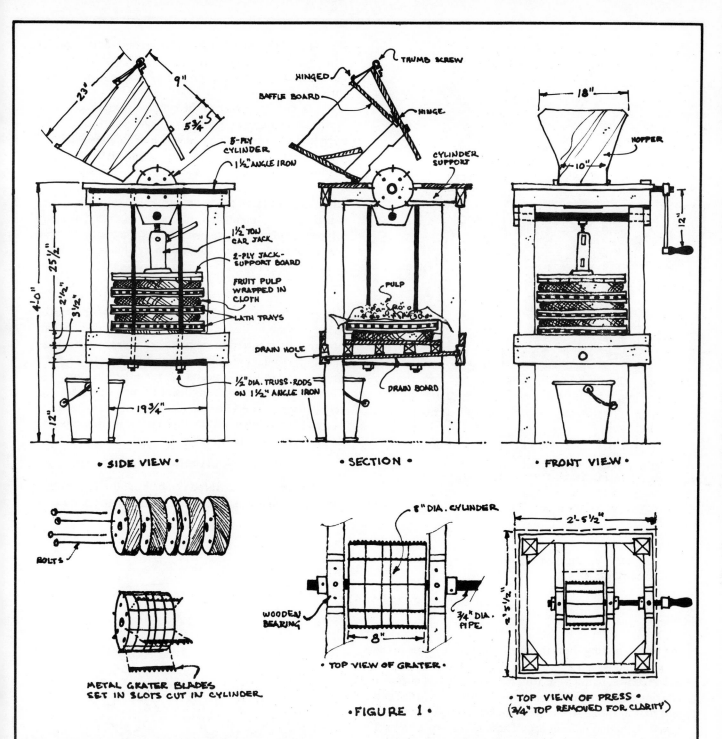

· SIDE VIEW ·

· SECTION ·

· FRONT VIEW ·

METAL GRATER BLADES
SET IN SLOTS CUT IN CYLINDER

· TOP VIEW OF GRATER ·

·FIGURE 1·

· TOP VIEW OF PRESS ·
(3/4" TOP REMOVED FOR CLARITY)

scribed in the side braces. The stringers and the 1'' x 1'' pieces should be made of the strongest wood available, as the rack has to withstand the full pressure of the jack. The two 1'' x 1'' pieces on each side of the rack are cut off flush with the first stringer to allow room for the corner posts. The rack is removable so as to facilitate cleaning.

Lath Trays

Standard laths or wooden strips 3/8'' x 1-1/2'' are cut to a length of 19''. A tray is 19'' square and consists of a single layer of laths placed parallel to one another and the thickness of a lath apart. These laths are crossed at each end (above and below) with laths that hold the

rack together. Copper clout nails, one to a lath, are driven in from both sides. Five lath trays can be used at a time. These are illustrated in figure 2.

Pressure Platform

This is made of three pieces of 1'' x 6'' x 19'' crossed by three other similar pieces. As this platform is subjected to considerable strain, it is wise to nail it thoroughly with nails long enough to clinch.

Wooden Bearings
Grater Supports

Take two pieces of 2'' x 4'' x 25'' for grater supports and bore the bearing holes as directed in the follow-

thickness of the board to make 8'', to bolt them together with four bolts countersunk at each end, and to turn the boards into a cylinder 8'' x 8''. A 1'' hole is also drilled through the centre.

The circumference of the cylinder is marked into eigths and lines drawn lengthwise on its surface. On each line a sawcut is made in which the blades will be fitted. The depth of these cuts will depend on the size of blades being used. In seven cuts, pieces of a coarse saw blade (such as a bucksaw or pruning saw) are placed with 3/16'' of teeth protruding from the cylinder. In the remaining cut, the blade is placed down so that a smooth edge protrudes to the same extent as the teeth. An example of the teeth used and also a smooth blade are shown in figure 3.

Shaft

A 23'' piece of 3/4'' pipe is used as a shaft. Quarter-inch holes are drilled at each end of the cylinder so that pins may be inserted to keep the cylinder from turning on the shaft. Collars are also used on the shaft to keep the cylinder properly spaced between the bearings. These collars are 3/4'' lengths of 1'' pipe with a set screw through one side. The bearing caps should be marked so that they will be replaced in the same position as they were originally made.

Hopper

A hopper as illustrated can be built to fit over the grater. Notches are cut out of the sides of the bottom to

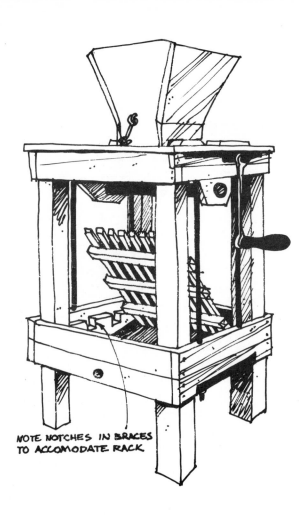

NOTE NOTCHES IN BRACES TO ACCOMODATE RACK

• FIGURE 2 •

ing before nailing them in place. Mark the centres of the 2'' x 4'' and attach 2'' x 2'' x 6'' pieces on the 2'' edge at the centre, using 6'' x 3/8'' bolts at each end of the bearing cap. Bore a 1'' hole at the centre, half in the cap and half in the 2'' x 4''. Quarter-inch oil holes can be bored in the top of each cap. These two pieces of 2'' x 4'' are now nailed lengthwise through the frame braces 8-1/2'' apart. They are 6-1/2'' from the inside of the side 2'' x 4''.

If the hole for the bolt through the bearing cap on the side of the shaft farthest from the drain hole is 1-1/2'' from the centre of the shaft, the end of the bolt may be used to attach the scraper roller later described.

Grater

There are two ways of making this part. The easier is to take a solid piece of wood and turn it down on a lathe or plane it to obtain a cylinder 8'' long and 8'' in diameter. The disadvantage of this method is the possibility of splits developing. The second method is to take sufficient

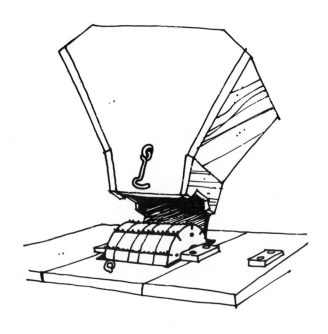

• FIGURE 3 •

fit over the bearing caps. The hopper may be removed to facilitate cleaning by releasing the 4'' hook and eye at each end (figure 2). The baffle board is hinged at the bottom and can be adjusted to different positions by loosening the thumb screw. The lower edge of the baffle board is tapered to a 1/4'' thickness; this taper extends back 2-3/4''. The taper is on the side of the baffle board facing the grater. The purpose of this board is to force apples against the grater. The position in which this board works best will be found in actual operation. If it is not possible to obtain an 8'' piece of flat iron slotted except at each end, with which to adjust the baffle board, then holes may be drilled through the side of the hopper to match a hole in the baffle board, and pegs or nails used to hold the board in different positions.

Top Covering

The top of the press may be covered with any 3/4'' material. The boards covering the side through which the shaft must be notched on the under side so as to fit properly over this item.

Pressure Bar

This is a piece of 1-1/2'' shafting and is sufficiently strong to resist most of the pressures used. However, if sufficient pressure is being used to bend the shaft, then a piece of 4'' x 4'' can be placed on the under side of the shaft. This 4'' x 4'' can be notched so that it fits over the support for the shaft. This notching will prevent the 4'' x 4'' from turning on the shaft.

Scraper Roller

When the grater is turned by hand, there is not sufficient speed to keep it clean. Consequently grated pulp rides around on the cylinder and eventually clogs the throat where apples are ground. To overcome this, a piece of 1/2'' or 3/4'' garden hose 8'' long can be placed on a piece of 3/16'' rod or heavy wire, as illustrated in figure 4. This roller is secured by the nuts of the bearing bolts on the throat side of the grater. The ends of the wire are flattened and slightly bent so as to maintain a small tension against the grater. The hose thus lies lengthwise on the cylinder and scrapes off the pulp. When it is hit by the blades, the hose rolls on the rod. If the grater is driven with an electric motor, the roller *must* be removed as the increased speed causes the rubber to be cut by the blades.

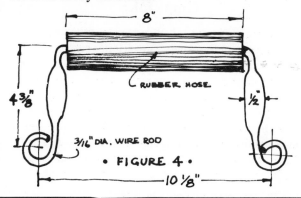

· FIGURE 4 ·

Painting

It is desirable to paint the press with white paint or four hour enamel. This prevents warping and checking of the wood and helps to keep the apparatus clean.

Operation of the Press

Apples are placed in the hopper. A piece of unbleached factory cotton, 36'' x 36'', is placed on the slatted rack, with the corners of the cloth in the middle of the sides of the rack. The apples are grated until the resulting pulp forms a layer 2'' to 3'' thick and 18'' square. The corners of the cloth are then folded over the pulp, completely enclosing the mass. This is commonly called a "cheese". A lath tray is then placed on top of this apple pulp and cloth, and the operation is repeated. If a short jack is used, five cheeses can be pressed at one time, yeilding approximately 10 gallons of juice. The pressure platform is placed on top of the last cheese. The jack is worked between this and the shaft. If this shaft is bent or the jack becomes too short, the piece of 4'' x 4'' previously described can be used. If it's desirable to press only one box of apples, a few pieces of heavy timber can be used on top of the pressure platform to raise the jack up to the shaft.

Where power is available, a 1/3-horsepower motor, 1,750 r.p.m., can be used to turn the grater. A 3'' sheave for a V-belt is placed on the motor and a 12-1/2'' sheave on the grater shaft. An automobile V-shaped fan belt makes a suitable drive. This is illustrated in figure 5. Care should be taken not to feed the apples too fast and not to feed any apples until the grater has been started.

· FIGURE 5 ·

Preserving Juices

Apple Juice

Although there are several methods of preparing sterile sweet apple juice, most of these are too cumbersome or too expensive for use in the home. The following simple method is suggested for home use, where only a few dozen bottles may be desired and no special equipment is available. This method does not give extreme clarity, but it does retain the pleasing flavour and health-giving properties of the fresh juice.

1. Strain the sweet juice. Fill clean beer bottles with juice until they are brimming full.
2. Place a wash-boiler containing 3-1/2 to 4 inches of warm water and a slatted wooden false bottom on the stove. Fill the boiler with the full beer bottles. A full bottle in this case has juice within 1/2 inch of the top of the neck. As the juice expands, the bottle should overflow. If the bottles are stood close together, the boiler should hold 29 to 30 bottles. If the proper amount of water has been used, it should reach halfway up the necks of the bottles.
3. Allow the water in the boiler to heat until it just starts to boil. This is evidenced by the upward movement of the water and the bubbles of steam that reach the surface and burst. Be sure this stage is reached, then move the boiler back to the cooler part of the stove and commence capping the bottles. There should be no air in the bottles when they are capped. If a thermometer is available, a test at the centre of a bottle should show a temperature of 180°F. It is wise to use an aluminum or parchment-spotted cap. These caps are the ordinary crown cap, with a circular disc of aluminum or parchment on the cork. The aluminum or parchment is much easier to sterilize than plain cork.

A handy "gadget" for removing the hot beer bottle from the boiler, and one which can be made from 1/8-inch steel wire, is illustrated in figure 1. In making this holder, two pieces of wire 32 inches long are bent as illustrated in A and B. B is placed beside A and the wires pressed into the open round bends at C. Then the wires E and F are bent at right angles, as illustrated. The open joint at C is next pressed closed with a pair of pliers. Both sets of wires are then bent to form the handles.

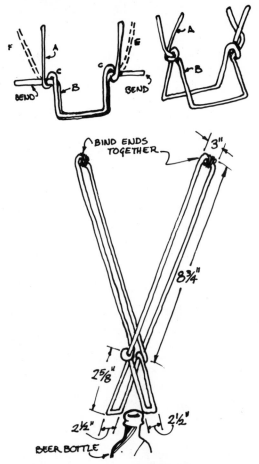

FIGURE 1

In the process of capping, it is wise to lay a few layers of newspaper on the base of the capper to avoid cracking the hot bottles on the cold metal. It is also a good plan to lay newspapers on the table where the hot bottles are to be laid. Lay all bottles on their sides after capping, to sterilize the neck of the bottle and the cap.

Nutritionally, freezing is the best method of preserving. This can be easily done by using old (or new) milk cartons as containers to freeze the juice in.

If you press winter apples and find the juice sour, allow it to sit in crocks of some sort for a short time (2 to 10 days), in order to age before bottling or freezing.

Grape Juice

A very pleasant grape juice may be prepared in the home from any of the American varieties such as Concord. The grapes are removed from the stem and placed in an enamel or aluminum utensil. They are then thoroughly broken to release the juice, and heated to 160°F., a very light simmer, for 10 minutes. This step serves to release the colour from the skin and other soluble solids from the pulp. The resulting juice, pulp, and skins are then passed through a cheesecloth sack. A small sample of the juice should be cooled and tasted for sweetness.

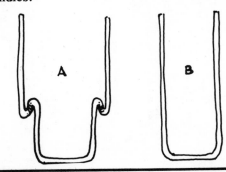

Sometimes as much as one pound of sugar or honey may be needed for every gallon of juice. The sweetener is thoroughly dissolved by stirring. The sweetened juice may then be sterilized in the same manner as described for sweet apple juice. Cream of tartar crystals usually settle on the bottom of the container during storage. These crystals are not harmful.

Juices with Suspended Pulp (Tomato, Apricot, and Prune)

Thoroughly vine-ripened tomatoes are stemmed and cored. The fruit is slightly pulped and placed on the stove in a covered kettle. It is heated to boiling. As much fruit as possible is placed in the kettle at the commencement of this step in order to exclude the air and prevent destruction of vitamin C. After the pulp has boiled four to five minutes, it is ready to be passed through a sieve to remove the skin and seeds. At this point, the necessity of haste cannot be over-emphasized, as the juice will lose much of its vitamin value if exposed to the air. If the juice is kept near the boiling point, the vapour given off during the extracting will keep the air away from the product.

Return the extracted juice to the kettle and bring just to boiling. At the same time, have enough sealers or beer bottles being kept hot in the oven. Fill these with juice, seal, and place in boiling water. If the juice is kept hot, beer bottles may be filled to within one inch of the top of the bottle. If beer bottles are used, sterilize caps in boiling water for five minutes before use. Aluminum or parchment spotted caps do not require this treatment. Cook beer bottles on their sides for 10 minutes in boiling water. Quart sealers should receive 20 minutes cooking.

Apricot juice and prune juice can be made similarly to tomato. The addition of a little water to the pulped apricot or prunes just prior to heating will reduce any tendency to scorching. About two to three cups of water to each 10 pounds of fruit is normally sufficient. Apricot can be sweetened by adding about 1-1/2 to 2 pounds of sugar or honey to each 10 pounds or gallon of cooked pulp. Dilute one to one with water before use. Prune juice, if made from thoroughly ripened fruit, does not require additional sweetner.

Extractor for Juice with Suspended Pulp

This extractor (fig. 2) is simple to make and can be used for any of the juices containing pulp. The size will depend on the utensils with which it is to be used.

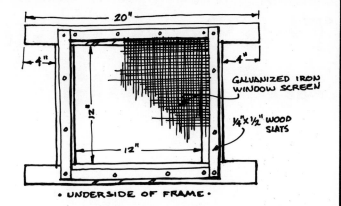

· FIGURE 2 ·

Making Vinegar

The process of making vinegar consists of two distinct steps; namely, the fermentation of the fresh juice and the acetification of the fermented juice.

Fermentation

1. Use a clean sound barrel, cask, or crock. Scrub with scalding water and lye if the container is not new.
2. Fill with fresh juice and add one yeast cake to every five gallons.
3. Fermentation will be complete when the small bubbles stop rising to the surface.

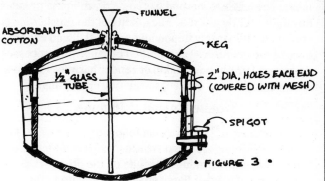

· FIGURE 3 ·

Acetification

A 10-gallon keg is a suitable container in which to conduct the process of acetification. Place the keg on its side and bore a two-inch hole near the top of each end. Screen these openings with wire to prevent entrance of insects, while permitting passage of air. A spigot should be placed in one end of the keg near the bottom. The fermented juice, to which some old vinegar or "mother" has been added, is then poured in through a funnel, as shown in figure 8, until the keg is half full. This apparatus works best when placed in a location where a temperature of at least 70°F. is maintained. If trouble is encountered from the staves on the top side of the keg "drying out", the apparatus can be arranged so that the same system is used, but the keg is kept in an upright position and filled only half full.

Finished vinegar should be ready in six weeks. As it is drawn off, more of the fermented juice may be added. Small batches may be finished in crocks or open casks.

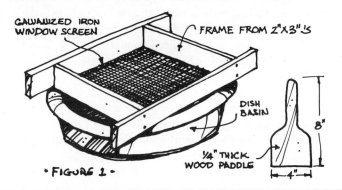

· FIGURE 1 ·

The Smoke Curing and Salting of Fish

by Iola I. Berg

The curing of fishery products by smoking has been carried out for many centuries. It's known that early man used a wood smoke cure in the preservation of fish and meat. The original method has come down to the present day only slightly altered. The quality of the finished product is still largely dependent on the skill and experience of the operator. Take *caution* because the processes described herein *may not* kill or render harmless all possilbe natural toxins or disease-causing organisms.

Smoke Curing Principles

Smoke curing involves the following processes: (1) salting, (2) drying, (3) heat treatment, (4) smoking. The final result of the product depends on the proper care and control of each of these processes, and upon the original quality and species of fish to be smoked.

Salting the product prior to smoking is usually done by soaking in brine for a definite length of time. The strength of the brine determines the type of cure of the product. Brining the fish is important; it firms the fish by removing moisture. Salt also imparts a flavour to the product. Fish may be lightly or heavily brined, depending upon the type of product desired. Lightly salted fish should be smoked immediately, since brining merely serves to impart flavour to the fish and to firm the flesh. Heavy brining is used in the development of special cures; for example, in the mild curing of salmon and also for preserving fish until the smoke curing process can be applied. The salt concentration reaches about 8 or 10 per cent, but it is not sufficient to preserve the fish indefinitely; thus the product must be kept in cold storage, preferably about 32 to 34 degrees F. Most of this salt must be removed from the fish prior to smoking. This is done by soaking the fish in cold running water.

Smokehouses

Simple smokehouses: There are three types of simple smokehouses that may be built cheaply and easily.

(1) *Converted icebox or refrigerator*: Drill some holes at the top to allow the smoke to escape. Use a hotplate at the bottom, preferably one with a temperature control. This provides a better control for hot smoking. Run a cord through the drain if an icebox is used. Into an old large pot, place a few pieces of alder to smoulder.

(2) *Oil drum, screen, and washtub*: Use a 50-gallon oil or gas drum with the top and bottom cut out. Set a three-foot square, one-half-inch wire-mesh galvanized screen on top of the drum. Place the fish on the screen and put an old washtub, upside down, over the fish. Then punch a few nail holes in the bottom of the washtub.

After suitable brining and soaking, the fish is subjected to a drying process. This is necessary to remove additional moisture from the fish. The more moisture removed from the fish, the greater will be the keeping quality. Drying is usually done outdoors, but can be done in the smokehouse. Maintenance of the proper humidity is quite important. Relative humidity should be below 75 per cent. Drying aids in the formation of the "pellicle." The pellicle is the glossy, firm surface imparted to the fish, which gives it the desired appearance and allows for the development and absorption of the delicate smoke flavour. Thus the formation of the pellicle is quite important in obtaining a good product.

The fish may be smoked in a cold or hot atmosphere. For cold-smoking, the temperature is held below 85° F. For hot-smoking, it may range from 120° to 180° F. and may be eaten immediately. It does not have good keeping qualities when cured by the hot method. Smoked fishery products are highly perishable and should be held under refrigeration at all times. For smoking most any kind of hardwood may be used, such as oak, alder, hickory, and mahogany. Alder is most commonly used in the Pacific Northwest. The soft woods are not recommended because of their resinous nature; they give an acrid flavour and odour to the product.

Some fish contain different amounts of fat or oil, and their salting and smoke curing may need to be adjusted accordingly. Small size fish may require as much smoke as a larger size fish of the same type, but the amount of drying may be varied. Those fishery products smoked prior to canning are smoked only lightly, just sufficient to produce the desired smoke flavour.

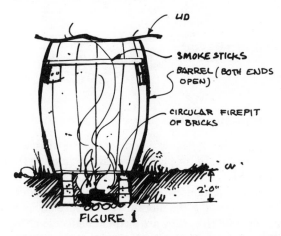

FIGURE 1

(3) *Barrel types (fig. 1)*: Knock the ends out of a large barrel, set it over a hole in the ground about two feet deep and a little narrower in width than the diameter of the barrel, and nail wooden strips in the barrel on two sides a few inches below the top. The ends of the smokesticks rest on these strips. Place a loosely-fitting cover on top (fig. 2). Dig a hole adjacent to the bottom of the barrel, connected with the pit, and fit it with a cover. The fire is fed through this hole, which also serves as a draft when the lid is partly raised. A smokehouse so constructed is best for hot smoking, but it may be used for cold-smoking if operated carefully. If the fire is permitted to flare up, however, the fish may be scorched. It is best to dig the fire pot on the side from which the prevailing winds come (fig. 2).

In hot smoking, the fish are hung near the fire, usually not more than three or four feet distant, and smoked at temperatures from 120 to 180 degrees, so they are partially or wholly cooked. In cold smoking, the fish are hung at some distance from a low smouldering fire and cured at temperatures usually lower than 90 degrees F. The degree of preservation depends on the length of time the fish are smoked; fish cold-smoked for a few hours, for example, will keep only a short time. If an extended period of preservation is desired, fish must be cold-smoked from a few days to a week or more.

Permanent Smokehouses (fig. 3)

(1) If a more permanent smokehouse is desired, and one that will handle a larger amount of fish, make a little shed, seven feet high and four feet square, inside measurement. About 12 inches above the ground, place a false bottom with 3/4 or one-inch auger holes at two-inch intervals. On the two sides, wooden battens are nailed at one-foot intervals, the first about 18 inches below the top. The ends of the smokesticks on which the fish are hung rest on these battens. The whole front of the house is hinged for a door. Three or four holes about two inches square are cut on the two sides a few inches below the roof, with slides to cover, for use as drafts or ventilators. The pit below the smokehouse and the fire pit may be lined with brick. A terracotta drain pipe may be placed in the trench connecting the two pits to act as a chimney.

(2) Smokehouse with the fire box removed from the house (fig. 4). In cold-smoking, it is preferable to have the firebox removed from the house, and the smoke conveyed through an underground pipe ending in an elbow joint in the bottom of the smokehouse. A common stovepipe damper is placed in the middle joint of pipe, the ordinary handle being fitted above when the pipe is covered with earth. This damper is the principal fire and smoke control.

A nice feature is added by the use of a ''smoke spreader,'' which is a rectangular galvanized-iron box, one foot square and two feet high, open at the bottom. Numerous 3/4-inch holes punched in the sides and top permit the escape of smoke. This box is placed directly over the mouth of the elbow and causes an even distribution of smoke throughout the house. It serves also to pre-

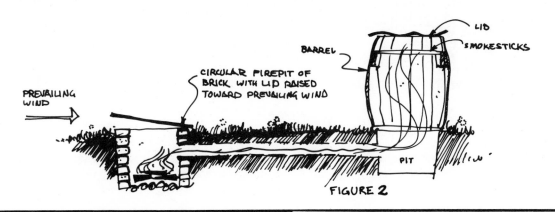

FIGURE 2

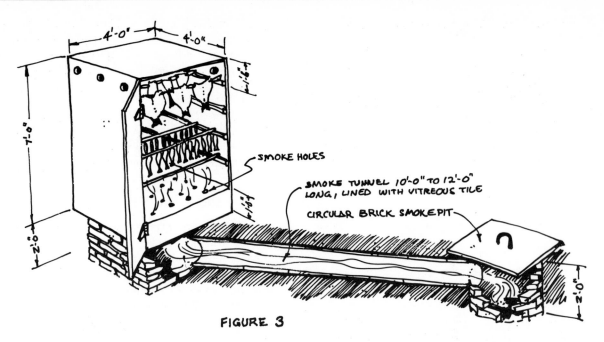

FIGURE 3

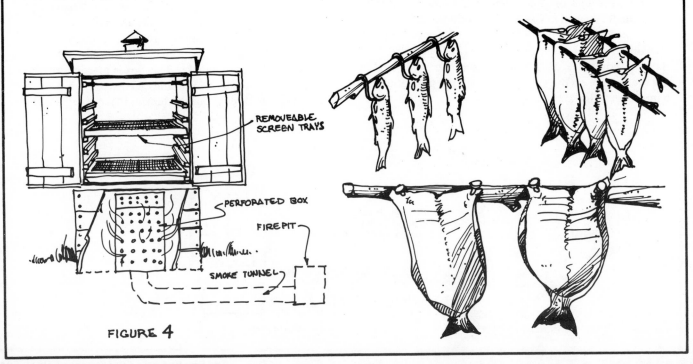

vent scorching of fish by direct draft, if at certain stages considerable heat is applied. The arrangement of fire box, smoke flue, and smoke spreader is made clear by the accompanying figures, which also illustrate (fig. 4) other possible modifications, such as construction of wood sliding trays and tip ventilator in roof. The screen trays should never be used if the fish can be suspended from rods, since the impression of the screen wire detracts from the appearance of the fish. In cold or rainy weather, condensation of moisture on the underside of the roof may occur, so that the dripping of water on the fish may injure the appearance, though not the quality, of the product. This difficulty has been overcome by stretching a double thickness of burlap just beneath the top. This has the double effect of reducing condensation and of absorbing the moisture as it is condensed.

Methods of Hanging Fish for Smoking

The fish may be hung on one or more S-shaped iron hooks, which are in turn hung over sticks running from one side of the smokehouse to the other. If whole, they may be hung on round wooden sticks inserted under the gill flap and through the mouth. When these sticks have been hung with fish, they are suspended from one side to the other of the smokehouse. If the fish are split, the smoke-sticks may be two-inch square sticks. Nails are driven through two sides at a 45-degree angle at intervals, depending on the average size of the fish smoked. The sides of the fish are hung on adjacent nail-points, just below the bony neck plate, thus holding the fish open so that all of the flesh surface will be smoked. Another method is to run 14-inch iron rods through the fish

FIGURE 4

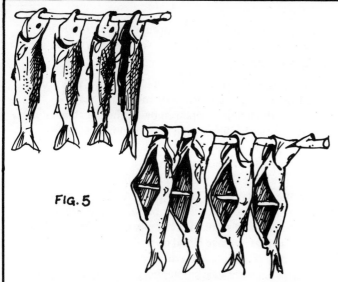

FIG. 5

just under the hard bony plate at the neck, one rod on each side. Thus, each fish hangs from two rods. Twelve or more fish may be hung on a set of two rods four feet long. Fillets may be hung over three-sided sticks of wood which, in turn, rest upon the sticks at each side of the smokehouse.

Do not crowd the fish in placing or hanging them in the smokehouse.

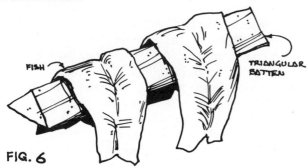

FISH

TRIANGULAR BATTEN

FIG. 6

Hot smoking

General method: This process may be used with almost any species, herring, shad, trout, etc. This method is recommended if it is desired to prepare a fish that can be used immediately without cooking. It may be kept longer without molding or souring, but even so, it will preserve for only a short time.

Split the fish along the back, just above the backbone, so that it will open in one piece, leaving the belly solid. Scrape out all viscera, blood, and membrane. Make an additional cut under the backbone for smaller fish. For the larger fish, cut out the forward three-fifths of the backbone. Wash thoroughly and soak in a 70-degree salt brine (one-half cup salt to one quart water) for 30 minutes to leach out blood in the flesh. Then prepare a brine using the following ingredients: 2 lbs. salt (use a fine grade of salt or sea salt), 1 lb. sugar (don't know how honey would work, but it's certainly worth trying), 1 oz. crushed black peppers, and 1 oz. crushed bay leaves. This is made up into a 90-degree brine solution. The amounts of ingredients are increased in proportion to the amount of brine to be made. Spices may be increased or

decreased according to individual taste.

The fish are held in the brine for periods of from two to four hours, depending upon their thickness, and the desire for a lightly or heavily cured fish. Weather conditions also make a difference; the exact length of time must be determined by experiment. Rinse off the fish in cold, fresh water and hang outside in a cool, shady and breezy place to dry for about three hours before hanging in the smokehouse, or until a thin shiny "skin" or pellicle has formed on the surface.

For the first eight hours, keep the fire low and smoldering during the smoking process. The temperature should then be built up. After four hours of heavy smoking, the fire is increased until the temperature is between 130 and 150 degrees F. The fish are cured at this temperature for two to three hours, or until they have a glossy, brown surface. This partially cooks, or hot-smokes the fish.

When smoking is finished, the fish must be cooled for two or three hours. They may be brushed over lightly with vegetable oil (usually cottonseed) while warm. This is sometimes done just after finishing the cold-smoking part of the process, before the temperature is increased. This gives a more attractive appearance and a light protective coating. For a better coating, the fish may be dipped in melted paraffin, but this coating is brittle and the fish must be handled carefully and the paraffin removed before eating. Each fish should be wrapped in wax paper and stored in the refrigerator. Spoilage occurs more rapidly if the fish are stored in a warm place or a cold damp place.

Cold smoking

General method: Small fish, such as herring may be cold-smoked in the round (without cleaning), but they should be gibbed. Gibbing is making a small cut just below the gills and hulling out the gills, heart, liver and leaving the belly uncut. Fish larger than 1 pound should be split along the back to lie flat in a single piece, leaving the belly portion uncut. All traces of blood, black skin, and viscera must be removed, paying special attention to the area just under the backbone. The head does not need to be removed. If the head is cut off, the hard bony plate just below the gills is allowed to remain, as it will be needed to carry the weight of the fish when they are hung in the smokehouse.

Wash the fish thoroughly, and place them in a brine made in the proportion of 1 cup of salt to one gallon of water. They should be left in the brine at least 30 minutes to soak out the blood diffused through the flesh. At the end of this time, rinse in fresh cold water and drain for a few minutes.

Each fish is dropped singularly in a shallow box of fine salt and dredged thoroughly. The fish are picked up with as much salt as will cling to the body, and packed in even layers in a box or wooden tub. A small amount of salt may be scattered between each layer. The fish are left in salt from 1 to 12 hours depending upon weather, size of fish, fatness, length of time for which preservation is desired, and whether the fish are split or round.

Salting is an important and essential feature in smoking, as smoking is not a sufficient preservative in itself. Unsalted fish will usually sour or spoil under temperature and humidity conditions found in the smokehouse before they can be cured. Fish such as halibut, herring, mackerel, or salmon may be smoked after being held in salt for a year. In these cases, the excess salt is removed by soaking the fish in fresh water. Fish given a heavy salt-cure and held in storage for some time before smoking are not so desirable in quality as those given a light salting and smoked immediately.

When the fish are taken out of the salt, they should be scrubbed off. They are hung to dry in the shed, as direct sunlight causes rusting of the fish. If the fish are kept shaded in a breezy location, they will dry well with a clear colour. If only a few fish are being dried, they may be hung in a shady undercover area where there is good cross-ventilation. An electric fan may be used if there is not much breeze. Drying racks may be made with chicken wire; the fish are placed skin side down and turned. They will dry on both sides, but the impression of the wire detracts from the appearance. The fish is dried until a thin skin, or pellicle, is formed on the surface. This should take about three hours under average conditions. If smoking is begun while the skin is still moist, the time required is longer, the colour will not be as desirable, the fish will not have as good a surface, and will steam and soften in smoking. In damp weather, fish are sometimes dried by hanging in the smokehouse over a low clear fire with little smoke, but the use of electric fans or blowers is a better procedure. A low smouldering fire is started an hour or two before the fish are hung in the smokehouse. The fire must not give off too much smoke during the first 8 to 12 hours if the total cure is 24 hours, or for the first 24 hours, if the cure is longer. The temperature in the smokehouse should not be higher than 90 degrees F. in California or the southern states, or 70 degrees F. in northern states, the Pacific Northwest, and Canada. If available a thermometer should be used in controlling smokehouse temperature; if not, a simple test is to insert the hand in the smokehouse—if the air feels distinctly warm, the temperature is too high. When the first part of the smoking process is ended, a dense smoke may be built up and maintained for the balance of the cure. If the fish are to be kept for about two weeks, they should be smoked for 24 hours; if for a longer time, smoking may require five days or more. Hard-smoked herring may require three or four weeks.

A few general rules must be followed in tending the fire. It must be kept low and steady; where hardwood sawdust is not available, chips and bark do almost as well. The fire must not be allowed to die out at night, nor should it be built up before leaving, as this will create too much heat. It must be tended regularly during the night. The general method of cold-smoking may be used with most fish, if the proper consideration is given to size, climate, humidity, salting, and other limiting factors.

Fillets: Any white-fleshed, "lean" fish which will produce fillets weighing more than one pound may be used. Cut the fish in fillets, removing the backbone and skin. Cover with a 90-degree brine and hold for two hours. Remove and drain for 10 to 15 minutes and air dry for two hours. Hang across a three-sided smoke-stick. Cure over a fire with a fairly light smoke for four hours at a temperature not higher than 90 degrees F. Turn the fillets so that the side resting on the smoke-stick is uppermost and smoke four hours longer. Smother the fire so that a dense cloud of smoke is obtained and smoke until the fillets are a deep straw yellow, turning the fillets once or twice so that both sides will be evenly coloured. This operation should take about six hours. Cool the fillets and wrap each separately in waxed paper. Store in a cool, dry place. They will keep about ten days.

Salmon: All species of salmon, steelhead, and lake trout may be smoked. The general cold-smoking method is most commonly used, but the following method gives a more appetizing product.

The heads should be cut off and the fish gutted. They must be split into two sides, and the backbone removed. To do this, the shoulder of the salmon is forced down on a sharp-pointed nail protruding from the cleaning table to prevent slipping. Short incisions are made under the anal fin, just above and below the backbone. With the upper lug or shoulder tip held by the left hand, enter the knife at the shoulder above the backbone, holding the blade steady, with the edge at a slight downward angle touching the bone. Take the whole side off with one sweep of the knife. If the work has been done well, little flesh will be left on the backbone; the side will be smooth. A thin line of backbone edge should run down the centre of the side. To remove the second side, a cut is made at the shoulder just under the backbone. With the edge of the knife blade resting against the backbone at a slight upward angle, give one sweep of the knife down to the root of the tail. This separates the backbone from the flesh without removing the fish from the nail. The two sides should be similar.

The sides are washed thoroughly and trimmed of ragged edges and blood clots. Blood remaining in the veins along the belly cavity should be removed by pressing it toward the back, either with the fingers or the blade of the knife. If the blood is not removed, it will harden and discolour the flesh. The sides are placed in a tub of 90-degree salinometer brine (a saturated salt solution) and chilled with ice. This removes diffused blood, makes the sides a little firmer, and stops oil from oozing out of the flesh. The fish should remain in the brine for 60 to 90 minutes.

The sides should be drained for 15 to 20 minutes. A shallow box is filled with a salting mixture made in the following proportions:

    2lbs. salt
    1 lb. brown sugar
    1 oz. saltpeter
    1 oz. white pepper
    1 oz. crushed bay leaves
    1 oz. allspice
    1 oz. crushed cloves
    1 oz. crushed mace

This amount should be enough for about 20 pounds of fish. The salmon is placed in the box, one side at a time, and dredged in the mixture, which is rubbed lightly into the flesh. The sides are packed in a tub or other suitable container with as much of the curing mixture as will cling to the flesh. A loose-fitting cover is placed on it and weighted down.

The fish are left for 8 to 12 hours, then rinsed and scrubbed to remove all traces of the salting mixture. The sides are fixed on hangers and dried in the air for six hours. If air drying conditions are not favourable, fans may be used. Hang the fish in the smokehouse and smoke in a gentle heat (not more than 100 degrees F.) for eight hours. Build up a dense smoke and continue the cure for 16 to 24 hours at a temperature not higher than 70 degrees F. To obtain a product having the maximum of preservation, the second part of the smoking period should be 48 hours.

The fish should be allowed to cool for several hours before handling, then brushed with vegetable oil, and stored in a cool, dry place.

Smoking Fish Indian Fashion

This will keep two weeks to one month in good condition. This method is especially recommended for trout, pike, or pickerel.

Cut off the heads, and gut the fish. A cut is made above the backbone almost to the tail. Another cut is made under the backbone, which is broken off, leaving not more than one-fifth of the tail section uncut. The fish should lie flat in one piece. The flesh is scored longitudinally from head to tail, with the cuts about one-half inch deep and one inch apart. After washing thoroughly and wiping dry, the fish are rubbed inside and out with a mixture of 1 oz. pepper to 1 oz. salt.

The fish are stored in a cool place overnight, and next morning are rinsed carefully. Two or three thin, flat wooden sticks are fastened across the back to keep the fish spread open. The roughly-pointed sticks pass through the skin. Dry the fish in a breezy place until the surface moisture has dried and a thin skin has formed on the surface.

A shallow fire pit is dug, about three feet in diameter, and a fire is started while the fish are drying, so that a good bed of red coals will be ready immediately. Hardwood should be used. When the fish have dried, about three hours under average conditions, each fish is fastened to the forked end of a stick about four to five feet in length. The other end of the stick is thrust into the

ground, so that it hangs over the bed of coals at an angle. The sticks should be placed so the fish will not touch each other

Two or three fish may be fastened across a stick, and thrust into the ground as in the first method, but must not be placed as close to the fire.

A tripod of poles is then erected above the smoke-sticks; on this is laid a thick thatching of green boughs and grass. A hole may be left in the thatching near the ground. Green wood is then placed on the coals, building up a dense smoke, and the hole is covered. It will be necessary to place additional green wood on the fire from time to time. The fish are smoked from six to eighteen hours, depending on size and degree of smoke-cure desired.

After cooling, the smoked fish are wrapped and stored in a cool, dry place.

Smoked Oysters

Shuck fresh oyster, drain thoroughly and dry on absorbant paper. Place the oysters on an oiled smoking rack, without overlapping, and cold-smoke for about 1 hour, or until oysters have taken on colour and their edges are curled and golden brown.

A Cardboard Smokehouse: Easy to Make

Anyone who can use a knife, saw, and hammer can make a low-cost smokehouse from a cardboard carton (fig. 7). It can be folded flat and moved easily. It is efficient and easy to operate. Its only disadvantage is that it cannot be exposed to rain. A 30-inch square smokehouse holds about 60 pounds of split fish.

Building the Smokehouse

Use a cardboard carton which is about 30 inches square and 48 inches high. Other sizes may be used, but they should be at least 25 inches wide and deep and 40 inches high.

(1) Remove one end by cutting along the edge folds. The open end is used as the bottom.

(2) Unfasten the flaps at the other end, so that they can be bent back and folded together again to make a cover.

(3) If the box is weak and tends to buckle when pressure is applied at the top, strengthen it by tacking a three-quarter-inch strip of wood vertically on the outside at each corner; attach the strip by driving large-head roofing nails (three-quarter inch or 2 centimeters) into them from the inside. Nail four more strips horizontally on the outside on opposite sides; nail two of them four inches from the top and the other two twenty inches from the bottom, driving large-headed roofing nails into them from the inside.

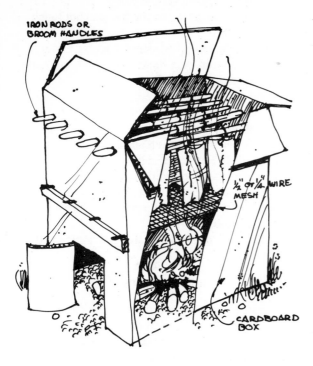

IRON RODS OR BROOM HANDLES

½" OT ¼" WIRE MESH

CARDBOARD BOX

(4) Cut a door 10 inches wide and 12 inches high in the centre of one side at the bottom. Make two cuts, one vertical and one horizontal. The door can then be bent out, with the cardboard on the uncut side acting as a hinge.

(5) Cut holes for the rods (which should extend at least two inches beyond the outside of the carton). Seven rods are used with a 30-inch size carton:

Two rods just below the fold at the top, to keep the flaps from sagging.

Three rods just above the upper horizontal wood strips, to support the fish. The two outside holes are six inches in from the corners, the third is in the centre. (Smaller cartons may need only two rods here.)

Two rods just above the lower horizontal wood strips, to support a tray to catch any fish that falls.

(6) Make a tray by cutting half-inch or quarter-inch wire mesh to fit inside the box. Bend the edges over and hammer them down flat.

(7) Make hooks from pieces of 8 - or 10-guage steel wire 14 inches long (or heavy wire coat hangers). Bend each piece in the middle around a hammer handle or a broomstick. Then, bend the hook end the same way to form a goose neck. The opening of the hook must be big enough to slip easily over the rod; the end must be bent so it will not slip off the rod during the smoking process.

(8) When the right size carton is not available, use two cartons of equal size, at least 24 inches high and 24 inches wide:

(a) Remove the top and bottom from one.

(b) Cut away the bottom of the other.

(c) Telescope the second over the first to get the desired height.

(d) Tack strips of wood on the outside of all four sides of the overlapping space to prevent further telescoping

and to seal the smokehouse.

Smoking

It takes five to six hours to smoke fish ready to eat. The exact period depends on the size of the fish.

The carton will not catch fire if:

(1) The ventilation is controlled to make the fire smoke rather than blaze.

(2) Not too much wood is placed on the fire. If too large a blaze develops, it can be smothered with sawdust or reduced by removing some of the blazing wood.

The fire should be built on a level plot of ground.

How to Salt Fish

By Daniel Casper

Salting, one of the oldest methods of preserving food, is an art as well as a science. The process of salting fish is influenced by weather, size and species of fish, and the quality of salt used. Therefore, experience is needed to adapt the process outlined here to your own situation. Start by salting small lots of different varieties of fish—whatever is available. By salting small amounts of fish at first, you will learn how much time is required for each step. Salted fish, if properly packed to protect it from excessive moisture, will not spoil.

Quality and Cleanliness

There are two things that are of special importance:

(1) The quality of the fish to be salted. The fish must be top quality. Salting will not help poor quality, old, or rotten fish.

(2) Cleanliness in all operations. All water used must be removed from working and drying areas. Whatever comes in contact with the fish, including all the equipment, must be kept clean.

One word of *caution:* Start by salting non-fatty, white-meated varieties of fish. The salting of fatty fish brings up problems of rancidity, rusting, and spoilage which can be handled better after you have experience in salting.

Salting the Fish

The process of salting fish has four operations: (1) Preparing the fish, (2) salting, (3) washing and drying to remove excess salt, and (4) air drying.

Preparing the Fish

The fish should be gutted and beheaded as soon as possible after catching.

(1) Remove the head by cutting on a slanted line following the gills. Sharks can be beheaded at the last line of gill slits. Fish which weigh one-half pound do not have to be beheaded, but they generally should be gutted.

(2) In gutting a fish, cut from the gill cavity along the ventral fold to the anal vent (fig. 1). All the guts must be removed. It is also good practice to remove the black membrane located in the visceral cavity (the hollow in the body of the fish which contains the guts) of many species.

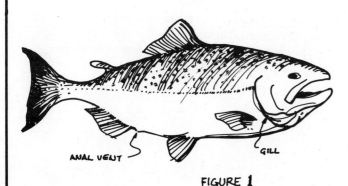

FIGURE 1

(3) All species of fish must be thoroughly bled. If the head has not been removed, cut the throat. Then remove the gills and all blood vessels. Blood clots can cause discolouration as well as bacterial infection which would make the fish unfit for eating.

(4) The shape into which the fish is cut depends on local custom. For a rule of thumb, under 1 pound, the fish may be left whole; from 1 to 10 pounds it should be split in half from head to tail (fig. 2); over 10 pounds, split the fish in two again from head to tail. The collarbone behind the gills should be left intact when a fish is split in half.

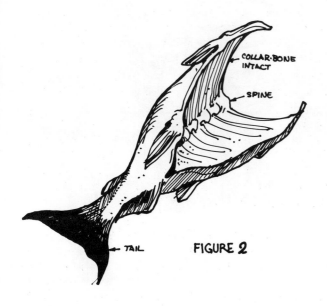

FIGURE 2

Salting

(1) Sprinkle a thin layer of salt, just enough to completely cover the bottom of a waterproof vat.

(2) Place a layer of fish, flesh side up, with enough room for each fish to avoid overlapping. Try for a neat pattern, alternating head to tail and tail to head.

(3) Cover the fish with salt—a thin layer, but with no open spaces.

(4) Repeat steps 2 and 3 up to two or three layers of fish from the top of the vat.

(5) Reverse the fish, packing them *skin* side up to the top of the vat, alternating with layers of salt. The top layer must be salt.

(6) The salt will extract moisture from the fish, forming a brine. Use boards and weights to keep all the fish under the salt.

(7) The brine must be kept saturated (90—degree salinometer—or when no more salt can be dissolved) at all times. As moisture is extracted, more salt must be added to keep the brine saturated. Too little salt will cause the fish to spoil. Too much will detract from the flavour and cause dehydration.

(8) As moisture is extracted from the fish, the level of fish in the vat will fall. More fish can be added—skin side up—alternating a layer of fish with a layer of salt, the top layer always being salt. Continue to add salt to keep the brine saturated.

(9) The fish are "struck through," or thoroughly impregnated with salt, in 12 to 15 days in warm weather. In cold weather the fish should stay in the brine for 21 days or more. The higher the temperature, the quicker the fish will be struck through. When properly salted, the flesh of the fish is translucent. It is firm but yields to gentle pressure, and has a whitish salt cover. An odour of fish and brine should prevail. There should be no spoilage odours.

Washing and Drying to Remove Excess Salt

(1) When the fish are struck through, they are removed from the vat and washed in unpolluted sea water or fresh brine to remove excess salt.

(2) Then place the fish on flat surfaces, using any arrangement of boards and weights to press them—as flat as possible—in order to:

(a) remove excess moisture and

(b) make the fish thinner, which will reduce the length of the air-drying process and improve the appearance of the fish.

Air Drying

(1) The final drying can be done either by sunlight and natural air currents or by artificial heat and air currents generated by fans. In most areas, in the proper season, drying can be done outdoors in the sun and fresh air. Choose an open area to get the most sunlight and wind. Avoid swampy areas, locations near human or animal waste, and especially fly-breeding areas.

(2) When freshly salted fish is first brought out to dry, there is danger of sunburn. If the fish is exposed at this stage to direct sunlight, it may harden on the outside and turn yellow. This will keep the inside from drying properly. To avoid this, keep the fish under shade or semi-shade for the first day.

(3) After the first day, expose the fish to as much sunlight and wind as possible. One method is to lay the fish on triangular slats—so that it rests on the least possible amount of surface—flesh side facing the sun (fig. 3). Another method is to hang the fish by the tail (fig. 4).

(4) Protect the drying fish against dampness. The fish can be moved into small roofed sheds built nearby for protection from rainfall and night-time dampness. The fish should be free of discolouration, mold, or other defects. Split fish should not have ragged edges.

(5) Generally, six warm days with winds of more than three miles per hour should dry the fish enough to prevent spoiling in storage or shipping, provided the fish is properly packed to protect it from excessive moisture.

Using Salted Fish

Salted fish is usually soaked overnight, with at least one change of water, to remove most of the salt before it is eaten. The longer it is soaked, the more salt is removed. Then it is used in the same way as fresh fish, except that it is not good for frying.

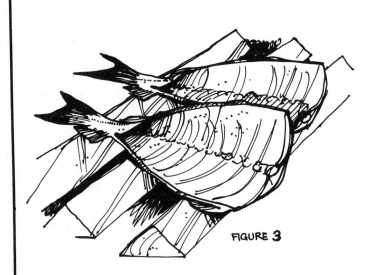

FIGURE 3

• FIGURE 4 •

Cheese Making

Cheesemaking is simple and lots of good fun. All you need is plain old milk. To produce a superior product, always be sure to use raw milk. Cheese can be made from top milk, bottom milk, fresh milk, sour milk, buttermilk, and even from the whey. Goat, cow, and ewe's milk are most common, although in some places the milk of the camel, the water buffalo, the donkey, and the mare are used.

Rennet is an animal product made from the stomach acid of young calves. When added to the milk, it causes the liquid to separate from the solid, thus "curds and whey." If the milk is cold and sweet, the curds are harder. (Extracts of the wild thistle and wild artichoke will also coagulate the milk). The extract of bruised marigold petals has been used for centuries in Europe to add a golden colour to cheese. After the curd has separated, the cheese goes through a drainage process. The process depends on the cheese you are making. Some cheeses are salted and eaten right away, such as ricotta. Another cheese is cut, kneaded, cooked, pressed, ground, and pressed again. This is called cheddaring. After the drainage process, the cheese may be ripened. This final stage varies greatly from cheese to cheese. Bleu cheese, which is originally made from ewe's milk, is innoculated with mold, and within a few months the characteristic green veins have found their way deep in the cheese. Bannon, a French goat cheese, is cured in chestnut leaves, dried, passed through the dregs of wine casks, and fermented in stone crocks. It is finally presented wrapped in fresh chestnut leaves. Prestost, a hard Swedish cheese, is washed in whiskey for five months during curing. Another French goat cheese, Selles-Sur Cher, is kneaded in charcoal until it takes a gray colour, and is then aged slowly. There are hundreds of thousands of different cheeses in the world. Each is part of its native soil— each is unique. Cheese is one of the most ancient foods manufactured by man. Simple and natural, cheese is a gift of the land, and of the slow, seasoned rhythm of country life.

Recipe for Basic Hard Cheese

8 qts. milk . . . 2 lbs. cheese

Allow 4 qts. to sour at room temperature overnight. In the morning, add 4 qts. fresh milk and heat on the stove to lukewarm. Add solution from one-half rennet tablet. (Solution is made by crushing and dissolving tablet in 2 tbsp. cold water.) Let stand until a smooth curd forms (45 minutes). Cut curd into small chunks with a knife. Gently stir with your hand; cut big chunks you may have missed. *Do not* squash the curds. Do this for about 15 minutes. Now, slowly heat the curds and whey to as hot as the hand can stand, stirring constantly. A very firm curd will form. Remove from the heat. Put somewhere to cool, stirring occasionally. When cold, pour curds into cheesecloth, salt to taste, hang to drain. Dress, press, wax, and store.

Bleu Cheese Culture

Take a culture of mold from aged bleu cheese and put it on a loaf of bread. Keep in a moist, dark place for 6 weeks. When the bread has crumbled completely and the mold has separated, dry the mold into a powder. Bottle and cork tightly.

To Use: sprinkle dried mold on the cheese, or pierce it in on the head of a needle in several places. Salt lightly, and let it rest for several days. When the mold has had a good start, pierce it at least 60 times to give air to the mold deep in the interior. Keep in a cool, dark place. Age 2 to 5 months.

Italian Cheese

Heat 10 qts. of fresh milk to 85 degrees. Add solution from one rennet tablet. Let stand until a firm curd forms (45 minutes). Break up curd with hands; heat slowly, stirring constantly, to as hot as the hand can stand. Gather curd in the hands and knead to form a firm ball. (Ricotta Romano is made at this time). Return to whey, and set somewhere to cool. Drain, press, wax, and store.

Ricotta Romano

Before Italian cheese is put back in the whey, heat the whey until a coat of cream rises to the top. Add one qt. milk (per 10 qt.), stir; heat until almost boiling. When curd rises, add one cup strong vinegar. Stir well; curd will come together. Drain curd, salt to taste, serve fresh.

Devonshire Cream

Allow the cream of whole milk to rise. Heat slowly to just below the boiling point. When the layer of cream is firm, skim it and place in a mould to harden.

Pennsylvania Pot Cheese

Prepare the curd from bottom milk. Drain, and grind in a meatgrinder; place in a covered crock. Keep curd warm for several days until it is covered with a tangled mass of mold. Remove curd. Heat slowly for about half an hour in water (or whey), stirring constantly. When it reaches the consistency of honey, put in moulds and cool.

Neufchatel Cheese

From whole goat's milk we make a soft cheese called Neufchatel, similar in appearance and method to cottage cheese, but much richer. Pressed, it makes delicious sandwich spread on wholewheat or rye bread for a cool lunch in hot weather.

Put one gallon of sweet, whole goat's milk in a larger kettle containing water at 72 degrees F. When the milk reaches 70 degrees (use a dairy or candy thermometer), add one Junket rennet tablet dissolved in ¼ cup cold water, and stir this in thoroughly. All utensils that come in contact with the milk should be scalded to kill unwanted bacteria or the flavour of the cheese will be ruined.

The warm milk should set overnight (12 to 15 hours). In the morning the curd will be firm and smooth, with a little whey on top. Spread a clean drain cloth (cheesecloth) over a colander and ladle the curd onto it. Tie the ends of the cloth together and hang the bundle up to drain. I tie mine to the water faucet. It is best to catch the whey and use it (or feed to the livestock). It is too valuable to waste, since it contains most of the milk sugar (lactose), minerals, and albumen: Scandinavians make a cheese from whey called mysost. We feed it to pigs and chickens; it tends to give goats diarrhea.

As the cheese drips, curds can be stirred occasionally. The more whey removed, the milder the flavour. For a very mild flavour, run cold water over the curds. After drainage is completed, add salt to taste, and it is ready to eat.

A Cheese Press

Here's a design a little bit different from the standard home-made press, which will allow you to use more pressure as well as pressing more cheese (see pg. 110.)

Basically it consists of an upper and lower one-inch board and four pieces of one-inch dowling rod set into the lower board. The upper board slides up and down on these four legs.

The picture shows a 3-lb. coffee can; for smaller amounts a 2-lb. can is more desirable. Both top and bottom of the can are removed, and for additional drainage a few holes can be punched in the sides. The round follower should be only a hair smaller in diameter than the coffee can, so that it can slide up and down inside the can. I use milk strainer pads so that the curd does not come in

contact with the wood.

Pressure is obtained by putting weights on the top board, which guides the follower down onto the curd and squeezes out the whey. You can use bricks or sand for weight. More pressure (40-60 pounds) will produce cured cheese.

Wash and scald your press after each use to guard the flavour of your cheese.

Cottage Cheese

The first step is to make clabber. This is milk which has been allowed to sour at room temperature. The souring process can take as long as a week during the winter and as short as a day in the summer. Use unpasteurized skim milk or buttermilk only, because pasteurized milk doesn't sour properly. The clabber is ready when it turns to a jelly-like consistency. Cross-hatch the clabber with a knife (fig. 5, p. 109). (Cream cheese can be made at this stage by hanging the clabber overnight in a cheesecloth bag. This separates the curds and whey).

Once cross-hatched, gently heat the clabber in a water bath (fig. 7, p. 111), stirring occasionally. The water should be too hot to touch, but never boiling; the clabber should never get too hot to touch. When the clabber has shrunk uniformly into small pieces, it is done—better underdone than overdone. Personal experience is the best way to get it right. Strain the mixture through a colander. If the curds run through the holes in the colander, it is underdone. If the curds are dry and rubbery, it is overdone. Add a little salt, honey, and cream to taste.

If you can't find rennet tablets in a drugstore or grocery store nearby, they can be ordered from Hansen's Laboratory Inc., 9015 W. Maple Street, Milwaukee, Wisc. 53214 or from Horan-Lally Co. Ltd., 26 Kelfield Street, Rexdale 604, Ontario.

How to Make Hard Cheese
(Makes 1½-2 Pounds)

1. Preparation of the Milk

Allow 4 quarts of evening's milk to ripen overnight in cool place (50-60 deg. F.). Mix in 4 quarts of next morning's milk. This will give a better cheese than if you use all fresh milk; however, milk must taste sweet. You may use either cow's or goat's milk with equally good results.

2. Warm the Milk to 86 Deg. F.

In an enameled or tinned pail, heat milk to 86 deg. F.

3. Add Cheese Rennet

Dissolve ¼ of a cheese rennet tablet in a glass of cold water; to help tablet dissolve, break and crush with a spoon in water; stir until completely dissolved. Put the pail of milk in a larger pail of warm water, 88-90 deg. F.; leave in a warm place, protected from draft. Add the rennet solution; stir milk thoroughly for a minute after rennet is added.

4. Let Set Until "Clean Break"

Let stand undisturbed until a firm curd forms, 30-45 minutes. Test the firmness of curd with your finger; put finger into the curd at an angle and lift. If the curd breaks clean over your finger, it is ready to cut.

5. Cut 2 Ways Vertically—Then 2 Ways at an Angle

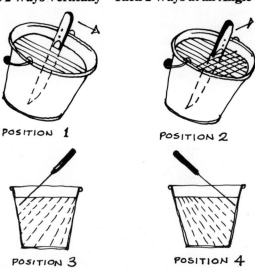

To cut the curd into small cubes, use a long butcher knife or spatula— long enough so that the blade will go clear to the bottom of the pail without the handle dipping into the curd. Cut into squares of about 3/8" as shown in positions 1 and 2 in illustration. Then use your knife at an angle—see position 3 in illustration—starting about 1" from the side of the pail; with angular cuts, slice the curd into pieces about 1/2-1" thick; begin at the top and make each cut about 1/2-1" lower. Then turn the pail and draw similar angular cuts from the other side (position 4).

6. Stir Curd for 15 Minutes by Hand

With your hand, stir curd thoroughly but very gently, with long, slow movements around the pail, and from the bottom up. Carefully cut up the larger pieces that come up from the bottom, but do not squash curd. Try to make the pieces of curd as nearly as possible the same size. Stir continuously by hand for 15 minutes, to keep the curd from sticking together.

7. Warm Slowly for about 1 Hour to 102 Deg. F.

Heat slowly to 102 deg. F. raising the temperature of the curd and whey about 1-½ degrees every 5 minutes. Stir (with a spoon) frequently enough to keep the curd from sticking together. Heating should continue slowly—if necessary a few degrees above 102 deg. F. until the curd holds its shape and readily falls apart when held on your hand for a few seconds without squeezing.

8. Stop Heating. Stir Occasionally for 1 Hour

Remove from heat. Stir every 5—10 minutes, i.e.,

enough to keep curd from matting together. Leave curd in the warm whey until it becomes firm enough so that the pieces in a handful when pressed together will easily shake apart. This will take about an hour.

9. Pour Curd into Cheese Cloth

Pour into cheesecloth 3-4 feet square. Then hold 2 corners of the cloth in each hand and let curd roll back and forth without sticking together for 2-3 minutes to allow whey to run off.

10. Salt Curd

Place cloth with curd in empty pail, sprinkle 1 tablespoon salt over curd, mix well with hands without squeezing; then sprinkle another tablespoon salt on curd and mix well again.

11. Form into Ball and Hang Up

Tie the four corners of the cloth crosswise, forming the curd into a ball. Hang up for 1/2 to 3/4 hour to drip off.

12. Dress the Cheese

Remove cloth from sides of ball. Fold a long cloth, shaped like a dish towel, into a bandage about three

inches wide and wrap tightly around ball, forming it into a round shape. Pin in place. With your hands, press cheese down to make the top surface of the cheese smooth. There should be no cracks extending into the center of the cheese. Your round loaf of cheese should not more than 6" across; otherwise it will dry out too much.

13. Press Cheese

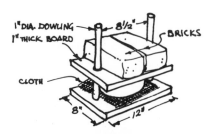

Place 3 or 4 thicknesses of cheesecloth on top and under the cheese. Put the cheese on lower board of press and push upper board down to rest on cheese; place 2 bricks on top. At night, turn cheese over and put 4 bricks on top. Let stand until morning.

14. Paraffin. Store in Cool Place

Remove cloths from cheese and place on board for half a day, turning occasionally until the rind is completely dry. Then dip in paraffin that is heated in a deep pan to 210-220 deg. F. Dip first one half, hold a minute, then dip other half. (If preferred, liquid paraffin may be painted on with a brush, or vegetable or mineral oil may be rubbed onto cheese instead of paraffining.) Then store in a clean, cool but frost-free cellar or similar place. Turn over each day for a few days, then 2-3 times a week. The cheese is usually good to eat after 3-4 weeks.

Some General Hints for Perfecting Your Cheese

If you want a harder cheese:

(1) You may cut the curd into smaller pieces.
(2) You may hold it a little longer, or bring the temperature a little higher when heating the curd (steps 7 and 8).

If you want a softer cheese:

(1) If your cheese becomes too hard, the reason may be that you have used milk which was over-ripened. Be sure it has not stood too long before you make it into cheese.
(2) You may cut the curd into slightly larger pieces.
(3) It may be that you can heat the curd to a lower temperature (step 7), or not keep it heated as long (steps 7 and 8).
(4) Maybe you have used too much weight in pressing.

A Homemade Forge

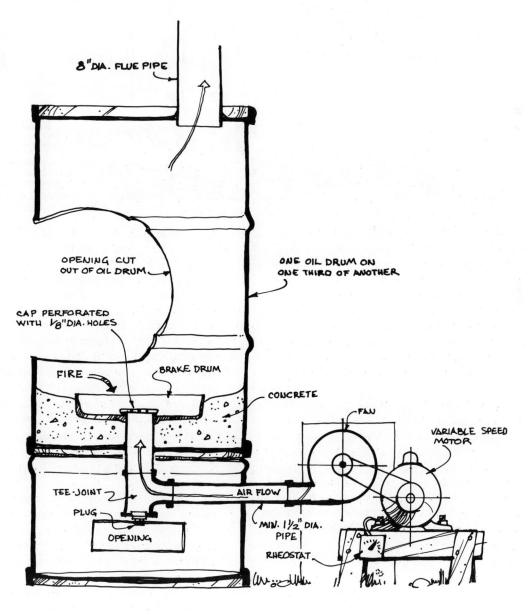

8" DIA. FLUE PIPE

OPENING CUT
OUT OF OIL DRUM

CAP PERFORATED
WITH 1/8" DIA. HOLES

FIRE

BRAKE DRUM

ONE OIL DRUM ON
ONE THIRD OF ANOTHER

CONCRETE

FAN

VARIABLE SPEED
MOTOR

TEE-JOINT

AIR FLOW

PLUG

OPENING

MIN. 1 1/2" DIA.
PIPE

RHEOSTAT

• SECTION VIEW THROUGH SIDE OF FORGE •

Rural Water Works

by M.J. Reese

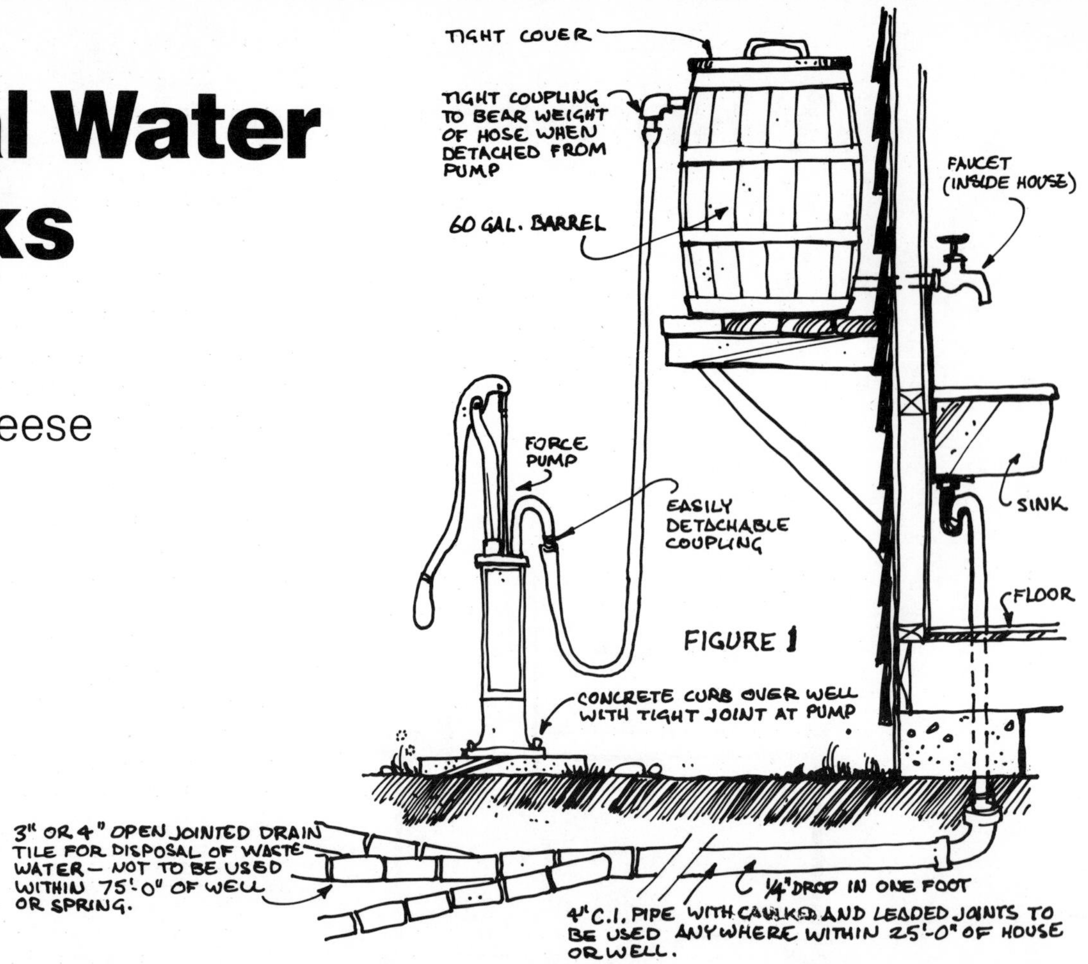

FIGURE 1

Labels in figure:
TIGHT COVER
TIGHT COUPLING TO BEAR WEIGHT OF HOSE WHEN DETACHED FROM PUMP
60 GAL. BARREL
FAUCET (INSIDE HOUSE)
FORCE PUMP
EASILY DETACHABLE COUPLING
SINK
FLOOR
CONCRETE CURB OVER WELL WITH TIGHT JOINT AT PUMP
3" OR 4" OPEN JOINTED DRAIN TILE FOR DISPOSAL OF WASTE WATER — NOT TO BE USED WITHIN 75'-0" OF WELL OR SPRING.
¼" DROP IN ONE FOOT
4" C.I. PIPE WITH CAULKED AND LEADED JOINTS TO BE USED ANYWHERE WITHIN 25'-0" OF HOUSE OR WELL.

If a well or cistern is located close to the house, one of the simplest and cheapest methods of obtaining running water in the kitchen in the warmer climates is to place a covered barrel or other supply tank on a shelf outside the kitchen wall and in such a position that it can be filled from the pump through a hose, as desired. A pipe attached to the bottom of the barrel or tank and passing through the wall has attached to it a faucet over a sink in the kitchen. The hose is detachable and can be removed from the pump when not in use (fig 1).

The sink is connected by lead pipe through a trap to a drain, which should consist of cast iron soil pipe when it is used anywhere in the immediate neighborhood of the well or cistern. Do not under any consideration use cemented tile for this purpose within 30 feet of any source of water supply. When far enough away from the house or well, this drain can empty into open jointed drain tile which may be placed in the garden soil or any other pervious soil, thus disposing of the waste water by absorption. The disposal tile should have a fall not to exceed 1 inch in 50 feet, else the water will rush to the lower end and water-log the soil. In very porous or sand soils 1 foot of 3 or 4-inch tile per gallon of discharge per day is sufficient. In heavier loam or clay soils, 2 feet of tile are necessary and sometimes more for every gallon. Aeration of heavy soil can be brought about by the use of coarse cinders or gravel laid in the bottom of the tile ditch.

Where there is danger of freezing or where the well is very close to the house, about the simplest and cheapest method is to place a pitcher pump or force pump over a sink in the kitchen. The suction pipe of the pump may be attached to the well or cistern and water obtained when desired merely by pumping. This is provided the vertical distance from the pump to the water in the well does not exceed 20 feet, as under ordinary circumstances a pump will lift water satisfactorily by suction only to about that height. The allowable distance from the well to the pump for this arrangement will vary with local conditions; cases have been noted in which the distance was as far as 200 feet. As water meets with resistance in pipes, due to friction, elbows, and bends, it is well to take off about 2 feet from the allowable vertical pumping lift for every 100 feet the water is drawn horizontally.

The Shower Bath

A cheap and convenient shower bath can be easily made and used in the kitchen or on the back porch (fig 2).

A hole is cut in the bottom of a 4-gallon bucket and a piece of pipe 2 inches long soldered in the opening. Rubber tubing 4 to 6 feet long is attached to the pipe and a nozzle is fitted on the end of the rubber tubing. A sprinkler from a watering can may be used instead of the nozzle. The bucket can be raised or lowered to suit the convenience of the person taking the bath by a rope fastened to the handle of the bucket and run through a pulley which is fastened with a staple to a joist in the ceiling. The end of the rope is looped over a hook, which is driven securely into the window or door facing, or into the studding in the wall.

A clothespin closed over the rubber tubing serves as a stopcock to cut off the water as desired. The shower can be better regulated by using a device such as is shown in the illustration. The end of a piece of No. 12 or 14 wire is fastened to a disk of leather or tin, or a cap of a tin can, by making a hole in the material used, running the wire through and looping the end. This disk is placed over the hole in the bottom of the bucket and the attached wire extends through the rubber tubing and the nozzle. The shower can be regulated by the disk being raised and lowered by means of the wire. The weight of the water in the bucket will form a sufficient seal when no flow is desired.

A large tub is placed under the shower, in which the bather stands.

A Progressive Water System

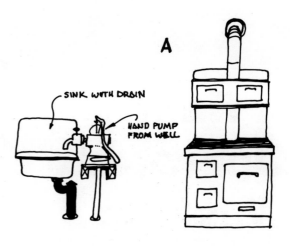

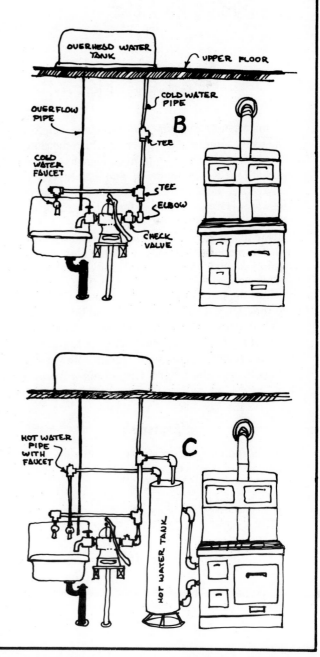

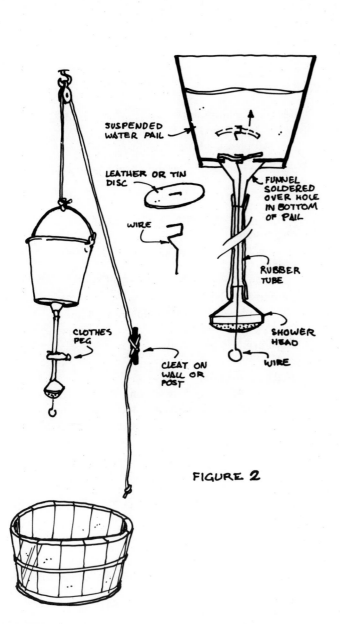

FIGURE 2

A Hand Operated Washing Machine

by C.C. Pettit and H. Holtzclaw

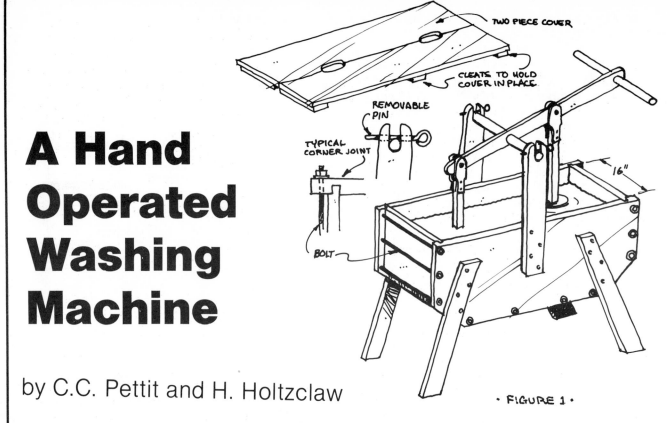

TWO PIECE COVER

CLEATS TO HOLD COVER IN PLACE

REMOVABLE PIN

TYPICAL CORNER JOINT

BOLT

16"

· FIGURE 1 ·

This washing machine reverses the principle used by the usual commercial washer, in which the clothes are swished through the water from various degrees of a circle until the water is moving, and then reversed. In this machine, the clothes stay more or less stationary while water is forced back and forth through the clothes by the piston action of the plungers.

One plunger creates pressure as it moves downward. The slopes at the ends of the tub bottom help the churning action of the water caused by the plungers.

A rectangular tub is best for this type of washing and churning process. In general, a moderately strong wood that will not warp excessively can be used for the tub. The sides should be grooved for the ends and bottom of the tub, as indicated in figure 1, and bolted with threaded rods extending through both sides with washers to draw them tight. The bolting will prevent leaks.

Materials

Tub Construction—moderately firm softwood, free from large heartwood growth.

sides—2 pieces—1" x 18" x 38"
ends—2 pieces—1" x 12" x 16"
bottom—1 piece—1" x 16" x 26"
bottom—2 pieces—1" x 6" x 16"
legs—4 pieces—1" x 4" x 30"
round plungers
    —2 pieces—1" x 10" diameter
    —2 pieces—1.5" x 5" diameter

cover (may be omitted)
    —2 pieces—1" x 8" x 36"
    —6 pieces—1" x 3" x 8"

Operating Parts—moderately firm hardwood

lever
    —1 piece—1" x 3" x 48"
plunger stems
    —2 pieces—1-1/8" square x 15" long
uprights
    —2 pieces—1-1/8" x 3" x 24" long
pivot and handle
    —2 pieces—1-1/4" diameter x 18" long

Metal Parts

plunger connections—
    —1/4" x 1-1/2" x 6" long
    10 rods—1/4" or 5/16" diameter,
    18" long with threads and nuts on each end
    (iron and brass)
    20 washers about 1" diameter with hole to fit rods
    1 rod—1/4" x 6" with loop end for retaining pivot
    6 bolts—1/4" x 2" long
    24 screws—1-3/4" x No. 10, flat head
    50 nails—2-1/2"
    strip sheet metal with turned edge
    —2-1/2" wide, 72" long

Small quantity of loose cotton or soft vegetable fibre for caulking seams. Oakum also works well.

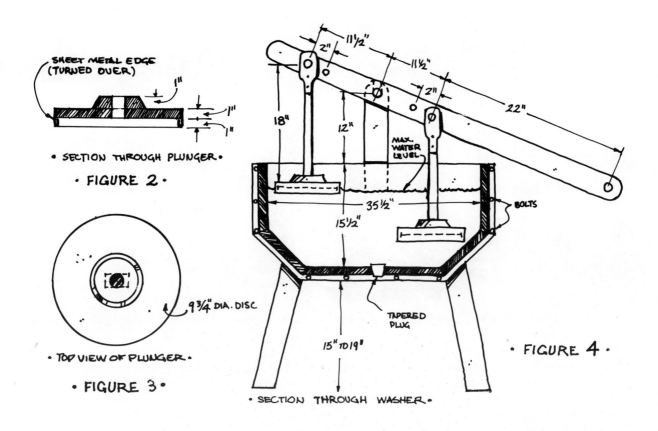

SHEET METAL EDGE
(TURNED OVER)

1"
1"
1"
1"

• SECTION THROUGH PLUNGER •

• FIGURE 2 •

9¾" DIA. DISC

• TOP VIEW OF PLUNGER •

• FIGURE 3 •

11½"
2"
11½"
2"
22"
18"
12"
MAX. WATER LEVEL
35½"
15½"
BOLTS
TAPERED PLUG
15" TO 19"

• FIGURE 4 •

• SECTION THROUGH WASHER •

Construction

(1) Mark and groove sides for end and bottom members.
(2) Drill holes for cross bolts.
(3) Cut off corner and trim ends of side members to length.
(4) Bevel ends and bottom pieces to fit into groove in side members.
(5) Mitre bottom and end members together.
(6) Assemble and bolt
(7) Cut and install legs.
(8) Caulk seams between ends and bottom members with **loose cotton or other vegetable fibre (or oakum) to make seams water-tight. If joints to side members are carefully made, they may not need caulking.**
(9) Bore hole and make plug for draining tub in the bottom.
(10) Make and install upright pivot members.
(11) Make and install plunger lever. *Note:* The cross pivot **member (round) should be shouldered or notched at each pivot to prevent side movement.**
(12) Make plungers and install (see illustration).

The size described in the drawings is large enough for an average family in North America. The same principle may be used for a larger or smaller machine, provided the basic proportions are maintained. The tub width should be slightly less than half the length to get a proper surge of water. The pistons should be wide enough to move within a couple of inches of each side of the tub. Likewise, the length of the rods on the plungers must be such that the plungers go well into the water and the clothes come completely out of the water at the highest position.

Operation

Fill the washer with 15 gallons of warm or hot water, depending on what is available. Remove stains. Rub soap into the areas of garments like cuffs and collars which come in close contact with the body. Soak very dirty clothes before putting them in the washer. Soap can be dissolved by shaving strips and then heating it in a small quantity of water before adding it to the wash water. A six pound load of clothes is the right size load for best cleaning. Wash at a moderate speed, about 50 strokes a minute, for 10 minutes or longer, if it seems necessary. After washing and rinsing the clothes, rinse the washer clean and replace the stopper. To keep the wood from drying out and causing the tub to leak, put about an inch of water in the washer when it's not in use.

Alternatives

The simplest method to wash clothes is to use a bucket with some sort of plunger device as an agitator. A drain plunger or a metal funnel attached to an old broomstick works well and is cheap.

Creative Recycling

by Jeanine Mitchell

Living in a cabin, or even just out in the country, you just naturally get into recycling—for two reasons, actually. First you can't afford a lot of waste, because that means bringing in extra supplies. When you have to carry stuff through the bush on your back, you quickly learn to improvise much of what you need from tin cans, jars, and so on.

Second, you are no longer compartmentalized. In the city, you can do the most atrocious things to the earth—pour Draino, phosphate detergents, paint, pesticides and so on down your drains—and never get your nose rubbed in it. Not for a while, anyway. You never see anything in its wholeness—all is hidden away—no blood on your money, no feathers in your crankcase.

But when you live off the land right under your feet, learn its secrets, listen to its songs, how can you destroy it? Now you have control back, and with it, sanity and responsibility.

There are so many real uses for most waste items, hardly any need be even collected for reprocessing. In the course of making your own, you drastically cut your consumption, which means the planet's wealth can be spread around to other people with nothing. This is only suitable for a whole-world economy, which is overdue anyway.

Newspapers are an exception. Too little is said on too much paper. Look at a city daily—most of it is covered in trash: ads for senseless products, stories that don't tell you anything, pompous editorials. The actual information could be condensed to fill a fraction of the space now used. Radios and televisions should be taking over a lot of the communication work, although not all of it.

You can burn newspaper, rolling it into tight "logs" so it will last a long time: a great fuel for poor people. You can make kites out of it, papier-mache, insulate your house with it, use it for a mulch to keep weeds out of the garden, pack things in it, sit on it, mop up with it.

But at the present rate of consumption, it must be reprocessed in large quantities as well.

You all must know that all your writing paper can be free—just stop throwing away envelopes, paper used on only one side, light-coloured bags, etc. Make note pads by cutting one side paper into pieces and stapling.

Tin cans are a trip. Many uses for the garden alone, including the following: cover young plants at night to protect from slugs and bugs, nail to posts or place around garden to attract magnetic forces of earth, which improves the harvest. Crush cans and bury them in a trench around garden if gophers are causing problems. Hang can lids on branches of fruit trees to help keep away birds. (Note: plant chokecherries, or some other sour or bitter fruit bush nearby, and the birds will eat those instead.) Start plants in them, laying stones on the bottom for drainage. Cut large tins up for bird feeders and bird baths, folding over any sharp edges. Birds eat hungry bugs off your plants.

Store food in cans, to keep it dry, bug- and mouse-free. Make windproof candle bug for night travel, if you live in the bush: cut off one lid of a medium size tin, cut a hole on the middle of one side, attach a wire handle to both ends of opposite side, stuff a candle up through the hole (fig. 1).

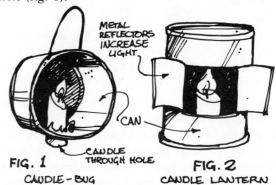

METAL REFLECTORS INCREASE LIGHT

CAN

CANDLE THROUGH HOLE

FIG. 1
CANDLE - BUG

FIG. 2
CANDLE LANTERN

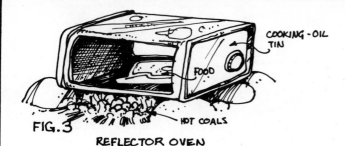

FIG. 3

REFLECTOR OVEN

Or make a candle lantern for bush or house (fig. 2). Makeshift bread pans a la Digger (just cut off top lid).

Pots for camping: add wire handles. A large square can (used often for large quantities of cooking oil and found in Chinatown alleys) can become a makeshift reflector oven if two sides are cut out, leaving ends intact. Put food in and place it facing the fire (fig. 3). Cans for camping dishes, too. Bury them when moving on. Cut tins, especially large ones, flatten metal, and save for fishing and building things. Cookie sheets.

Musical instruments: drums, with inner tube or an old skin over one end, wind chimes of tin lids strung together, makeshift steel guitar of wooden frame covered with tin cut from gas can—see *Living on the Earth* by Alicia Bay Laurel.

FIG. 4

Toys: stilts from large cans with string handles (fig. 4). Walky-talky of string tied between two cans; sound travels through string, you talk into the can and hold open end to your ear. Give kids small seafood cans to paint into ashtrays, snack dishes, thingamajigs.

Bottles

Rolling pins, candle holders, vases. Give them to kids to make water xylophones or water flutes: line up ten bottles, with varying water levels, tap them with a stick or blow across the top, and you play songs. Save them to fill again with homemade wine, beer, root beer, juices from your juicer capped for the winter. Make glasses by cutting off the tops and filing the edge, and make bowls and individual greenhouses for struggling plants by cutting tops off gallon jugs. Here are three more-or-less methods of cutting bottles:

(1) Wrap gasoline- or kerosene-soaked length of yarn around cutting point of cold bottle three times. Light, turning bottle slowly, as flame follows yarn. When flame has encircled bottle, turn until it cracks. If it

doesn't break after a moment, tap a little above cutting line with knife handle, repeating the burning if this too fails.

(2) Fill bottle just below cutting line with warm water. Melt paraffin (in a tin can) and let stand till warm. Pour about one-half cup warm wax into the bottle, using a funnel to keep all wax off sides of bottle. Refrigerate bottle until ice cold. Heat rest of paraffin over double boiler until as hot as you can (but NEVER heat wax directly over burner or flame—it can explode), and pour through funnel onto the hardened wax in the bottle. This should crack it to smooth edge.

(3) Buy a cheap glass cutter from hardware store, attaching it firmly to table top or inside a box. Using much force, push and roll bottle away from you against cutting edge of the tool. After circling the bottle smoothly suspend a string with nail or bolt tied to it into the bottle and tap at cutting line gently (or dip in hot, then icy water). File edge, sand edge until frosty looking.

If you plan to cut a lot of bottles, you might want a proper cutter, as the above methods are haphazard, wasting much glass and patience. Some people make a living with their cutter, turning bottles into candles, glasses, and hookahs.

Send $7.75 to—Fleming Bottle and Jug Cutters, 19432 Military Road, Seattle, Washington 98188. You'll get a reliable, adjustable cutter, postpaid.

Jars

Jars are also very useful. Save any screw-on jars with their lids for canning. Paint black and store film dry; and if you knit and have pets or babies in the house, punch a hole through the jar lid and keep your wool inside the jar, feeding through hole in the lid. Place jars over new plants: keeps away slugs and acts as a greenhouse, frost, and stormguard, keeping them moist and warm. If you travel keep food cold but dry with jars full of ice.

Cut off or smash the bottom of a large-based bottle and blow it like a trumpet—hang it by the door as a dinnerhorn. Cut off bottom and hang wooden bead inside for a bell clapper. Alicia Bay Laurel says: jug for the band—stretch some inner-tube ove the open end and secure with a leather thong. Vary the pitch of the jug by pressing and releasing the rubber.

Water carries. Self-waterers for houseplants: fill jar with water, wick(s) in to reach bottom and wrap other end(s) loosely around plant stem(s) just above the soil. Self-waterers for garden plants: poke small holes in lid and put short bits of heavy string, yarn, pipecleaners, then turn upside down by plants. Clothes sprinkler. Sand-salt sprinkler for icy walks. Containers for different size nails and screw, first aid stuff for trips, sewing kits, baking soda for fire extinguishers. Tape heavy jar around outside (to prevent breakage), fill with water and use for fire extinguishers. Tape heavy jar around outside

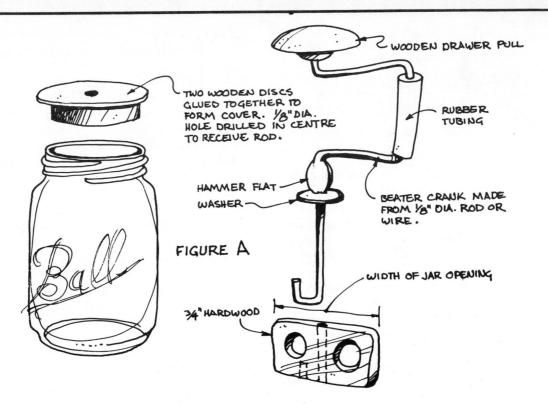

TWO WOODEN DISCS GLUED TOGETHER TO FORM COVER. 1/8" DIA. HOLE DRILLED IN CENTRE TO RECEIVE ROD.

WOODEN DRAWER PULL

RUBBER TUBING

HAMMER FLAT WASHER

BEATER CRANK MADE FROM 1/8" DIA. ROD OR WIRE.

FIGURE A

WIDTH OF JAR OPENING

3/4" HARDWOOD

(to prevent breakage), fill with hot water and use for bedwarmer on cold nights.

Butterchurn: (fig. A) half-gallon jar; for lid, glue smaller disc to larger one—must fit snugly. Drill hole in lid to fit beater rod. Those two holes on the wooden beater are one inch wide. The hole for the rod must fit tight; after passing the rod through it, bend the end up to hold. Rubber tubing is where you turn the beater, just like a drill. Drawer pull is your hand rest. To make butter, fill churn half full of thick cream. Push cover and beater attachment into place, and crank back and forth.

You can also make a food chopper by putting a drawer pull on one end of a dowel rod, fitting an open-wound spring underneath for easier action, poking it through the lid, fitting and wiring two blades (cut from tin cans) on the other end, which rests on a cardboard disc cut to fit the bottom of the jar (figure B).

There are lots of other uses for jars, of course—you can even make a small weather station for farms with jars, scrap wood, assorted odds and ends, and a thermometer.

If you know of more useful ways to cut down on garbage and consume less, send them by carrier pigeon.

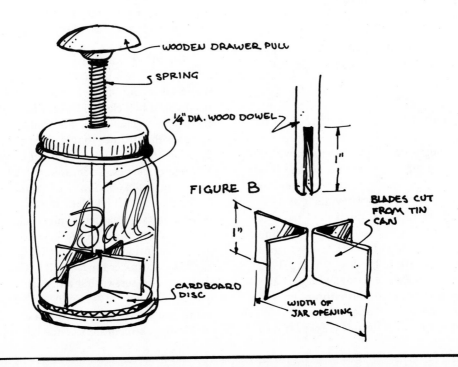

WOODEN DRAWER PULL

SPRING

1/4" DIA. WOOD DOWEL

FIGURE B

BLADES CUT FROM TIN CAN

1"

CARDBOARD DISC

WIDTH OF JAR OPENING

Practical Alchemy & Other Affairs of the Homestead

Eight-year Natural Finish

Raw Linseed Oil	3 gals.
Mineral Spirits or Turp	1 gal.
Burnt Sienna, Oil Colour	1 pt.
Raw Umber, Oil Colour	1 pt.
Paraffin Wax	1 lb.
Penta Concentrate 10:1	½ gal.
Zinc Stearate	2 oz.

Pour the gallon of mineral spirits into a five gallon open-top can. Put paraffin and zinc stearate in another pan and heat over flame, stirring until uniform mixture results. Pour this into the mineral spirits, stirring vigorously. Keep flame away from mineral spirits. When solution has cooled to room temperature, add pentachlorophenol concentrate, then linseed. Stir in colours until mixture is uniform, and it's ready for use. For redwood colour, use ½ pint raw umber, plus one pint pure red oxide colouring oil.

—Mother Earth News

Swedish Farm Paint

Red Iron Oxide	13.0 per cent
Ferrous Sulphate	3.2 per cent
Rye Flour	3.8 per cent
Water	76.0 per cent
Linseed Oil	4.0 per cent

Stir the rye flour into most of the cold water and boil 20 minutes. Dissolve the ferrous sulphate in a small portion of the water and add the solution to the rye flour gruel. Add the oxide, mixing thoroughly. Boil 15 minutes. Just before removing from the fire, add an amount of linseed oil equal to four per cent of the weight of the other ingredients. When cold, it is ready to use.

Quick Drying Paint

A paste is made containing:

Zinc Oxide	100 lb.
Hexamethylene Tetramine	3 lb.
Linseed Stand Oil	100 lb.

To the paste add:
Cobalt drier (cobalt resinate dissolved in an equal weight of mineral spirits) four pounds, and mineral spiris to give brushing consistency.

Filler for Fine Cracks Before Painting

Mix a little flour with the paint to be used to form a soft putty.

Paint for Pine Log Cabins

Formula No. 1

The best finish for peeled pine logs is warm linseed oil. The first coat should be thinned with 20 per cent turpentine; the second coat with 10 per cent turpentine, and the last coat should be straight linseed oil. Allow two weeks to elapse between each coat.

Formula No. 2

Use equal parts of boiled linseed oil and lead mixing oil. Apply two coats.

Paints for Cedar, Cypress, and Redwood

Priming Coat:

White-Lead	100 lb.
Raw Linseed Oil	4 gal.
Turpentine	1¾ gal.
Liquid Drier	1 pt.

This mix makes nine gal. of paint which will prime about 5,400 square feet of surface.

Second Coat:

White Lead	100 lbs.
Raw Linseed Oil	1½ gal.
Turpentine	1¼ gal.
Liquid Drier	1 pt.

Third Coat:

White-Lead	100 lb.
Linseed Oil	3 gal.
Liquid Drier	1 pt.

Barn Paint

Fish Oil, Heavy-bodied, refined	25 gal.
Red Iron Oxide	50 lb.
Mineral Spirits	15 gal.
Talc	5 lb.
Spar Varnish, Neutral	5 gal.

Paint for Buildings

A cheap wash may be made as follows: Take a clean, water-tight barrel and put into it ½ bushel of good lime. Slake it with boiling water; cover it six or seven inches deep, and see that it be thoroughly slackened. Then dissolve the slackened lime in water and add two pounds of sulphate of zinc and one pound common salt. This will harden the wash, and prevent its cracking after application. To colour it: For a cream colour add, in proportion to the above mixture, three pounds yellow ochre; for a lead colour, add a lump of iron black; for fawn colour, add four pounds umber, one pound of Indian red, and one pound lampblack; for stone colour, add two pounds of raw umber and two pounds of lampblack. To render it still more durable, and to give a glossiness to the work, before application to woodwork add a pint of sweet milk to a gallon of the wash.

Paint for Shingles

Slake stone lime by putting into a tub and keeping in the steam. When slaked, pass through a fine sieve, and to each six quarts add one quart of salt and one gallon of water; boil and skim off what rises to the surface. To each five gallons of this result add pulverized alum, one pound; copperas, one half-pound; potash, one half-pound; hardwood ashes, sifted, four pounds; apply with a whitewash brush. This is a very cheap paint and will last for many years.

Whitewash for Masonry

Casein	5 lbs.
Trisodium phosphate	3 lbs
Formaldehyde	3 pts.
Hydrated lime	50 lbs.

Dissolve the casein in 2 gallons of hot water, the trisodium phosphate in 3 gallons of water, the formaldehyde in 3 gallons of water. Add all this to 8 gallons of lime paste, which is made by mixing the hydrated lime with 6 gallons of water.

The lime coating is applied to damp walls, and dries to an opaque, hard, dust-free finish.

Canoe Finishing

Canvas canoes take a good finish, and remain not only water-tight, but also attractive, over a considerable period—if the job is done right.

1. Wash inside and out; then dry thoroughly.

2. Remove old paint, using any standard varnish remover according to the manufacturer's directions.

3. Dry entire canoe thoroughly. For this use a small motor-driven blower, taking warm air from around a heater improvised from one of the common "air-tight" wood-burning stoves. This warm dry air is blown gently into a canvas-covered box completely covering the canoe, the blower being tied in at the end while the other end is left open as a vent. After partially drying the canoe with the stern toward the blower, lift the cover, turn the canoe halfway around, and complete the drying.

4. After making sure that the canoe is dry, and regardless of the final colour desired, prime it with a thin coating—little more than a wash —of aluminum, using a long-oil varnish as the vehicle.

5. Then the canoe is given two colour coats of best grade marine paint, the material for each coat being cut with the addition of ½ pint of turpentine or wood spirits to the gallon as received. After the first coat has dried thoroughly, it is sanded lightly to assure a better bond with the following coat.

6. The job is finished with a coating of spar varnish. The varnish is flowed on with as little brushing as possible, beginning at the keel and working toward the gunwales.

Where any lettering, initials, or decorative design is desired, it is put on over the last coat of colour and covered with the spar varnish along with the rest of the canvas.

Jobs turned out in the manner outlined last from three to five years, depending upon usage (care being taken to drain the craft after each trip) and the amount of abrasion suffered from sandy beaches and rocky shoals.

Mosquito Repellant Oil

Oil of Citronella	16 oz.
Oil of Cedar Leaf	1 oz.
Oil of Pennyroyal	2 dr.
Creolin	4 dr.
Mineral Oil	1 gal.

Mix thoroughly.

Apply a few drops on the hands, face, and other exposed parts of the body and spread lightly over the skin.

More Mosquito Repellant

Oil of Citronella	6 oz.
Turpentine	6 oz.
Kerosene	4 oz.
Phenol Crystals (U.S.P.)	10 gr.

Dissolve the phenol in the kerosene, add the other ingredients, and mix thoroughly.

To keep mosquitoes out of the room, darken the room; saturate blotting paper or cotton with this liquid and place it near the door.

Care of Farm Tools

Carlessness in regard to farm tools, both as regards their replacement after use and their protection from atmospheric exposure during indefinite periods when they are not required, is accountable for depreciation and loss to an extent more than the average farm manager is aware. Necessary tools demand attention just as does any other part of the farm working equipment, and their oversight should be an essential part of thorough supervision. Indeed, they should be included in every periodic machinery overhaul or treatment in preparation for between-seasons storage. A recommended method for keeping both machinery and tools free from rust and in perfect condition for their work after long intervals of disuse, is to give them a coating of beeswax, dissolved in benzol. The benzol speedily evaporates, leaving the steel or iron covered with a thin coating of the protective wax. The advatage of this treatment over the application of paint is that plough mouldboards, shovels, and hoes remain polished and ready for instant work, whereas paint and grease coverings have the effect of making soil adhere. The beeswax coating is equally effective in hot or cold weather, but as benzol is highly volatile and flammable, the mixture should be kept in a tightly-corked bottle and kept far away from any exposed light. Where small tools, such as spanners, bits, and pliers are to be given this treatment, an effective method is to dip them in boiled linseed oil and let it dry on them; or the tools may be warmed on a stove and then smeared with white beeswax, after which they should be heated again to permit the wax spreading thinly and evenly over the surface to penetrate all interstices in the metal. One treatment of the metal of machinery or tools by one or other of the methods described will keep the machinery and tools rust free and bright for as long as a year, if need be.

Hints on Buying Second-hand Tools

Having in my youth worked at the bench for 12 months with an old tool-buyer, and learnt the art with him, I mostly buy all my tools second-hand, and save about 60 per cent, thereby, and tools run into money. The following hints from my experience may help others:

(1) In buying second-hand tools, go round the pawnshops and second-hand places devoted to such.

(2) Know what tools you want, their proper brands, and their present price, new.

(3) Look around each shop as you go in; if the articles you want are not readily procurable, do not waste time stopping.

(4) If they are not, and you see a tool you want, good and cheap, snap it up at once; it will be gone when you want it.

(5) Look carefully at each tool for flaws, and reject any that have been patched up, unless you can patch them up better with little trouble.

(6) Never, under any circumstances, believe anything the salesman tells you as to the tool's quality: the more emphatic the seller, the bigger liar, as a rule.

(7) Do not leave deposits on any tool; buy it right out, or you will most likely have trouble about it later on.

(8) Some salesmen try to bluff a buyer into taking a thing; the minute one starts this game, throw down the tool and prepare to leave; this will bring him to reason.

(9) Carry an up-to-date price list in your pocket; it saves argument.

(10) A fair price for good second-hand tools is 35 to 50 per cent of their new price, according to quality.

(11) All nuts rusted tight, rusty tools, etc., can be fixed up with a little kerosene.

(12) If possible, go round once with a good buyer, and get him to show you how to pick good tools.

Waterproofing Boots

One pint linseed oil, ¼pt. oil of turpentine, ¼ pound beeswax, ¼ pound pitch. Melt ingredients by standing tin container in boiling water away from a fire, renewing hot water till all are blended. The vapour is flammable. When dissolved pour the liquid into a tin to set. When required for use, melt a small quantity and rub well into the soles of the shoes.

Or: Melt in a tin over a low flame 1pt. boiled linseed oil, ½ pound mutton suet, six ounces clean beeswax, and four ounces resin. See that boots are dry and clean, and give a plentiful dressing; it must be put on warm with a soft brush. The leather will become quite pliant and resist all moisture.

Or: Rub a lump of wax on the boots until they become a grey colour, then heat a piece of old linen or soft calico in the oven and smooth over with the hot rag till the leather has absorbed the wax. Allow the shoes to cool, then give a good brushing and apply a good boot polish.

Identifying Poisonous Bottles

A sure way to avoid mistaking a poison bottle for another is to push two ordinary pins crossway through the top part of the cork at right angles, with the points projecting. That identifies the bottle even in the dark.

To Pull Out Stumps

When pulling out a stump with a chain and team only, hook the chain round the bottom of the stump, not the top, with the hook on the opposite side to the team, and pass the chain over the top of the stump. This gives a leverage and increases the pulling power. A better way, with a little grubbing, is to get the chain round a big root, and pass over the top of the stump as before.

To Square a Corner

To square a corner when plotting out the site for a paddock or building, lay a four-foot straightedge along one line from the corner peg, and another of three feet along the adjacent side. Then bring their ends exactly five feet apart and you will have a perfect right angle. From the height and base of the angle, the sides may be then lined out.

To Mend Troughs

To mend tanks or troughs that have pinholes rusted through, fill a kerosene tin with cold water. Throw in washing soda until the saturation point is exceded and undissolved soda can be seen lying on the bottom of the tin. Next get a flat vessel, such as an old baking dish, and mix cement with this water until it becomes a thick paste (make only a small quantity of cement at a time, as it sets very quickly). Apply this paste thickly to the holes with a brush, spreading some around them also. Moisten and wring out a piece of unbleached calico and press it down on the cement firmly and smoothly, as if sticking paper on a wall. Put another coat of cement paste on this, then apply another strip of calico, and a final coat of cement will finish the job. Two people are needed to make it a success—one to mix the plaster, and one to do the work. The person mixing the cement must keep briskly stirring and mixing the paste, turning it over with a small trowel till all is used. Water should be shut off from the tank for twelve hours. The patch will have set hard and will not crack when the tank expands or peel off when dry. Sheep troughs stand

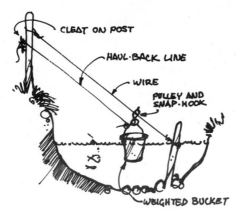

for years after this treatment, and a tank made of flat galvanized iron was successfully treated while full of water. No soda was available on one selection, and waterglass was used to mix the cement, and used while the tank was full of water.

Water Elevator

A length of No. 8 fencing wire is stretched from a post at the top of the bank to a stake driven into the creek bed in such a position that the lower end of the wire will be completely under water. A bucket is suspended from the wire by means of a pulley and snap hoop. A weight must be attached to the side of the bucket in order to sink it. The buket is operated by a rope, either with the hand or with a small windlass.

Fireplace Brick Cleaner

Make a past of:
2 oz. powdered pumice
2 oz. soda
2 oz. salt
plus as much water as is needed to bring it to a creamy consistency. If the bricks are very sooty, add 1 tbsp. of ammonia. Apply with a stiff brush, covering the bricks completely, and scour with a will. Rinse with clear, warm water. Be sure bricks are dry before fireplace is used again.

For a soapstone, sandstone, or chuckanut stone hearth, clean with pure water, then sprinkle on some powdered marble or soapstone, and rub with a piece of stone as large as a brick with one flat side.

Stove Black for Stove Grates

Melt 1 lb. asphaltum in an old tin or kettle. When melted, add one-half pint linseed oil, and one-quarter pint oil of turpentine. Beforehand, clean the grate well. Apply blackening while still hot with a small painter's brush that will get into all the crevices. Leave the grate to dry.

Stove Polish

Add to 1 pt. benzine, 1 oz. pulverized resin. When dissolved, mix any good and finely ground black lead. Use the liquid as you would water for mixing polish. Apply with a small paint brush, rub smooth, as it dries rapidly. When dry, polish with a soft stove brush.

Home-made Fire Kindlers

Melt 3 lbs. resin, 1 qt. tar and stir in as much sawdust and pulverized charcoal as possible. Spread on a board to cool. Break into walnut sized lumps. You can light these with one match—it burns for some time with a good blaze.

Leaky Laundry Tubs

If you have a cement laundry tub, it is probably an oldie—and the older they are are, the more porous and fragile they become. If it begins to leak water through decomposing cement, there's nothing you can do but buy (or make) a new one, since paint won't adhere to the soap-saturated surface. But cracks can be patched really easily. Regular cement mixed in finish proportions (1 part cement to 3 parts sand, or a bit leaner on the sand) is just fine. Undercut the crack to insure good binding—and your oldie will remain a goodie as long as you care.

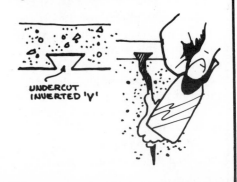

Chick Food

(starter and developer)

	lb.
Hulled Oats	10
Corn Meal	50
Wheat Middlings	20
Millet	2
Rape	1-1/4
Caraway	1/8
Gentian	1/8
Ginger	1/4
Black Pepper	1/4
Bone Meal	2
Shell Meal	2
Epsom Salts	2
Dried Buttermilk Powder	10

Have all ingredients finely ground before mixing. Mix thoroughly.

Feed as any standard chick food, giving no more than will be cleaned up at each feeding.

Liquid Manure—Chinese and Japanese Style

Into a sealed jar put a collection of putrid animal substances, consisting of fish, blood, etc., to which is added a certain quantity of urine, but the vessel is not completely filled. It must remain sealed in this vessel for six months. Before using, it is always diluted with four or five times its bulk of water and it is used extensively for garden crops, but universally in drills.

Non-slip Log Sawhorse

Refitting Axe Handles

A new axe handle, as purchased in the store, often does not fit an axe head. It was made for use in a number of heads, and thus needs to be shaped. A wood rasp is probably the best tool to do the job.

The handle should fit the axe eye snugly at all points Never drive a nail in the end of the handle after it has been fitted to the head to hold the head on the handle. It will split the wood, and allow the head to slip off. Use a wooden wedge as shown. The wedge should be dry, soft wood. Cut off one inch of grip end of handle so it won't split when driven in head.

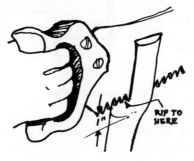

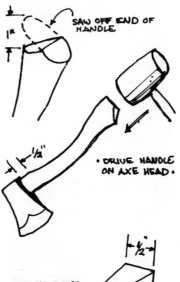

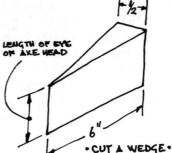

Handle should fit axe eye snugly at all points. Tap in handle to test it for hand.

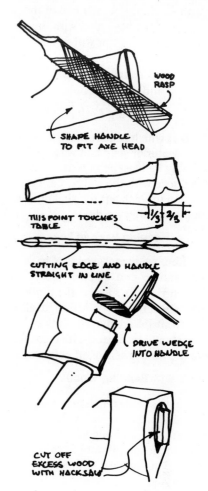

Wedge should be dry, soft wood. Drive it squarely. Soak handle with hot linseed oil.

Sterilizing Soil For Planting

The presence of weed seeds in potting compost interferes with the raising of plants from seeds in trays, pots, and frames. It is therefore advisable to kill off any noxious seeds before sowing. A simple method is to put the earth into a fine-mesh sieve and pour boiling water over it. When the water leaking out at the bottom is uncomfortably hot to the hand the process is complete. Another way is to spread the earth on shallow trays and put it into the oven, turning it over at intervals until it becomes heated right through.

Siphoning Hint

When water has to be drawn from a deep tank by siphoning, and the action cannot be started by mouth suction, hold the end of the long leg of the hose level with the top of the tank, fill it with water and drop it. The suction of the column of water will exhaust the air in the short leg and start the siphon.

Cleaning Bottles

Dirt which cannot be dislodged by hot water or soap and water will probably be loosened by shot or sand introduced with the water. Care must be taken to wash out the shot or sand completely afterwards.

Keeping Bark on Logs

Remove narrow strips of bark from end to end of each piece, one on each side, as soon as the timber is felled (best in early autumn), to allow bark to shrink freely. The cuts and ends should be coated with creosote and the timber seasoned before use.

Bending Wood

In most cases moisture and heat are wanted. Boiling reduces strength, so steaming is better wherever practicable. Bamboos can be softened sufficiently with a gas or spirit flame passed to and fro so as not to burn the surface, which should be wiped over repeatedly with a damp cloth. The object bent should be tied or clamped in the shape which it is required to assume and be left for some days. It will be found useful in some cases to make saw cuts across the grain on the inside of the bend(fig. A), or along the grain (fig. B) at the end of a piece. Any piece selected for bending should have the grain running straight. If it "runs out" at any point on the outside of the bend, there is a danger of the wood slivering-out there.

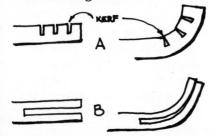

Gate Catch

A is a block of oak or other hard wood shaped as in (a) of the figure below. The latch,*C*, is of the same wood. A long slot cut in *A* allows it to rise on nails sufficiently for *C* to lift it clear when the gate closes. Plate *B*, of metal, prevents a jamming on nail heads.

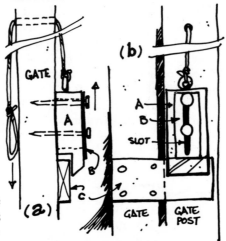

A Self-closing Gate

A gate will swing to of itself if its hinges or hooks be so arranged that opening the gate causes the free end to rise gradually as it moves. If the lower hook be vertically under, but somewhat farther out from the gate than the upper (fig. a), the gate will rise until it is at right angles to its closed position; but if moved through more than a quarter-circle will automatically swing through the next quarter-circle and remain open. This may be convenient in some cases; but usually is not so, and a stop is placed to prevent it opening more than "square." Assuming the two hinges to be of exactly the same shape, the gate is not parallel to the hook side of the hanging post, and the closing post must be inclined somewhat for the gate to touch it top and bottom. This objectionable feature can be overcome if the top hinge has the ring in the centre line of the gate, while that of the bottom is in line with the outer face (fig. b), as the gate can then be hung vertically, though the lower hook is farther out than the upper.

To make a gate swing to through a *half-circle*, the hooks project the same distance from the post, but the lower one is somewhat farther from

the closing post than the other (fig. c). If the hinges be similar, the gate will necessarily droop at the closing end. If, however, the lower hinge has its ring farther from the hinge end of the gate than is that of the other (fig. d), the gate may be hung level and yet be self-closing.

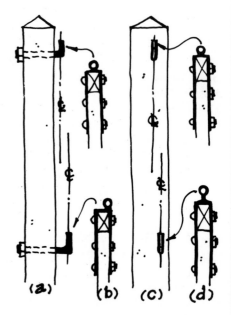

When a Door Sticks

Before cutting, try the effect of a little vaseline or soft soap at the point where the door "binds." Sticking is sometimes caused by a slight expansion due to damp weather, and disappears when the air dries again.

Extinguishing Chimney Fires

Throw some salt and powdered sulphur on the fire, to create fire-killing fumes, and cover the fireplace with a sheet or blanket soaked in water to cut off the air supply and starve the flames. All windows and doors should be closed to assist this. If air can be prevented entering the chimney, the fire cannot last long.

Gate Fastener

How to Build a Compost Shredder

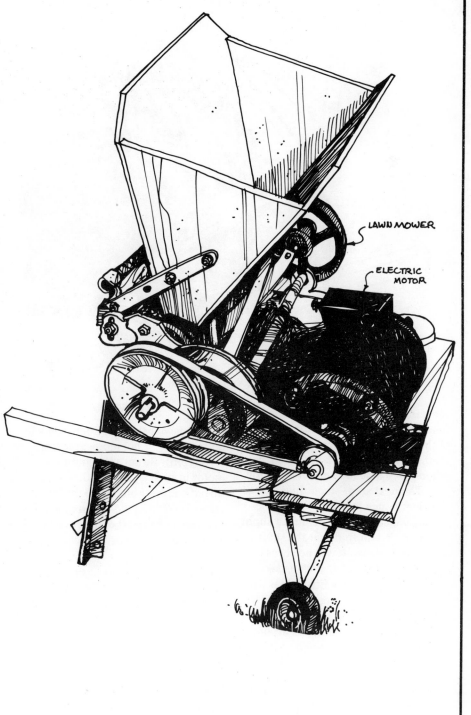

LAWN MOWER

ELECTRIC MOTOR

A simple and easily constructed tool for compost making is the compost shredder. High quality 14-day compost can be made with the shredder. Get an old push-type lawn mower, easily come by from a second hand store for a moderate price.

The Stand

Get some recycled 2x4s so you can build a stand for the mower. The frame has to be built about 20 inches high, perhaps adding a couple of wheels to the front legs for mobility. The size depends on the lawnmower.

The Mower

First remove and recycle the handle and roller from the machine. Then mount the machine upside down on the frame that you've just built. Next remove the wheels (usually by removing the centre bolts, or a couple of cotter pins). This will expose the two small pinion gears, and

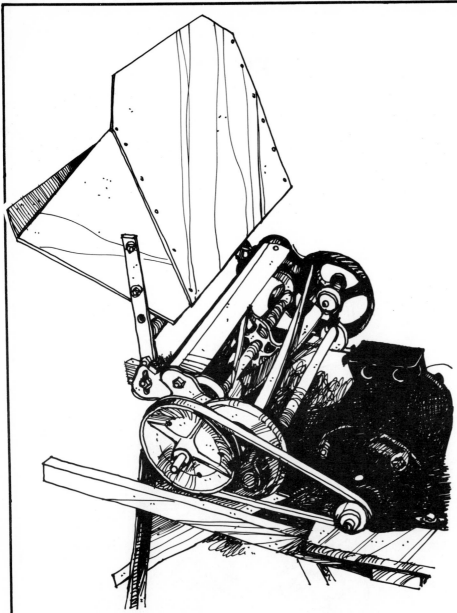

the pair of rectangular "pawls" found in the small slots near the ends of the blade-assembly shaft. Remove all these so that the blades spin freely when given a push in either direction.

The next step—mounting a large 5 inch or 6 inch V-belt pulley on the end of the blade shaft—offers a slight problem. You'll find that the shaft is too short to do so. It will be necessary to have a local machine shop make you a shaft extension fitting that will lengthen the shaft enough for the pulley to be clear of the rest of the machine. The exact dimensions of the piece will depend on the size of the shaft and the diameter of the hole in the pulley. The easiest way to indicate what you need is to take both the mower and the pulley to a machinist and show him what the problem is.

The Motor

To power the shredder, you will need a ¼ or ⅓ horsepower motor (1750 rpm). Be sure to mount the motor in such a position that it will turn the mower blades so that they move TOWARD the cutting bar. If you can't change the direction of rotation of the motor, you can accomplish the same result by putting the large pulley on the other end of the mower-blade shaft. Put a small (1½ inch) pulley on the motor shaft and mount the motor so the two pulleys are exactly in line. V-belts are sold in sizes that indicate their total length. Find the size you need by stretching a rope around both pulleys in place of a belt. If there is no electricity, try an old gas mower as a drive source instead of the electric one.

In order to guide the materials to be chopped to the cutting-bar, make a v-shaped "hopper" of either plywood or sheet metal. It should be about a foot wide at the top and taper to about 1½ inches at the bottom. Make it almost as long as the cutting-bar. Hold it in place by a couple of strips of iron bolted to the roller holders screwed to the ends of the hopper.

The ⅓ horsepower motor shredder can cut up green twigs almost ½ inch in diameter, provided they are fed in slowly. But always remember the damned contraption eats fingers too.

14-day Compost

The keystone of the 14-day method is the grinding or shredding of all material going into the compost pile. Grinding has these effects on compost:

(1) The surface area of material on which micro-organisms can multiply is greatly increased.

(2) Aeration of the mass is improved, because shredded material has less tendency to mat or pack down.

(3) Moisture control is improved.

(4) Turning of the heap is easier.

No layering of material is used in the 14-day method. Material is mixed either before or after shredding, then piled in heaps no more than five feet in height. After only three days, the heap is turned. Turning is continued at two- or three-day decreased intervals. After 12 to 14 days, the heat of the pile has dropped, and the compost is sufficiently decayed for use on the soil.

Jim Buckey, of New Alchemy Institute, West, built the compost chopper and offers the following criticisms and improvements:

1) Mount the chopper on 50 or 30 gallon drum to assure safe flow of compost material—you never know when there might be a rock flying out. Also, as is designed in the article, the compost comes flying out the bottom in all directions, including at your legs and feet. See diagram No. 1.

2) Secure the motor firmly to the stand (i.e. with lock washers) because of vibrations.

3) Use either channel iron, angle iron, or aluminum for making the stand instead of wood. (Get used material.)

4) Extension shafts may be available at hardware stores, so look there first before taking your machine to a local machine shop. (They're expensive.)

5) Use a ¾ horsepower motor, ball bearing, instead of ¼ or ⅓. The smaller ones just don't have enough hp to shred your materials well. Also the ¾ is better built and will last longer.

6) Add a safety bar for the back edge of the hopper to rest on. See photograph on this page.

7) Tack weld a piece of light gage sheet metal to the blades so that the size of the chips can be controlled. Otherwise large pieces of stick will go through the blades. See diagram No. 2.

8) And use a pair of safety glasses, even sun glasses will do. You never know when something might come whirring out.

METAL BAND AROUND CIRCULAR SHREDDER BASE HOLDS SHREDDER ON DRUM

OIL DRUM (SHOWN IN SECTION)

OIL DRUM CUT AWAY AT BOTTOM

FIG. 1

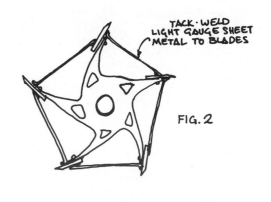

TACK·WELD LIGHT GAUGE SHEET METAL TO BLADES

FIG. 2

Index

Cloudburst 2

A
HANDBOOK OF RURAL SKILLS
AND
TECHNOLOGY

Contents
Cloudburst 2

by Philip Brachi

Plumbing in the Sun

The theory is simple. Even our notorious British climate offers an average 1400 hours of sunshine annually, delivering some 900 kilowatt hours to each square metre of Wales and England. A black surface will absorb most of the energy and turn it into heat; so trap this beneath a layer of glass or plastic, opaque at those longer wavelengths, and carry the heat away somewhere useful.

Unobscured and unobtrusive, a roof is the obvious place to erect such a sliver of a greenhouse; sensible too, because the same structure keeps the house dry. Programs exist to compute optimal orientation (a wee bit west of south?) and slope for solar roof siting. Orientation, though, will often be dictated — as here at Eithin-y-Gaer — by an existing building; and the programs have demonstrated their own redundancy, by proving that pitch is far less critical than area. So build big if you can; ours is 60 square metres.

Set on a north-facing hillside, with some shading from apple, ash, and elm, our home-built home is a compromise; having a southern horizon above which the Sun never rises for six mid-winter weeks, and an orientation 30° west of south, meant that our roof could never be optimal. But then reality rarely is. We chose a 30° pitch, angled for the six months of high summer Sun, which contains almost 80 per cent of the year's energy harvest in these climes. We are living at about latitude 52½° north — approximately on a line with the Northern tip of Newfoundland, Saskatoon or the Queen Charlotte Islands. Elsewhere, follow the plans.

Our solar system is indirect; as the plumbing diagram (Fig. 1) shows, the hot water drawn at the tap is not the water which passed over the roof. This choice was made for several reasons. The circulating pump is happier without new water all the time to corrode its impellor; and there is less furring-up by salts depositing on the hot aluminium. Additives, too, can be experimented with. Inks to darken the

water and aid heat absorption, perhaps; copper sulphate to prevent algae growth, should that prove problematic; and we've found that a little detergent (Sunlight, of course!) lowers surface tension, helping the water to spread out as it runs down the roof.

An eminiently do-it-yourself proposition, the intermittent man and woman-hours between basket-making and baking amounted to perhaps 6 or 7 people-weeks.

Mid-July experiments have shown a steady state, in which water was running up to the roof at 62½°F (17°C) and returning at 113½°F (45°C), at the rate of one goat bucketful (4.9 litres) every 27 seconds. That is 21.5 kilowatts, or about seven domestic immersion heaters. The 60 square-

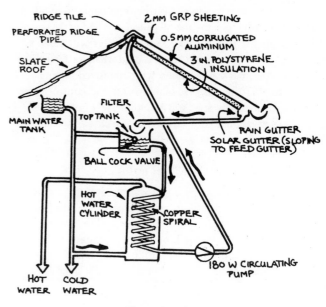

FIGURE 1

metre roof was extracting 40-45 per cent of the Sun's energy offering, which, an hour past its highest, we guessed to be 800 - 900 watts per square metre.

Stefan's Law suggests that the 50°C kitchen tap record-to-date will not easily be bettered, as efficiency falls off sharply above these temperatures. But this also means that the roof performs best when needed most — when starting with a cold tank.

And how does the system know when to start?

Sensitive controls of the solar system is very important, as a glance at the water circuit will confirm. If, after warming up the hot-water cylinder, the Sun clouds over, then the system left running will be heating the mid-Wales sky for those lucky buzzards! The roof must be switched off. If, however, a couple of baths are then taken, cold water replacing the hot water drawn will so cool the cylinder as to make it worthwhile turning on the pump once more.

What is required, then, is a continual comparison of roof temperature with that of the hot water cylinder. The black box to do the trick has proved invaluable. Awake day and night, it occasionally has the roof using diffuse sunlight before 7 a.m. solar time.

As yet, there have been few problems. Filtration, though, must be careful and continuous, or live beetles, elm seeds, and other aliens somehow intrude. Running a bottle-brush through the ridge pipe is a drag! Condensation on the under surface of the GRP sheets affects the upper (hotter) half or third of the roof, and must be reducing efficiency; it causes some water transfer to the rain gutter, too. To counter this, we are going to increase the flow-rate, lowering the steady state temperatures. Or should we do a little lateral thinking, and use this effect to distill our elderflower wine?

There was, of course, that imperial snarl-up when I forgot the aluminium roof was the only item in the house not built to an 18-inch module. Three feet into 900 millimetres won't go! Embarrassed consultations of "GRP Technology" advised diamond-tipped circular saws at 10,000 s.f.m. Being caught short on these, we used garden shears.

Some improvements to eke further ergs come to mind. A 300-gallon tank replacing the 39-gallon one will make much fuller use of the roof's power; the hot water will be at a lower temperature, so we'll add less cold when bathing. Fine-tuning of the black box, along with improved thermal contact for the thermistors, should make the control even more responsive. The attic still gets amazingly hot, though, so perhaps we should go up from 3 to 6 inches of insulation below the roof.

The place of Alternative Technologies

Alternative technologies could well be evolved on a lab bench in the city; but to do so would miss the point. Like the good Peter Harper says, "AT is not really about new pieces of hardware, but about our whole approach to living, production, consumption, and fulfilling our goals."

Decentralisation is of the essence. How does the Sun's energy arrive, after all? The effort to promote hectare-gobbling solar stations for the electricity grid is technocratic tunnel-vision. Or has it something to do with the way in which power, in that other sense, is distributed within our parlous state. Ambient energy from sun, wind, and water is hard for anyone but the user to control, and correspondingly unlikely to be misused.

Against the advocate of solar roofs are ranged various objections: "How do you heat water in winter?" and "How much energy went into making all that aluminium and plastic?" The answers are: a heat pump, to give 12 kilowatt-hours of heat out for 3-4 kilowatt-hours of electricity in; and about 15,000 kilowatt-hours, which we should be able to collect as hot water in year or two. More serious is the criticism that such AT gadgets affect only the technology of consumption, ignoring the organisation of production and its attendant horrors. In a word, it's bourgeois. What about inequality, alienation, exploitation? How does Amalgamated Greed treat its black workers in the bauxite mine behind the aluminium roof?

Maybe we now have a more realistic view of what AT can achieve. Alone, it is not going to change the world, or any-thing very much, but will be lovingly co-opted by big business. Yet AT is not alone, but a part of something far larger, less obvious. The manifestations are everywhere: free schools and housing associations, food and craft co-ops, white bicycles, squats and work-ins; even at the production end, things are changing slowly. Together amounting to a movement, rough but real, such developments can only multiply the potential of this cheerful roof.

Being a community, we do not see this as a purely technical achievement, nor an economic one to save us $250.00 a year. There is, though, the rare sensuality of bathing in rainwater warmed by the sun. And as part of the home that we and our friends built for ourselves, it perhaps has a certain spiritual dimension, contributing a little to that softest, least palpable technology of them all; a group of people slowly coming together communally under one roof.

Completed in June 1974, our solar roof supplied hot water for about ten people through a poor summer till early October. These plans should enable handymen and women to build their own, giving 6-8 months hot water yearly, for about 3 cents a day, and lowering winter fuel bills too.

How It Works

A dark surface — in this case a corrugated **aluminum roof** —will absorb most solar energy and turn it into heat; a layer of glass or plastic **glazing**, secured on **glazing bars**, prevents this heat escaping skywards. The corrugations run down the aluminum roof's slope, each "valley" being fed a trickle of water from a perforated **ridge-pipe** running along the roof's ridge. The water, warmed in its passage down the aluminum, collects in a plastic **gutter** and gravity feeds indoors. Flowing through a copper spiral within the hot water cylinder of the domestic **plumbing** system, it yields up its heat, and is then recycled by a small pump back up to the ridge. A top-up tank in the system allows filtration, and any occasional water losses are made good there. South is the best orientation, but wide variation seems possible; our roof faces 30°W of south. A 30-35° slope is optimal for the six months of the summer sun which comprise nearly 80% of Britain's solar energy input. Elsewhere, make the slope latitude minus 20° roughly, for summer use. *** More important is to build big**, ours, 60 square metres (60m²), has given 21.5 kilowats on a sunny July lunchtime.

Construction

These plans assume working with exposed rafters, but the techniques could be used to build smaller panels, skylight fashion, or to make free-standing solar collectors for backyard experiments.

The Aluminum Roof

This was made from Granges Essem TRP 40 corrugated sheet, 0.5 mm gauge, factory coloured dark grey. Allowing for overlap, each sheet covers 900 mm width, supplied cut to length required. Fixing the lightweight aluminum roof to the rafters **must** be done with aluminum nails, **not** steel, to avoid electrolytic corrosion between these metals. Plastic washers (W in fig. 2) cushion the heads of the 4" (100 mm) nails (X) tight against the roof (Y); a plastic snap-fit dome (Z) attached to the washer seals the fixing. Nail the aluminum sheets through their ridges, because the valleys will later run with hot water. If the attic rafters do not coincide with the ridges of the aluminum sheets (the TRP 40 sheets have ridges every 100 mm), nail noggins 4" x 2" (100 mm x 50 mm) wood between the rafters, and fix the aluminum to them. Remember to leave the complete length of every ninth ridge of the aluminum roof free of fastenings, so that glazing bars can be attached later. The house now has a strong aluminum roof, quite capable of carrying two people, provided weight is spread by working from a ladder secured over the ridge of the house.

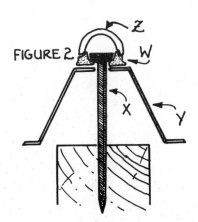

FIGURE 2

The Gutters

The **solar gutter** collects water from the aluminum; it slopes about one inch in 15 feet (0.5 per cent) toward a convenient point to enter the house and join the plumbing system. Using ordinary 3" (70 mm) plastic guttering, seal the joints between sections with "Plastic Padding": hot water leaks easily! Secure the gutter to the ends of the rafters. Insulation beneath and beside the solar gutter is well worth-

*Much steeper is best for facing the lower winter sun, but this is architecturally harder, reduces the roof's summer performance and, of course, much less solar energy is available in winter.

while. A downspout connector (A in fig. 3) and a 45° angle piece (B) are fitted to the gutter where the solar water is fed indoors. Roughen their joining surfaces and glue with "Plastic Padding" (C); again use it (D) to connect the 45° angle piece to the polythene plumbing (E) emerging from the wall of the house (F). The **rain gutter**, attached to the house **fascia**, collects rain from the glazing. (N.B. Until all glazing is in place, the solar gutter acts as rain gutter; think, and plumb, carefully, or you may divert a cloudburst indoors! Don't connect the plumbing to the solar gutter until the glazing is completed.)

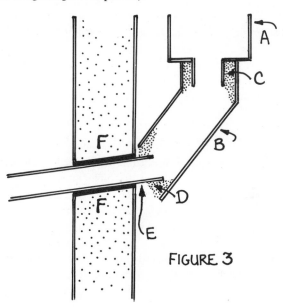

FIGURE 3

PUTTING ON THE ROOF

The Ridge Pipe

Ours is ¾" (18 mm) internal diameter copper tubing; because of increased costs, plus the possible electrolytic problem of copper near the aluminum roof, we now favour rigid PVC tubing. Holes 5/64" diameter (2 mm) are drilled every 100 mm to coincide with each valley of the corrugated roof. With a bottle-brush, clear out any swarf after drilling, as this may clog the small holes when the ridge-pipe is operating. Leave the installed ridge-pipe's ends sealed with a threaded openable plug: if filtration ever fails, the pipe can be flushed out, or the brush drawn through with a stiff wire. The ridge-pipe is secured to the wooden ridge-plate structure of the house, positioned so that its holes drop water directly into the valleys of the corrugated aluminum. Water reaches the ridge-pipe via two connections, spaced a quarter of the way from each end; this makes the water flow from the pipe more evenly than if the supply is pumped only to the centre or end of the roof.

The Glazing Bars

These run from top to bottom of the roof along every ninth ridge of the aluminum, forming frames 900 mm wide to hold the glazing sheets. The recess in the bottom of the glazing bar fits the square head of an aluminum bolt 7/8" (20 mm) long; (the bolts and nuts, plus self-tapping screws, capping strip, and PVC seals are all supplied with the Frampton Furguson C70 glazing bar). Their bolt makes a simple fixing direct to the aluminum roof, but on our windy

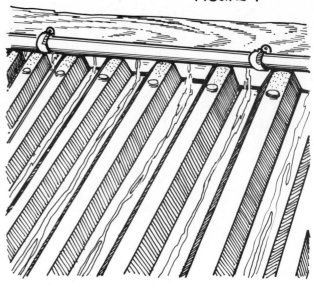

FIGURE 4

THE RIDGE PIPE

hill we chose the more secure fix shown. Brackets (12 in fig. 5) made from one inch angle iron are fixed to the attic's rafters directly beneath each ninth ridge of the aluminum roof. Bitumin damp-proofing material (DPM) cut into strips (8) helps the glazing bar to seat tightly and offers some heat insulation, preventing the glazing bars from cooling the roof. Electrolytic corrosion between the steel nut (6) and aluminum glazing bar is avoided by a home-made polythene

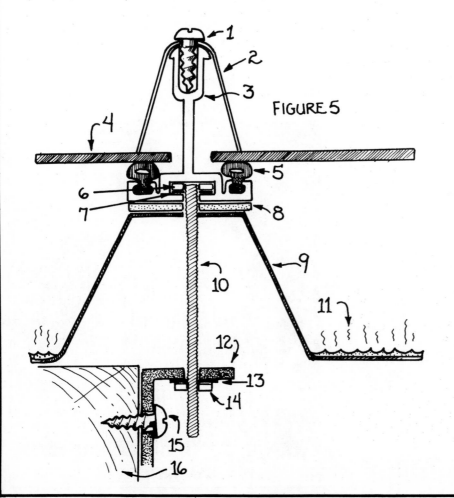

FIGURE 5

1. SELF-TAP SCREW
2. CAPPING STRIP
3. GLAZING BAR
4. GRP SHEET
5. PVC SEAL
6. NUT
7. POLYTHENE WASHER
8. DPM STRIP
9. ALUMINUM ROOF
10. THREADED BAR
11. HOT WATER FLOW
12. ANGLE BRACKET
13. WASHER
14. NUT
15. WOOD SCREW
16. RAFTER

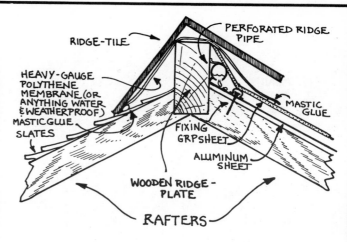

FIGURE 6

washer (7); the threaded bar (10) is protected by gloss paint where it passes through the aluminum roof. The entire fixing occurs every 59" (1.5 m) for each glazing bar.

Glazing the Roof

Using plastic may seem nonsense: glass is half the price and more transparent; besides, to glaze with plastic is hardly good English! But, from experience, glass is problematic: weight, fragility, sharp edges, and impossibility of placing weight on glass once laid in place — all combine to favour glass-reinforced plastic (GRP) sheeting; e.g., Mitra's Mitlite, 2 mm thick. GRP is light, safe, flexible and extremely tough; made to size, each sheet runs from ridge to gutter; ours were over 16 ft. (5 m) long; a glass version would require several separate sheets, with algae and dirt problems where they overlap. However, GRP does sag between the glazing bars, reducing efficiency by touching the aluminum roof; extra plastic domes (Z in fig. 2) are nailed to the ridges of a few corrugations to lift the GRP. Longer than the aluminum, since they run beyond the solar gutter to the rain gutter, the GRP sheets are easily lifted and laid in place between two glazing bars. (With glazing bars spaced at 900 mm intervals, 885 mm is a good width to order the GRP sheets.) At its top end, the GRP can be flexed to ride up over the ridge-pipe and fit tightly against the wooden structure of the house (fig. 6). The sheet is secured, starting from the lower end, by screwing the capping strip (2 in fig. 5) onto one supporting glazing bar. The second glazing bar is left uncapped, ready to receive the next GRP sheet. Gaps at the top and bottom of each sheet, where air might circulate, should be sealed with plastic foam cushion, visible in fig. 7.

Plumbing

All pipes carrying solar circulating water are "Class C" polythene, using the Tubelock connection system. Plumbing from the pump to the ridge-pipe is ¾" (18 mm) internal diameter, the remainder 1" (25 mm). The 39 gal. (177 litre) hot water cylinder, with its copper spiral, is commonplace; most centrally-heated homes have one. For winter, an immersion heater can be fitted. The SMC Commander S circulating pump lifts 2.4 gal./min. (11 litres/min.) through a maximum 14 ft. (4.3 m) head; beyond this, a larger pump is

needed. Flow rates can be experimented with by varying pump speed or size; for the 650 ft.^{2} (60 m^2) roof, our rate may be a bit low. Keep the slope of the gravity feed from the solar gutter to the top-up tank constant, without sagging, to prevent airlocks when the system is switched off.

Operation

Using its sensors (fig. 8: TH1 on the hot water cylinder, TH2 on the back of the aluminum roof), the **Black Box** controls the pump, on and off, only running it when the roof is warmer than the cylinder by a few degrees, adjustable by VR1. Filtration must be continuous, or else insects, etc., enter the system, blocking the ridge-pipe's holes; hence the kitchen sieve above the top-up tank, emptied monthly; and now a tea-strainer across its exit, too. A little detergent in the tank promotes inner cleanliness, helping the water to spread out as it runs down the roof. Temperatures have reached 126°F (52°C), way too hot to touch, at the kitchen tap; but heat losses are less and efficiency greater if a larger

GLAZING THE ROOF

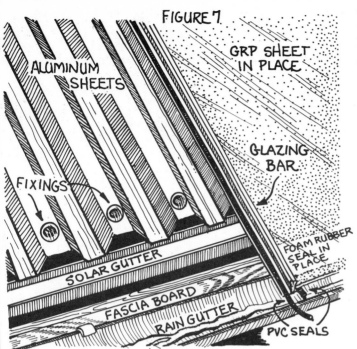

FIGURE 7.

GRP SHEET IN PLACE

ALUMINUM SHEETS

GLAZING BAR

FIXINGS

FOAM RUBBER SEAL IN PLACE

SOLAR GUTTER

FASCIA BOARD

RAIN GUTTER

PVC SEALS

efficiency; yet we still get more hot water on a sunny day than we can use. Perhaps an increased flow rate might help, by lowering the roof's operating temperature.

Bibliography

"Undercurrents" — "The magazine of radical science and peoples' technology." Bi-monthly (well, almost!) from 11, Shadwell, Uley, Dursey, Gloucester, England, $6.50 U.S. per year or equivalent — $8.00 U.S. for airmail. Plenty of items on do it yourself Solar Energy.

"Alternative Sources of Energy" — $6.00 (U.S. currency only), from ASE Subscriptions, Route 2, Box 90A, Milaca, MN 56353, USA. Highly practical information on development of technologies for a decentralised society. No. 15 is a classified access list of over 1000 articles, books, addresses — $1.50. No. 17 — "Spectrum" is an equipment directory of alternative technologies — $2.50.

volume of water is stored at somewhat lower temperatures. Insulation is vital. We have 3" (75 mm) polystyrene block behind the aluminum roof, costing about $1.25 per square metre; the hot water cylinder, top-up tank, and return pipe are each boxed in with at least 3" of polystyrene. Frost damage cannot occur, since the roof drains whenever the pump switches off — a major advantage of this system. Condensation on the under surface of the GRP sheets affects the upper third or half of the roof, and must be reducing

BRAD's solar roof: what it cost (1973-4)		
Component:	Cost (£)	Cost/sq.m (£)
Corrugated aluminum	132	2.20
Glazing bars + fittings	50	0.83
Plastic sheeting (GRP)	246	4.10
Copper ridge-pipe	18	
Top-Up tank	4	
Extra plumbing	10	
Black Box control system	5	
Solar gutter	8	
Pump	17	
Fastenings, etc.	4	
Total cost in English Pounds	494	8.23
Total cost in Canadian Dollars	($1185.60)	($19.75)

The Black Box — Components

VR1	Potentiometer/4K7 Lin/P20
R1	Resistor/1K 1/3 watt/UPMO33
R2	Resistor/1K 1/3 watt/UPMO33
R3	Resistor/1K 1/3 watt/UPMO33
R4	Resistor/1K 1/3 watt/UPMO33
R5	Resistor/3K3 1/3 watt/UPMO33
R6	Resistor/100K 1/3 watt/UPMO33
R7	Resistor/78K 1/3 watt/UPMO33
R8	Resistor/33K 1/3 watt/UPMO33
R9	Resistor/4K7 1/3 watt/UPMO33
R10	Resistor/250 ohms 1/3 watt/UPMO33
C1	Capacitor/0.1μF 400v/Siemans
C2	Capacitor/4700μF 25v/Siemans, axial lead
TH1	Thermistor/VA 1055
TH2	Thermistor/VA 1055
1C1	Integrated Circuit/LIC741C8, etc. (any 8-pin 741 type)
D1	Diode/silicon/IN916
D2	Rectifier Diode/S2CN1
D3	Rectifier Diode/S2CN1
S1	Main Switch/SPDT type/centre off 1019C
RS1	Reed Switch/250v 1 amp/SR1
I1	Reed Coil/12v > 800 Ω /SS/12
Z1	Zener Diode/10v 400mW
Z2	Zener Diode/3.3 400mW (optional)
T1	Mains Transformer/9-0-9 volts 100mA (e.g. Norman type CT1)
N1	Mains Neon Indicator/NR/R
O1	Mains Output Socket & Plug/P438
TR1	Transistor (PNP, Si)/2N3703

Also required: Integrated Circuit Holder (8-pin) EF 722-2-8; Veroboard 0.1 inch matrix, copper-clad, 3¾" x 5"; Aluminum Box 6" x 4" x 2"; Terminal Block 2 amp 12-way; Mains Wire (3-core); Knob for VR1 JV18; Mains Input Socket and Plug P340; 16 6BA Nuts & Bolts 0.375 inch, roundhead; Twin Coaxial Wire lightweight (links box-to-roof and box-to-tank); Mains Plug 3-pin fused; Fuse 1 amp for mains plug. Total cost for the black box is under $25.00 after VAT & postage, from Electro Value; or $12.00 shopping around, NB. THIS CIRCUIT IS NOT FOR BEGINNERS! Inquiries about the black box should be sent to John Wood, 899 Kingsway, Manchester 20, England; enclose an international postal reply coupon please.

Addresses of Suppliers

Granges Essem, Leon House, 233 High Street, Croydon, Surrey, England. **Frampton Furguson**, Barton Road, Comberton, Cambridge, England. **Mitra Plastics**, Whittington Road, Oswestry, Shropshire, England, **Bricell Plastics** (polystyrene), Worsley Road North, Walkden, Worsley, Manchester 28, England, **Electro Value**, 28 St. Jude's Road, Englefield Green, Egham, Surrey, England (Their catalogue codes are given in the Black Box components list.)

Questions about the roof may be addressed to the National Centre for Alternative Technology, Machynlleth, Powys, Wales. International postal reply coupons must be included in all correspondance to John Wood or the National Centre.

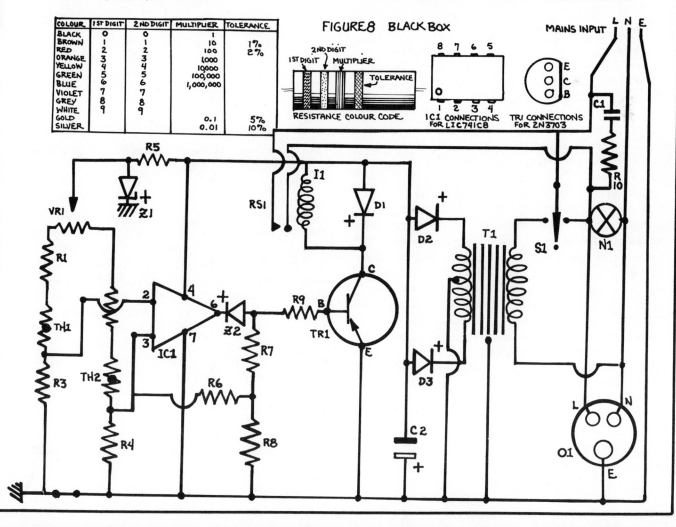

FIGURE 8 BLACK BOX

COLOUR	1ST DIGIT	2ND DIGIT	MULTIPLIER	TOLERANCE
BLACK	0	0	1	
BROWN	1	1	10	1%
RED	2	2	100	2%
ORANGE	3	3	1,000	
YELLOW	4	4	10,000	
GREEN	5	5	100,000	
BLUE	6	6	1,000,000	
VIOLET	7	7		
GREY	8	8		
WHITE	9	9		
GOLD			0.1	5%
SILVER			0.01	10%

RESISTANCE COLOUR CODE

IC1 CONNECTIONS FOR LIC741C8

TR1 CONNECTIONS FOR 2N3703

The Eco-Cabin

by Lance Bohlen

designed by Jim Bohlen

The eco-cabin is a unique structure, the shape being derived from a geometric solid called an icosahedron. The crystalline form is made up of 20 equilateral triangles. If a group of 5 interconnected triangles are removed, the shape of the cabin results. To aid in visualizing the structure, construct the model from Fig. 1. As is evident, the base or floor is a pentagon — 5 sided. It is interesting and convenient that any one side of the base is equal in length to any side of the remaining 15 triangles. In the actual cabin, the roof triangles are extended past the sides to form protective eaves.

This shape was chosen for a dwelling because of its simplicity of design, economy, ease of construction, great structural strength and maximum utilization of a minimal amount of materials. It has an advantage over "pure" domes in that placement of windows, doors and skylights is more conventional. Owing to its simplicity, most of the major components (foundation, floor and struts) may be pre-fabricated. This dramatically cuts down on construction time at the site. Another "plus" is that absolutely no power tools are required for construction, suiting remote locations. It is estimated that a well insulated eco-cabin will cost well under $1,000, even in inflationary 1975, complete with air-tight wood heater.

Tools

As mentioned before, only hand tools are necessary for construction. The required tools are:

> brace and bit drill with a 3/8" bit
> a **quality** crosscut saw, approx. 8 pts. per inch
> 4 foot level

> hammer
> shovel
> axe
> chalk line
> adjustable wrench
> screwdriver
> 12' tape measure
> staple gun
> carpenter's square
> protractor square (available at most hardware stores)
> bevel square
> cheap hard-point saw (for ripping and cutting plywood)
> bow saw (optional)

Materials

The most important factor in keeping the cost of your cabin low will be your ability to scrounge materials at the lowest possible cost. Although it is desirable to use re-cycled materials such as those obtained from wrecked buildings etc., many of us lack the facilities or capabilities to do it. An alternative is to scrounge in local lumberyards. Most lumberyards have a section reserved for utility grade lumber. It is usually in bundles of random lengths, although of the same stock size (2" by 4", 1" by 8", etc.). If you can obtain permission to pick through the bundles, you will find enough wood of suitable quality to fit your needs. Remember to keep the bundle orderly, so you can keep a good thing going! Here are some pointers to look for when sifting through the pile. Sight along the edge, and look for warp and straightness of grain. If the grain is very wavy, reject it. The same goes for a bad warp, unless it's near the end where you can cut it off and still have a good-size piece of wood left. Then check the knots. If

* minimum ECO-logical and ECO-nomic Impact.

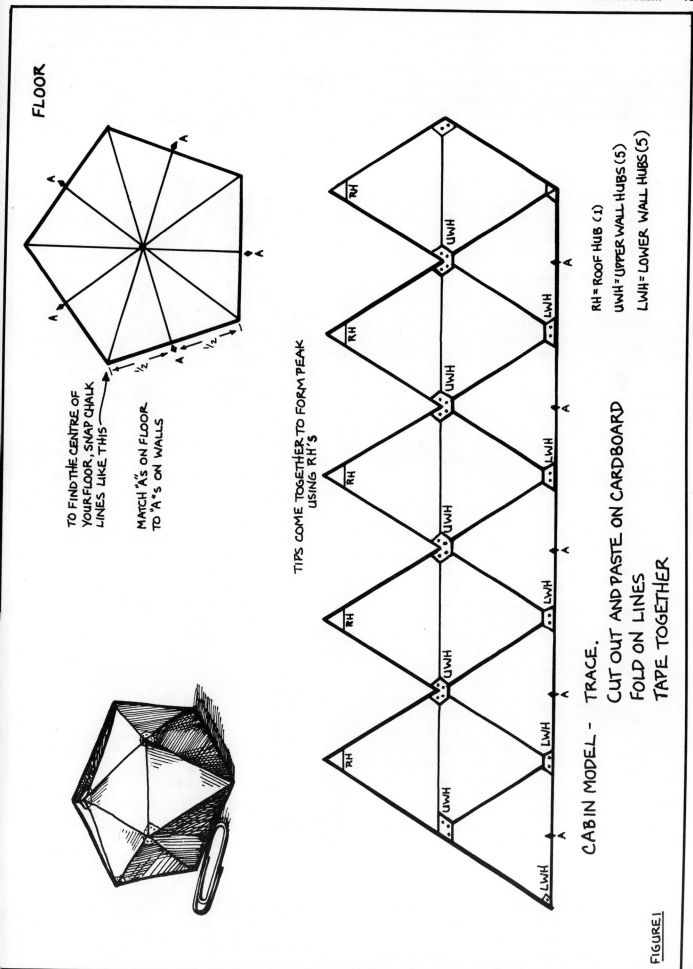

FLOOR

TO FIND THE CENTRE OF YOUR FLOOR, SNAP CHALK LINES LIKE THIS

MATCH "A"s ON FLOOR TO "A"s ON WALLS

½   ½

TIPS COME TOGETHER TO FORM PEAK USING RH'S

RH = ROOF HUB (1)
UWH = UPPER WALL HUBS (5)
LWH = LOWER WALL HUBS (5)

CABIN MODEL — TRACE.
CUT OUT AND PASTE ON CARDBOARD
FOLD ON LINES
TAPE TOGETHER

FIGURE 1

they are more than ¼ the thickness of the wood in depth, reject it, unless it's near the end. This criteria does not apply to sheathing material. Look especially for decay. If it can be cut out, okay; if not reject. Some lumber may be badly checked (split) on the ends. This is alright, if it does not extend too far up the board. Planer skips are okay, unless they visibly weaken the board.

Materials List

35 – 5" long, 3/8" diameter carrage bolts, nuts and washers
5 – 4' by 8' sheets of tongue and grooved ¾" plywood
15 – 8' long 2 by 4's construction grade (for wall struts)
250' lineal feet of 2 by 4's for roof, door, etc. (utility) 12' - 16' lengths
14 - 10' long 2 by 6's for foundation
1000 board feet of utility grade 1 by 8 shiplap (for sheathing)
1 roll of roofing felt
2 boxes (1000 each) 5/8" staples and gun
1 qt. roofing cement
2" and 4" common nails
chimney jack, vent, door hardware, rope, etc.
urethane or styrofoam insulation for roof
fibreglass insulation for sides and floor
windows
materials for outer skin

Construction of Foundation

Before you begin actual construction, decide exactly where you want the door and windows to go. If you want a large window oriented south, decide whether you want it slanting in or out. Use your model and sketch in the windows, door, and skylight. Then mark the orientation at the construction site.

The first step is to prepare the skids. The skids are two logs of equal length, on which the foundation is attached. Locate two logs approximately 15' long and over 6" in diameter. They should be peeled so no destructive insects are harboured. Next, adz or flatten one side to provide a level surface. To do this, sight along the log to find the straightest edge. Then snap two parallel chalk lines 4" apart. Use an axe to chip away the wood between the lines, sighting along the log as you go. When this is done, lay the skids on the ground, surfaced side down. Divide the skids into thirds. At each third point, cut notches about 6" wide and 2" deep. These are to accommodate the uprights posts that keep the cabin off the ground. The next step is to raise and level the skids. First, decide the height you want your cabin floor to be off the ground. Don't forget to take into account the thickness of the floor and joists (6¾"). Then take two pieces of scrap boards and nail them to the end of one of the skids as shown in Fig. 2. Swing them apart until you have the desired height, then repeat the entire procedure to the other side, making sure the skid is level. When that is done, dig 2 holes directly under the notches, deep enough to remove the sod layer and large enough to accommodate a rock with a flat surface at least 6" in diameter (cement pier blocks can be substituted). Make sure the rock is at least 2" above the surface. Then measure the distance between the rock and notch and cut and peel a post about equal to the width of the notch. If you find that the skid isn't perfectly level, shim the post at the notch (a wood

shingle works well). Repeat the entire raising operation to the other skid, making sure that the centre of one skid is

FIGURE 2

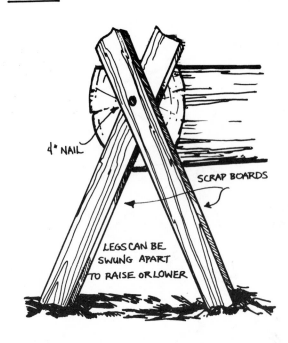

4" NAIL

SCRAP BOARDS

LEGS CAN BE SWUNG APART TO RAISE OR LOWER

exactly 4' 8" away from the other and that they are mutually level.

The next step is to prepare the perimeter floor joists. Select 5 ten foot long 2" by 6"s that are relatively straight. Set your protractor square to 54° and lay out five 9' lengths with 54° angles at either end. Place the joists as shown in the floor plan (Fig. 4), fastening the ends lightly, with 2" nails. Juggle the joists around until they form an accurate pentagon, then dig holes under the three points shown, and lay rocks and posts as was done on the skids. When this is done, secure the ends with 2 4" nails each (Fig. 3). Make sure the joists are level with respect to each other. A little precision and time here will save hours of frustration later.

FIGURE 3

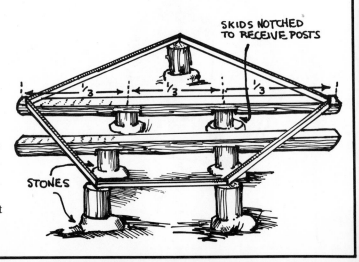

SKIDS NOTCHED TO RECEIVE POSTS

STONES

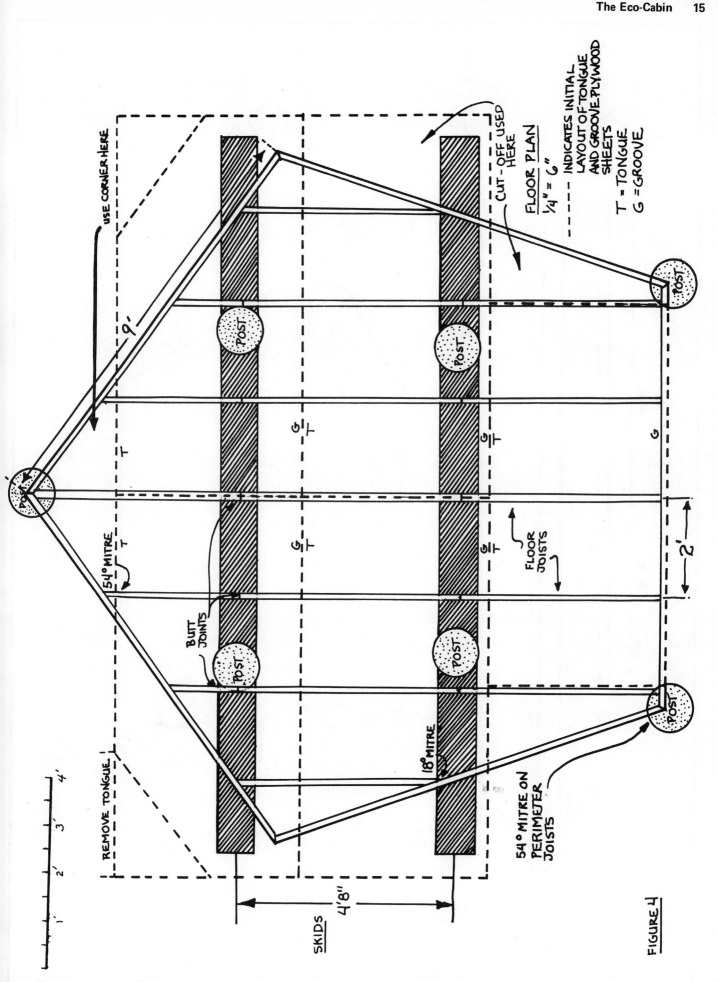

USE CORNER HERE

CUT-OFF USED HERE

FLOOR PLAN
¼" = 6"

INDICATES INITIAL LAYOUT OF TONGUE AND GROOVE PLYWOOD SHEETS

T = TONGUE
G = GROOVE

9'

54° MITRE

BUTT JOINTS

POST

POST

POST

POST

POST

POST

FLOOR JOISTS

2'

18° MITRE

54° MITRE ON PERIMETER JOISTS

REMOVE TONGUE

1' 2' 3' 4'

SKIDS

4'8"

FIGURE 4

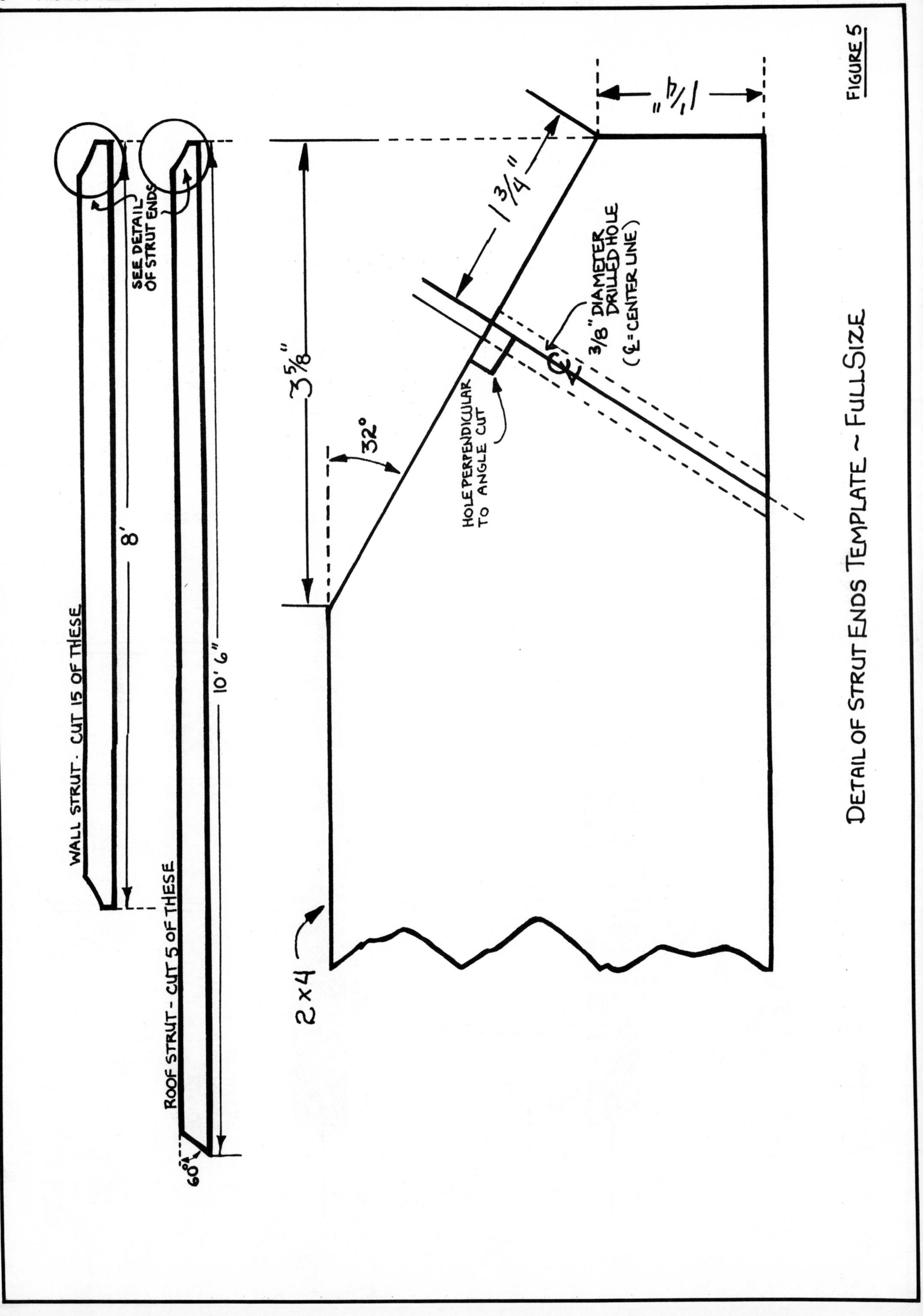

WALL STRUT - CUT 15 OF THESE.

SEE DETAIL OF STRUT ENDS

ROOF STRUT - CUT 5 OF THESE.

8'

10' 9"

60°

3/8" DIAMETER DRILLED HOLE
(℄ = CENTER LINE)

HOLE PERPENDICULAR TO ANGLE CUT

2 × 4

32°

3 5/8"

1 3/4"

1 1/4"

DETAIL OF STRUT ENDS TEMPLATE ~ FULLSIZE

FIGURE 5

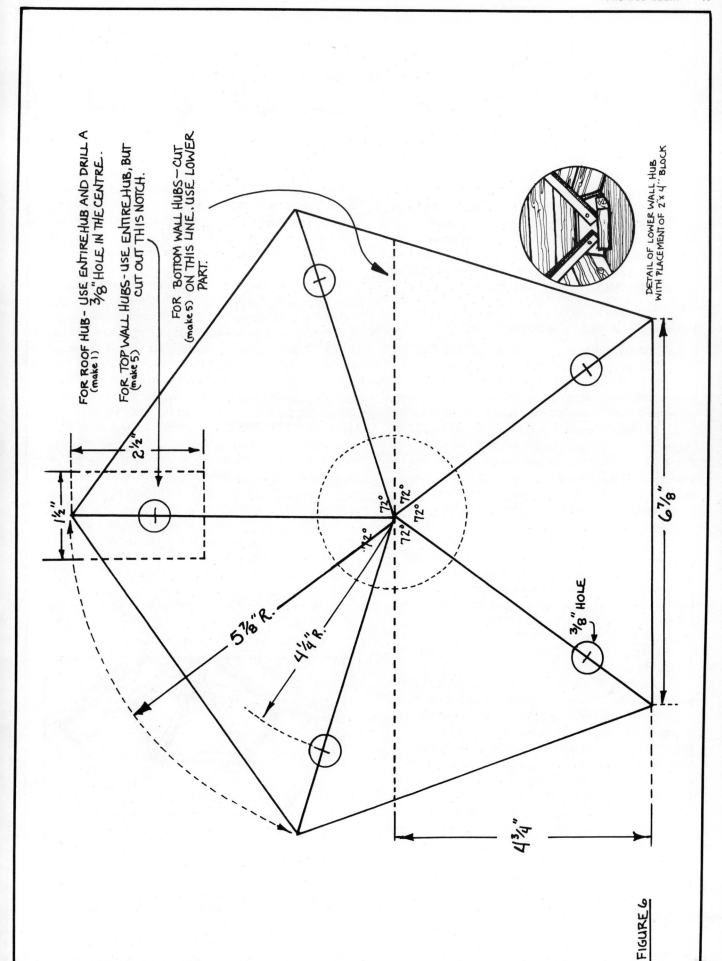

FOR ROOF HUB - USE ENTIRE HUB AND DRILL A 3/8" HOLE IN THE CENTRE.
(make 1)

FOR TOP WALL HUBS - USE ENTIRE HUB, BUT CUT OUT THIS NOTCH.
(make 5)

FOR BOTTOM WALL HUBS - CUT (make 5) ON THIS LINE. USE LOWER PART.

DETAIL OF LOWER WALL HUB WITH PLACEMENT OF 2"x 4" BLOCK

2½"

1½"

72° 72°
72° 72°
72° 72°

5⅞" R.

4¼" R.

3/8" HOLE

6⅞"

4¾"

FIGURE 6

Next, position the floor joists as shown in Fig. 4, and nail securely with two 4" nails. Notice that most of the joists (the five longest) are two pieces of wood joined at a skid. Here again, take time to level accurately.

We tried pre-fabricating the floor, which proved to be very time consuming. Besides, you have to be extremely accurate as one slightly curved cut can result in strange gaps in the finished floor. A better method, we found, was to simply lay the 4' by 8' sheets of plywood (as illustrated by the dotted lines on the floor plan, Fig. 4) and saw around the perimeter of the floor. Before you saw though, nail the floor with 2" flooring or common nails on 8" centres. You should use the cheap hard-point saw for cutting plywood, because the glue used in laminating tends to dull saws very quickly. Use the plywood you cut off to form the 4 remaining pieces of the floor (as indicated) and for the hubs. Don't forget to check for level as you go along.

Fabrication of Hubs and Struts

Cut and drill the hubs and struts as shown in Figs. 5 and 6. Two people can reduce preparation time here. The hubs can be drilled five at a time if they are clamped together Note: a hole should be drilled through the centre of the roof hub for a safety rope (which will be explained later). Two people working in harmony should be able to prepare all the hubs and struts in about 2 hours. The next step is all fun. Assemble the struts and hubs according to your model (Fig. 1). Place the lower wall hubs on the floor. Do not tighten the nuts until all the struts are connected and the hubs are straight. To connect the frame to the floor, first find the centre of the floor as shown in Fig. 1. You must spot the lower wall hubs accurately in order for all the angles to be true. To do that, measure exactly 85½" from the centre to all five points. Place the inside edge of the lower wall hubs centred on that mark, and nail them to the floor. Then block both sides of the hub with 5" long 2 by 4's and nail them too. A way to check the whole assembly is to check the top struts for level. Twist the hubs until levelling is achieved evenly around the perimeter.

Loosely bolt the five roof struts to the roof hub. Cut a pole exactly 137¾" long and nail a 2" nail halfway into the centre of one end. Insert the nail into the hole in the centre of the roof hub. Then hoist the entire assembly, fitting the roof struts into the notches of the top wall hubs, up until the butt of the pole rests exactly on the centre mark on the floor. Temporarily nail the pole into the floor, remembering that it will have to be removed later. Nail the struts to the hubs, then tighten the nuts at the peak. The overhang from the struts forms the basis of the eaves. Measure, cut, and nail the "rafters" as shown in Fig. 8. When that is done, the support pole can be safely removed.

Sheathing

Normally, one starts the sheathing with the roof, the reason being that once it's finished, it doesn't matter whether or not it rains, you can still work on the walls.

However, we did just that, and when it came to sheathing the very top of the walls, we found the space between the overhang and the wall was not large enough to swing a hammer! So, before you start on the roof, nail one board of sheathing around the top of the walls.

Before you begin to sheath the roof, nail a board of shiplap around the very perimeter of the roof struts to provide a nailing surface for the very ends of the sheathing boards. It should be mentioned that, in the interest of safety, a panic rope should be installed. Tie a ¼" rope, about 12' long, to a 7" long stout stick. Pass the free end through the hole in the roof hub, then nail the stick into the hub (to counter gravity). This rope should always be near the person working on the roof so that it can be grabbed at in a hurry. Start sheathing the roof from the centre of each section of the roof, working out to either side. Here again, two people working together should be able to sheath the roof in 2 days. Our method was to have one person on the roof marking the angles and nailing the boards, the other person marking the lengths and cutting. If rain seems imminent, you should waterproof the roof as soon as possible. First cut holes for the stovepipe "jack" assembly, skylights and vents as required, then nail the above on. A vent might be desirable during the summer but during the winter, it just lets out heat. An off-on device would be ideal. Install insulation if you want it (see section on insulating). A serviceable one-season temporary roof can be made with two layers of roofing paper. Start by sealing all the nails used to secure the vent, etc, with roofing cement. Staple the two layers of roofing material, starting from the bottom, overlapping 6". When you get to a chimney jack or whatever, cut an oversized hole, not so big that it extends over the flange. Then liberally cement the paper to the flange. If you get confused while roofing, just "pretend' that you are a drop of falling water.

When the roll roofing is in place, cut "shingles" out of the scraps about one foot square, and staple them to the

FIGURE 7

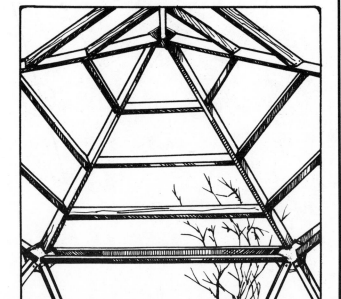

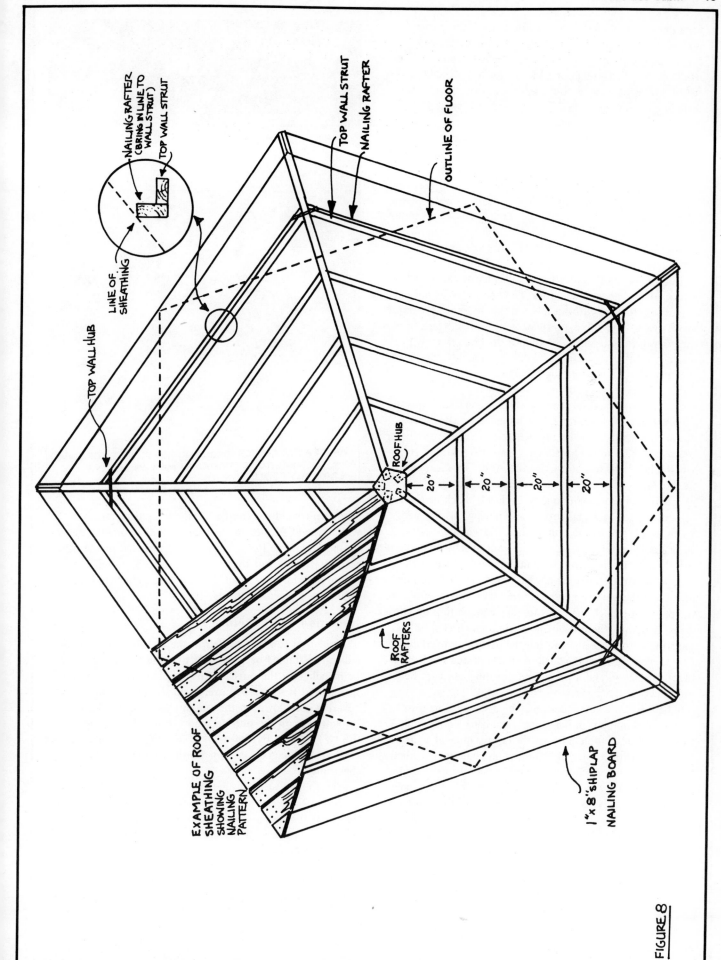

NAILING RAFTER (BRING IN LINE TO WALL STRUT)

TOP WALL STRUT

TOP WALL STRUT

NAILING RAFTER

OUTLINE OF FLOOR

LINE OF SHEATHING

TOP WALL HUB

ROOF HUB

20" 20" 20" 20"

ROOF RAFTERS

EXAMPLE OF ROOF SHEATHING SHOWING NAILING PATTERN

1" x 8" SHIPLAP NAILING BOARD

FIGURE 8

intersecting edges of the roof sections, from the bottom up, overlapping 6". When you are all done, no staples should be exposed except at the top. This temporary roof has proved itself through one Vancouver Island rainy season on two cabins, without leaking a drop. When installing a permanent roof, just use the roofing paper covered over by the roofing material. To waterproof the peak, cut an oversized hub (about 1' on an edge) out of ½" plywood, and bolt it on to the existing roof hub, using extra nuts and washers. Cement the nuts with roofing cement. The safety rope should be passed between the two hubs so it can still be used. Cover the whole cap with a layer of 4 mil. polyethylene film. A note about snow. The roof has been designed to withstand 40 pounds per square foot. We have measured 24" of snow on the roof without adverse effects. (1" of snow = 1 lb. per sq. ft.).

Before you start to sheath the walls, decide exactly where you want the windows and door. The door must be put in one of the triangles with the base on the floor, not the point. Leave one side open (not the door side) to sheath last, so you can conveniently use the elevation of the floor as a saw-horse in the event that you don't have one. It should be mentioned that any acceptable sheathing material can be used instead of shiplap. Shiplap was chosen because when it shrinks, you don't have to look at tarpaper between the cracks. For water-proofing purposes, sheath so the lap is under the board above it. Sheath from the top, where you nailed the first board earlier; from the bottom, on the other sections. Hack-saw the hub bolts just above the nuts so the sheathing will fit properly. A fast way to sheath the walls is to have two people hold up the board, one on each side. Each person is responsible for marking, cutting and nailing, his/her side. When you get to where you marked the windows, either leave a hole or build a window frame out of 2 by 4's and nail sheathing to it. One word of caution: never cut into the supporting struts! They are all that holds the roof up. The outside of the walls should be covered with one layer of roof-ing paper. Although the eaves are long enough to protect the walls from rain, there might be a wind which could blow moisture onto the walls. Just roll the paper out, overlapping 6" and working from the bottom up. Cut it and staple it in place. Insulation and a permanent covering can later be installed over the paper.

There are two ways a door may be installed. One is to fit two parallel uprights in the triangle and hang a door from them. The only problem is that the door is hung at an angle, so it closes with considerable force. This could be remedied with a hydraulic screendoor closer, but who wants to look at that? A better way is to build an upright frame and hang the door vertically. Because of the triangular shape of the doorway, a rectangular door wouldn't fit the frame. So, a door must be built to fit the frame. A serviceable door can be made out of shiplap lumber. Trace the outline of the door and transfer it to a few boards laid together. Make two thicknesses, one vertical and one horizontal, and nail them together. A little extra work and you can make a Dutch door (Fig. 9).

The holes that are left for windows can be temporarily covered with 4-mil poly reinforced with lath strips, or

FIGURE 9

AN IDEA FOR A DUTCH-DOOR AND FRAME. NOTE HORIZON-TAL SUPPORTS. TOP OF DOOR FRAME CAN SUPPORT CROSS-LOFT POLE.

permanent windows can be installed. Used rectangular windows will fit into the wall sections that originate at the points of the floor. They can be installed in the other sections as well, but they would have to be rather close to the floor or very small. Instead, triangular windows can be installed as shown in Fig. 10.

Insulation and Covering

Insulation can be installed in the conventional manner (fibreglass stapled between struts on the inside) or it can be installed on the outside. The problem with inside insula-tion is that it has to be covered on the inside and inside covering cuts down on the amount of room inside. If the insulation is on the outside, you can install shelving in the "V" formed by the struts (Fig. 11), plus you have an attractive woodgrain interior finish from the shiplap sheathing.

The roof must be insulated with rigid panels but the walls and floor can be insulated with fibreglass. First, find out what the insulation requirements are for your area, then obtain the amount of insulation needed according to the materials list. For the roof, nail lath strips that are the thickness of the solid insulation, horizontally spaced the distance of the width of the permanent roofing material nail spacing. Tack in the insulation and then nail the roof covering over it, be it shingles, roll roofing, etc. The principle is the same for the walls. Just make sure the paper backing (vapour barrier) on the fibreglass insulation is next

FIGURE 10

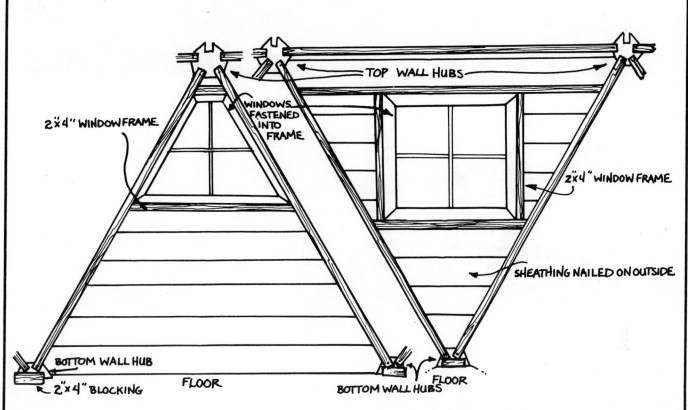

2"x4" WINDOW FRAME

WINDOWS FASTENED INTO FRAME

TOP WALL HUBS

2"x4" WINDOW FRAME

SHEATHING NAILED ON OUTSIDE

BOTTOM WALL HUB

2"x4" BLOCKING

FLOOR

BOTTOM WALL HUBS

FLOOR

to the sheathing. For the floor, buy insulation 2' wide, then press it up between the joists, making sure the paper backing is next to the floor. Covering can be just about anything as long as it's waterproof. Some ideas are: cedar shakes, cedar shingles, board and battens, and asphalt shingles.

Miscellaneous

The roof is high enough for the installation of a storage loft. Poles or dimension lumber can be used. Lay the pole from any 2 upper wall hubs, securing it with a 2 by 4 block underneath. Supports can be screwed into the roof struts or poles can go to the floor. Horizontal supports should be installed every two feet, nailed to the top wall strut. Planks may then be laid over the framework. Warning: it gets quite warm up on the loft so don't store any perishables or musical instruments there.

The cabin described has a floor area of 140 square feet, quite adequate for one person. By increasing the floor perimeter one foot in length for each side, an area of 172 square feet with an additional space provided in a ½ loft, appears adequate for 2 compatible persons. This is the practical upper size limit to the eco-cabin design. If incompatibility is inevitable, then perhaps 2 of the smaller cabins interconnected but spatially independent may prove to be more viable.

By using more basic structural elements, poles, etc., the eco-cabin could also serve as a crop shelter, animal housing

or tool shed, sauna, out-house, etc.

If you have any specific questions or want more detailed plans for insulating, roofing, and exterior finishing, write: Eco-Cabin, Greenpeace Experimental Farm, General Delivery, Denman Island, B.C. V0R 1T0, Canada

Paul Bailey

AN INTERIOR SHOT OF ECO-CABIN. NOTE THE SHELVING IS SET INTO STRUTS.

Subsistence Architecture

by W.C. Tinkess

Sod Construction

Sod construction, in contrast to either loose earth or excavated holes, is distinctive. The sod blocks were, and are, employed as actual building blocks. This method of structuring was found in the British Isles, Scanadinavia, and across northern Europe. Sod and/or earth was used by the Vikings, and remnants have been located in Greenland and Iceland. The earliest authentic sod structures, excavated in Newfoundland, date from approximately 1000 A.D.

The attributes of earth/sod — especially the insulation value — have·been known for some thousands of years. The insulation value of two inches of sod/earth is said to be equivalent to one inch of fibreglass.

In true sod construction, the use of wood was minimal, with the sole exception of the rafters. Pieces of sod were used and laid like bricks or flat stones. The sod dwelling was usually 12, 14, or 16 feet wide and 16, 18, or 20 feet long. The size was largely dictated by the economics of heating. Fuel was scarce: wood often had to be hauled and coal was expensive. Certainly there was nothing pretentious about sod buildings, but they were warm in winter and cool in the sultry summer. There were few window and/or door openings in order to make the walls as stable as possible. From 40 to 60 tons of sod were required for the average structure. The sod was chosen from a relatively dry coulee, where the roots were long, tough and fibrous. The breaking plough was used to cut a furrow from 12 to 14 inches wide; the sod averaged four inches in thickness. Depending upon the builder, the type of building, and the conscientious care expended, these long furrows were then cut into 24, 30, or 36 inch long strips. For true sod construction, the latter was preferable. In many cases the floor was excavated one to two feet below the ground surface. This was not always the case, but since it was only common sense to use the sod from the site itself, this was quite common. It also effectively cut down the height of the walls and increased their stability, and made it easier to construct when standing on a wagon bed or box. This lowered floor was also warmer and more draft-free. In careful building, the corners were squared and perimeter lines were drawn. The virgin sods were then laid, always **grass side down** using three 12 inch by 36 inch slabs together. These were laid as smoothly and as accurately as possible, with the cracks and crevices levelled and filled with a spade or shovel. Three or four layers were thus laid like bricks; the adjoining ends of the sods were staggered, and particular care was taken at the all-important corners. Next, a layer of sod was placed crosswise to bind and tie the lower longitudinal lengths. Then the lengthwise layers were resumed. These alternate layers were built up until the walls

FIGURE 1

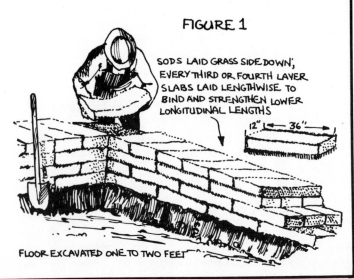

SODS LAID GRASS SIDE DOWN; EVERY THIRD OR FOURTH LAYER SLABS LAID LENGTHWISE TO BIND AND STRENGTHEN LOWER LONGITUDINAL LENGTHS

12"   36"

FLOOR EXCAVATED ONE TO TWO FEET

reached a height of six or seven feet. It was essential to have a gradual inward slope of both the outer and inner wall surfaces. This was roughly one inch for every foot rise in height. In this manner, the finished wall was about three feet thick at the base, and two feet thick at the top under the line of the rafter ends. With a six-foot high wall, stability was asssured and maintained, but there was a full seven feet of head-room because the floor was excavated one-foot deep.

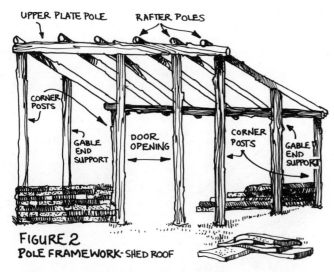

FIGURE 2
POLE FRAMEWORK - SHED ROOF

There were two methods of constructing a sod building. One was to erect an open frame work consisting of poles or posts planted at each corner, possibly at the appropriate door and window openings and perhaps the gable ends. These were then all joined together by the upper plate pole. The ends of the rafter poles rested **solidly** on this plate. Inevitably as the sod dried, there was shrinkage of the walls. Around both window and door openings this was of little or no concern, since these were easily re-plugged. The roof edges posed a more critical problem, because the walls shrank away from the roof or eaves. This meant that sod had to be continually cut to fit into and close the widening gap exposed. Since the

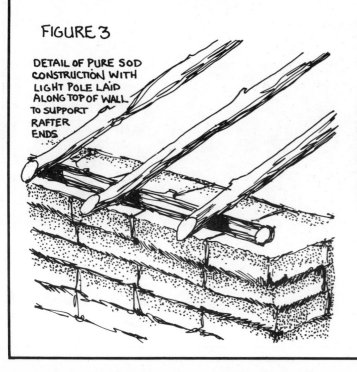

FIGURE 3

DETAIL OF PURE SOD CONSTRUCTION WITH LIGHT POLE LAID ALONG TOP OF WALL TO SUPPORT RAFTER ENDS

rafters rested upon the ridged plate, they could not follow the settling of the walls. The other method did not call for posts, with the exception of central ridge supports when a gable roof was employed. The four walls were "pure sod build-up", minus the dubious contribution of built-in supporting posts. Here, the ends of the rafter poles rested directly upon the top of the solid sod embankment wall. The very slight rise of pitch directed the roof pressure downward. In some cases, a light pole loosely laid lengthwise along the top of the wall supported the rafter pole ends, and in this way the pressures were somewhat more evenly distributed throughout the wall. With the inevitable shrinking of the sods in the wall, the rafter ends and the entire roof settled as a unit, ensuring tightness without awkward repairs.

The door and windows were framed in wood and then built into the sod walls in the planned spaces. Over the window/door openings, small lengths of poles or logs were placed to bridge the space and to support the final layers of sods.

The most practical and convenient roof for a small soddy was the flattish "shed" type. The front walls were from six to eight feet high, and the rear from five to six feet. The rafter poles were simply laid across.

In larger structures of dwelling houses, the traditional gable was attempted. The extra weight rested upon the end walls, pressing downward, and should the building be hurried and sloppy, tended to produce outward pressures on the ends of the side walls. So, when using the gable, practical experience dictated that a stout post be planted either against each gable and inside, or actually built into the gable end walls to support the heavy ridge log or pole. To assist in bearing the weight of the roof, there were one or two extra posts in the interior of the building to support the central portions of the ridge pole or log. By its very nature, a sod-layered roof has tremendous weight problems, and its supports had to be sturdy. It has been estimated that about one hundred pounds per square foot was the ideal. However,

Built in 1906, this is a very well constructed "soddy". Several essential details should be noted. The thickness of the walls reveals the gradual inward slope of both surfaces of the wall. And notice the box made of plank filled with earth for the stove pipe, and the cottage-type roof. This is free-standing sod construction.

FIGURE 4
FRAMEWORK FOR GABLE ROOF

The cottage-type roof illustrated in the first photograph ensured careful construction, and despite first impressions to the contrary, was ideal. The weight was borne equally by all four walls and the outward thrust was distributed equally as well. A minor benefit was that a much shorter ridge pole could be used. This, in turn, was supported by two posts planted inside the building interior under each end, with possibly a third being placed centrally. This roof had to be made in a wholesome manner to ensure satisfactory function.

No matter what type of roof was erected — whether shed, gable, cottage — the rise or the pitch was of necessity very gradual. Although the average builder lacked formal engineering knowledge, this instinctive low pitch minimized the outward thrusting pressures of the roof on the walls and held the sod in place securely.

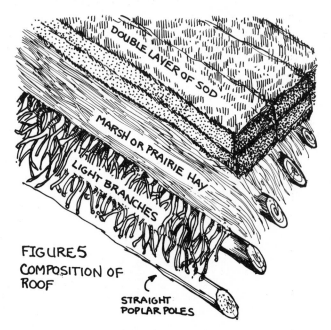

FIGURE 5
COMPOSITION OF ROOF

the settlers did not have the benefit of engineering formulas. From the river bottoms, the settlers obtained reasonably straight poplar poles. These were laid about 12 inches apart. Over the rafters was usually laid a layer of lighter branches and shrubbery. This in turn supported a layer of marsh or prairie hay or straw up to one foot in depth. Reasonable care was taken to see that the hay lay in a fairly even direction aligned from ridge to eave. When this was securely and evenly packed, then a double layer of sod was laid to make a total of eight inches of sod. Ultimately, this grew again as grass and further enhanced the roof's durability. Most of the literature and stories available mention the sordidness of these roofs, and that rain for a day outside meant about two days rain inside, as the roof leaked. Yet one wonders. With reasonable caution and care and without skimping on materials, such a well-made roof as outlined should give little trouble, except with prolonged tropical downpours.

A stable built about 1908. Several interesting features are evident. Notice the "sky-light" in the peak of the roof. This is an established homestead, with a later addition to the original stable to the side. There is a possibility that this was a post framework with sod walls, since the walls are straighter than expected. Located near Anglia, Saskatchewan.

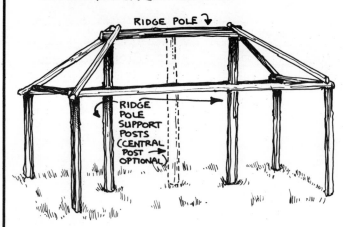

FIGURE 6
FRAMEWORK FOR COTTAGE ROOF

RIDGE POLE →

RIDGE POLE SUPPORT POSTS (CENTRAL POST OPTIONAL)

Baled Straw Construction

In this age of mechanical balers, it requires very little imagination to see straw bales as building blocks and to visualize a structure. These "building blocks" must be quite firm, well shaped, and well tied. Such blocks or bales lend themselves most suitably to either square or rectangular construction. As with common brick and/or concrete block, the joints are staggered. Half-blocks are needed at the corners and window and door openings. These can be made by gently untying a full bale, removing the unwanted portion, and re-tying the shortened bale to fit the smaller area. Depending upon the conceptualization of the building — its use and relative permanency — the construction methods may vary. For a basic crude stable or poultry shed, the bales may be laid directly upon the ground, and this way suffice for several years. A much better method is to use a foundation or several widths of concrete blocks, concrete patio squares, or stone and cement on the ground site. The walls can then be a double course of the straw bales, with every second course being "headers" as in any common English bond brick construction. This results in a substantial wall — thick, secure, and tight. Take care to use only the better bales as noted. Joints will then be quite snug. Cracks or spaces between the courses may be judiciously stuffed with fine hay or straw. The corners are built in the conventional way of all brick construction. Openings for door and windows should be anticipated and the required half-bales prepared. Such openings may be framed of heavy plank or suitable boards, set and braced into place, with the resultant straw block wall built up to and embracing the openings. **Plates** on the wall tops under the roofs may be standard **scantling**, pinned into the under straw bale layers with long spikes. Upon these plates rest the rafters, as in any usual construction. The "shed-roof" may be the roof of ease and choice, but any type of roof is acceptable. Such roofs may be either sawn lumber and shingles, or asphalt roll roofing. Other circumstances may dictate that the roof be made of poles covered with light branches and a 12-inch depth of straw or hay loosely combed, the whole topped with four to eight inches of sod. To prevent livestock from nibbling the walls inside and out, a layer of cheaper poultry netting may be stretched over both wall aspects. A further improvement and long-range preservation may be secured by a coating of stucco or cement mortar over the walls inside and out. To complete this, place a polyethylene film over the basic concrete blocks and under the first course of the straw bales. This, with the addition of the stucco/mortar, preserves the walls from moisture, both ground and rain. Conceivably, a well-built straw-bale walled structure, with stucco coating,

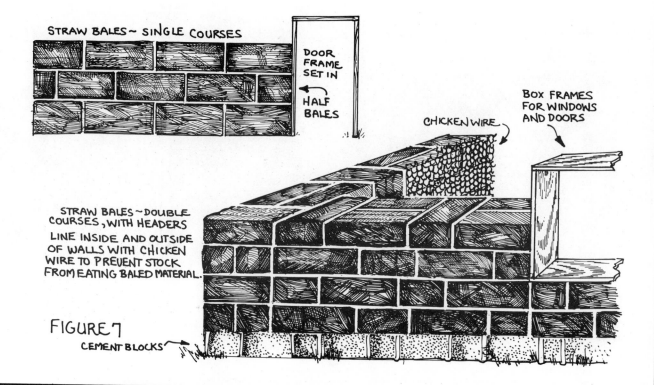

STRAW BALES ~ SINGLE COURSES

DOOR FRAME SET IN

← HALF BALES

CHICKEN WIRE

BOX FRAMES FOR WINDOWS AND DOORS

STRAW BALES ~ DOUBLE COURSES, WITH HEADERS
LINE INSIDE AND OUTSIDE OF WALLS WITH CHICKEN WIRE TO PREVENT STOCK FROM EATING BALED MATERIAL.

FIGURE 7
CEMENT BLOCKS

could serve as a house, it would be warm in winter, and keep cool during the summer. No interior framework is required, with the possible exception of one or two planted posts to help support the roof ridge, especially if an earthen roof is used.

Loose Straw Construction

Loose straw/hay construction follows the techniques of building with rammed earth. Two lines of posts are dug and planted to form and to outline the wall. These two lines may be from 24 to 36 inches apart. The posts themselves should be approximately three feet apart, and as high as the structure is planned to be. Poultry netting is stretched and stapled to the inner aspect of the outer line of posts, and to the outer aspect of the inner line of posts. In other words, the two stretched layers of screening face each other, separated by two to three feet of space. Should a realtively permanent structure be required, it is advisable to place either concrete blocks or concrete slabs on the ground surface as a beginning, with perhaps a layer of black polyethylene film. Loose hay or straw is then placed within the "wall" between the two lines of posts and securely tamped. The material is placed in as evenly as possible without bunching and firmly tamped into a tight hard mass. If care is taken, this should result in a tight substantial wall. The tops of the outer line of posts may be connected and joined by a plate, either of sawn scantling or pole. This, of course, is for the rafter ends to rest and to build upon. Either the shed or the cottage-type of roof can be built to alleviate the building of

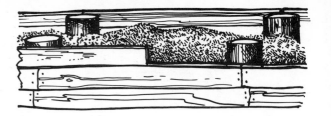

WHEN BOARDS ARE USED AS WALLS, SAWDUST MAY BE USED AS FILLER.

gables. To facilitate the placement of doors and/or window openings, several posts may have to be moved closer together and door/window frames nailed directly thereon, resembling a box minus the top and bottom.

In the case of a window, the straw is paced tightly underneath the "box". The screening should be stapled to the box frame and removed from the opening itself. This type of structure serves admirably for outbuildings such as poultry houses, goat sheds, small stables, and such. Incidentally, in place of the poultry netting or fencing, old boards, or even reasonably long straight branches or saplings may be used, all fastened to the respective faces of the posts. A coat of stucco or mortar may improve the usefulness immeasurably and prolong the life of the building. The interior can be covered with some form of plaster board, and the outer line of posts strapped and the covered with shingles, roll asphalt roofing, or siding to convert the building into quite a creditable cheap human home, serviceable for many years.

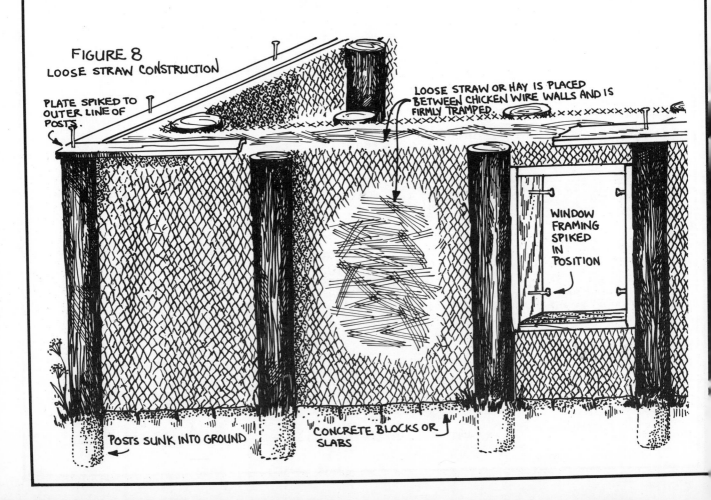

FIGURE 8
LOOSE STRAW CONSTRUCTION

PLATE SPIKED TO OUTER LINE OF POSTS.

LOOSE STRAW OR HAY IS PLACED BETWEEN CHICKEN WIRE WALLS AND IS FIRMLY TRAMPED.

WINDOW FRAMING SPIKED IN POSITION

POSTS SUNK INTO GROUND

CONCRETE BLOCKS OR SLABS

Post and Beam Design

by Norman Polster

When our family decided to build a house, we studied all possible designs, decided on post and beam, calculated structural members and built a model. I submitted our plan to Tom Michener, a mechanical engineer architect, for a structural analysis. From his study and Harry Parker's **Simplified Design of Structural Timber**, Wiley Press, 1967, $9.75, I learned some basic structural considerations.

Our house was designed for space for living, utilizing a 64 inch module, a 1:3 slope shake roof, 7 modules long and 4½ modules wide on two levels. Four inch square posts surround the house and 4" x 6" posts run down the centre.

The roof was designed to support 50 pounds on each square foot and the floor 40 pounds. The roof beams were 4" x 8" to span the 2½ modules of the living room. The beam height was then calculated as follows:

$$h = 3L\sqrt{\frac{w}{bf}}$$
$$= 3(13)\sqrt{\frac{250}{4(1600)}}$$
$$= 7.7 \text{ inches}$$

h—height of beam in inches
L—length of beam in feet
b—width of beam in inches
w—force on each foot of beam in pounds
f—fibre stress in wood in pounds per square inch
    (allowable stress is 1600 psi.)

If we had selected round beams, the diameter would have been:

$$D = \sqrt[3]{\frac{48\ w\ L^2}{\pi\ f}}$$
$$= \sqrt[3]{\frac{48\ (250)\ 13^2}{\pi\ 1600}}$$
$$= 7.4"$$

D— diameter of round beams in inches

If we had used round beams they would have weighed 240 pounds, whereas our rectangular beams weighed only about 100 pounds.

The vertical force supporting the beam at each end is:

$$V = \frac{1}{2}\ Lw$$
$$= \frac{1}{2}(13)\ (250)$$
$$= 1630 \text{ pounds}$$

V—vertical force in pounds

The compressive stress on the beam where it rests on the 4" x 4" post is:

$$c = \frac{V}{a}$$
$$= \frac{1630}{16}$$
$$= 102 \text{ psi}$$

c—compressive stress in psi. (allowable stress is 400 psi.)
a — area in square inches

The compressive stress on the central floor beams where they meet over a 6" x 4" post is:

$$c = \frac{1.8\ (1630)}{12}$$
$$= 244 \text{ psi.}$$

Note: 1.8 is the effect of both roof and floor loads.

The foundation under the central posts was made one foot square to support the roof and floor load of half the beam loads.

$$V = \frac{1}{2}\ (24)\ (90)\ (5)$$
$$= 5400 \text{ pounds}$$

Note: the total width is 24'.

The stresses parallel to the grain along the central plane of a beam are:

$$q = \frac{1.5V}{bh}$$
$$= \frac{1.5\,(1630)}{(4)\,(8)}$$
$$= 76 \text{ psi.}$$

q—stress in psi. (allowable stress for fir is 120 psi.)

If we had used an 8" diameter round beam:

$$q = \frac{5.33V}{\pi D^2}$$
$$= \frac{5.33\,(1630)}{\pi\,64}$$
$$= 43 \text{ psi.}$$

Our floor beams extend 5' to form a deck, the length length we might have extended the deck based on the allowable stress on the wood is:

$$L = 6.7h\sqrt{\frac{b}{w}}$$
$$= 6.7(8)\sqrt{\frac{4}{250}}$$
$$= 6.7'$$

Had we chosen a round beam this length would have been:

$$L = \sqrt{\frac{D^3 \pi f}{192\,w}}$$
$$= \sqrt{\frac{8^3 \pi (1600)}{192\,(250)}}$$
$$= 7.2'$$

Our tallest pole is 12 feet in the upper centre of the house and the allowable unsupported post 4 inches in width should not be more than 16 feet. The compressive stresses on the ten foot post in the lower centre of the house is:

$$c = \frac{V}{A}$$
$$= \frac{5400}{4 \times 6}$$
$$= 225 \text{ psi.}$$

c—compressive stress in psi. (allowable in fir is 1000 psi.)

There is another calculated allowable stress:

$$c = \frac{3E}{\left(\frac{L}{D}\right)}$$
$$= \frac{.3(1,760,000)}{\left(\frac{(10)\,(12)}{(4)}\right)^2}$$
$$= 590 \text{ psi.}$$

E—modulus of elasticity—psi. (for fir this is 1,760,000 psi.)
D—smallest width of post-inches

There are other structural considerations in building a post-beam house, especially the diagonal bracing and attaching the beams to the posts. We put bracing in all solid walls, interior and exterior. To attach a beam to a post we used 12" x ½" lag screws and, where two beams joined over a post, an 18" x 2" x ¼" metal plate on top of the beams.

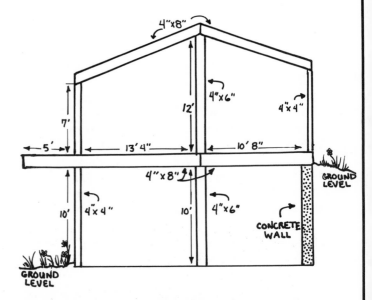

A Post and Beam Shed

by Jur Bekker

A couple of years ago I built an 18' x 24' post and beam shed. Since it has been such a useful building, I thought I might pass on the way I built it.

The shed was built to meet a variety of needs. At the time of building, we needed space to house our goats and to store hay. Eventually the shed will be used for wood storage and workspace.

After cutting down the trees in the area where the shed was going to be, I staked out the locations of the posts. To get a square, I used a string and checked the two

diagonals. When they are equal, the layout is square.

The posts stand on top of seasoned cedar foundation posts (1½' - 2' in diameter and 3' long) which are dug in, leaving about 6" above the ground. A 12" piece of 5/8" reinforcement rod, drilled 6" into both the foundation and posts, stabilizes them. For the posts I used 18" diameter fir and larch logs. I left the posts a little longer than needed. After erecting the posts, I snapped a horizontal (using a line level) chalkline on the posts and cut them off even, with a power saw. After the posts were up, I braced them

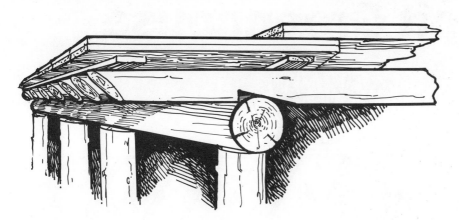

to each other and to trees and stumps with thin poles and 1" x 4"s.

For beams (horizontal members) I also used fir and larch logs (8" - 12" diameter.)

These beams were flattened where they sit on top of the posts. I drilled ¾" holes in the beams right over the posts. The holes go half way into the beam. A 7" spike was then driven into the hole with a heavy hammer. An old bolt, used as a drift pin, enabled me to drive the spike all the way to the bottom of the hole. This way, I did not have to use 12" spikes. For rafters, I used straight poles (larch, cedar and pine) with little taper, about 6" at the butt and 4" at the top. With a regular double bitted axe, I hewed a 2" wide flat face on one side of the rafters. This flat face later received the purlins.

Over the beams I reduced the rafters to the same thickness (determined by the diameter of the thinnest rafter), so that the upper side of rafters ended up even. If they are not even, the purlins will not lie flat and this will cause difficulty with the shaking.

I chose a 1:3 pitch because I used shakes on the roof. Any flatter roof and it would have leaked.

For purlins (the boards that lie on top of the rafters and support the shakes), I used 1" x 4" rough white pine. For raising the posts and putting the beams on top of

them, I used a tripod made from 15' cedar poles and a block and tackle.

I did not put skylights in the roof and now I wish I had. I have put them in another building and it is very simple. I used pieces of flat car window and put them in the same way one would put on a shake on a roof. The only difference is that I put in 1" wide strips of flashing material (galvanized iron or aluminum) bent in an S-shape. One half stuck in the space between the shakes, the other half supporting the glass.

Although diagonal bracing is stronger, I did not use it because it gets in the way of doors and partitions. I put in horizontal braces, which were notched in.

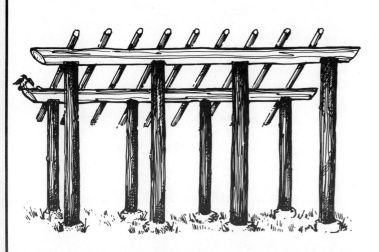

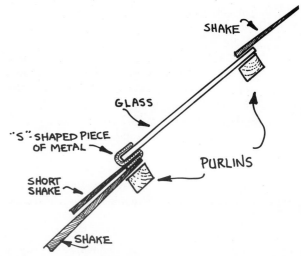

The Sunpit Greenhouse

by Hal & Judy Hinds

Wintering in cold temperate, or more aptly, intemperate, parts of the world is guaranteed to be much more endurable if you combine a bit of autumn with a lot of spring inside a sun-heated, sunken greenhouse or Sunpit. In a nutshell, a rectangular hole about 4 feet deep is dug with the long axis running NE and SW. A concrete foundation is constructed against the walls of the hole and covered with a roof insulated all around except on the SE side which is fitted with plastic. In the east end a half-size door opens out, and although you have to bend down to enter the Sunpit, a full-size door would mean an exterior stairwell that would fill with snow and ice. In the west end there is a hatch, hinged at the bottom, that is opened for cross ventilation. Earth-heat and moisture rise from the floor and solar radiation through the plastic front heats the interior. Insulated panels cover the plastic at night and during prolonged periods of stormy weather, holding in the heat.

Because the temperature in the Sunpit greenhouse ranges ideally between 35° and 70° F, it is classed as a "cool" greenhouse, a type of structure capable of favouring a wider and more practical spectrum of plants than the tropical or semi-tropical greenhouse built above ground with wall-to-wall glass. The five major types of cultural activities we have tried successfully in the Sunpit indicate its possibilities: we have grown salad greens of several varieties all winter long in broad flats; we have brought a great range of beautiful plants into flower; we have forced many pots of bulbs; we have over-wintered and propagated tender plant material, especially herbs; and we have started flowers and vegetables from seed for the summer gardens. The potential for experimentation and enjoyment is endless.

The Excavation

The excavation for the Sunpit can either be dug by hand or by heavy equipment. We dug ours, four feet deep, nine feet wide and about 19 feet long. We were in no hurry, and used the soil dug from the excavation to fill potholes in the driveway and construct an elevated ramp to the barn. All the larger-than-fist-sized stones were set aside and were later embedded in the mortar of the foundation. Two trenches were also dug, both sloping away from the Sunpit. One trench carries a plastic water line and an electrical cable from the cellar of the house, while the other holds a four inch drainage pipe to carry off any extra water that might enter the Sunpit. The drain pipe goes under the foundation wall and the electrical/ water line goes through the foundation in a 2-inch plastic pipe.

The Foundation

Once the trenches were filled, I squared off the excavation by delineating the corners of the forms with batten boards and strings. I decided to use the earthen sides of the excavation as the outer part of the form. In this way, I had only to construct the inner part of the form, carefully reinforced and braced across the centre, and a low form around the outer edge of the excavation where the final foundation would extend above ground level. I used recycled lumber for the foundation forms, plywood, old doors, old floor boards, etc.

Next was to pour the concrete, a big, one-day job. We rented a small gasoline-driven cement mixer for the event. We used a formula of 10 parts mixed sand and gravel to one part cement with enough water to make a rather runny mix. The stones from the hole were incorporated in the foundation as it was poured and one worker stood inside the excavation and pounded on the form to help settle the mortar around the stones. On the last loads we were careful to level the top of the foundation so that the sills of the superstructure would lie even all around. Just before the last batch set, I inserted two long bolts, thread end up, along each side. These bolts went into the concrete about two inches and were long enough to go up through the sill beams and be fitted with a washer and nut. Our mix of concrete cured rather slowly, but we were not in a hurry. It produced a strong set, and when the forms were removed about three weeks later, it could be seen that only a very few cavities were left unfilled by the concrete. It is best at this time to cover the floor of the pit with 3-4 inches of crushed rock to help drainage.

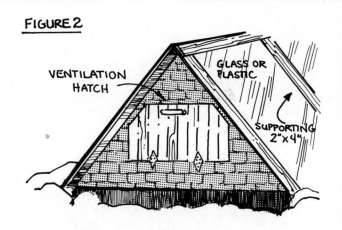

FIGURE 2

pit, the back side was boarded up and styrofoam pellets were used as insulation. Plastic sheeting was used liberally throughout to seal cracks between boards to keep the insulation from leaking out and as a vapour barrier. The ends of the Sunpit were treated in the same manner, and the door and hatch were built with a space for the pellets also. Styrofoam sheets would be easier to handle for the door and hatch, however.

The Panels

The insulating panels are styrofoam sandwiches. Three inch styrofoam sheets are bonded and bolted to two ¼-inch plywood sheets. The size of the panels will vary with the size of your Sunpit. We used five panels about 5 ft. by 3 ft. You might not need the carriage bolts if you do a careful bonding job. There are special caulking gun adhesives formulated just to bond styrofoam to wood. Make sure the adhesive and panel components are fairly warm before using. At first we tried fastening the panels to the super-structure with hinges at the bottom, but snow tended to pack in and spring the hinges, so it seems best in our climate to leave the panels loose. A canvas cover rolled down over the panels would make the Sunpit a little tighter and protect the panels from rain and snow damage.

The Interior

The success of the Sunpit is immediately apparent upon opening the door: the warm, moist, fragrant air; the mass of variegated foliage greens; the liberal sprinkling of such colours as cyclamen pink, delphinium blue, larkspur orange, snowdrop white, Christmas cactus red and primrose yellow. We used unplaned spruce and fir left over from the superstructure for the interior stagings.

On the left as you enter, underneath the plastic-covered southeast side, is a table three feet wide and four feet high, running the full eighteen foot length of the Sunpit. This table, or front bench, is supported by cedar poles resting on flat rocks, two poles on each corner and two front and back half way along. The entire structure was carefully leveled during the building and is anchored to the sills that rest on the concrete foundation. This bench is bordered all around by a six-inch wooden rim. Within the rim, forming the table top, are three-foot boards of random widths set apart about one inch for drainage. These boards are not

FIGURE 1

The Superstructure

The 4" x 4" sills were attached by drilling and counter-sinking the bolts, washers and nuts. The straightforward carpentry and the new, unplaned lumber that we splurged on made the job of building the superstructure move along very quickly. In one weekend the roof on the north side was boarded up and covered with tarpaper and shingles. The Sunpit really started to take on a finished look. The front side was covered with a layer of 6 mil plastic fastened down with lath strips. Later another layer was added inside producing a 2-inch space between. Inside the

FIGURE 3

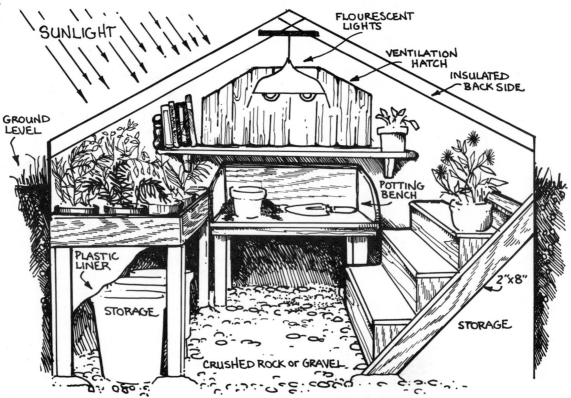

SUNLIGHT

FLOURESCENT LIGHTS

VENTILATION HATCH

INSULATED BACK SIDE

GROUND LEVEL

POTTING BENCH

PLASTIC LINER

STORAGE

2"x8"

STORAGE

CRUSHED ROCK or GRAVEL

nailed down, but merely rest on two by fours that are attached to the bottom of the bench rim.

The extensive area underneath the front bench makes an ideal storage space for pots, soil ingredients, compost bucket, germination chamber and bulbs for forcing. Care must be taken to avoid drenching these materials with water from the plants above. The problem is easily solved by underlining the front bench with a sheet of 4 mil polyethylene plastic. It is stapled to the underside of the front rim and slopes gently down toward the back.

In the corner immediately to the right of the entrance I have a tub of water under the water faucet. This tub was cut with a chain saw from the bottom half of a wooden barrel and serves admirably as a water reservoir for watering the plants and also as a repository for my stock of watercress that I replant into our little brook each spring. Without this tub I would have to drain the Sunpit water line back to the cellar during frigid weather and turn it on again each time I wanted to fill my watering can.

The staging under the north roof is in the form of bleachers, three long shelves about a foot apart running nearly the full length of the Sunpit. Four 2" x 8" boards running diagonally from the back sill to the floor and resting again on flat rocks make up the supports for the shelves. The shelves are ordinary boards, eight inches wide and fourteen feet long, carefully leveled along their length and supported by brackets cut 45°-45°-90° from the 2" x 8" stock. Two cuts produce two brackets. Near the top of the bleachers where the roof meets the foundation there is a fourth shelf cut and fitted between the diagonal supports of the bleachers. This holds small 3-inch pots with head-

room for about 6 inches of growth.

On the end of the Sunpit under the hatch I built a small potting bench, attached on the left to the front bench, supported on the right by another cedar post and nailed at the back to the concrete foundation with four inch nails. This useful little bench is about 2.5 feet wide, 2 feet deep and rises in the back about a foot. It is constructed of 1-inch plywood. Having sides, this bench serves very well to hold a quantity of potting soil at the back available for quick potting of rooted cuttings or for repotting. It is also a good work surface for starting seeds. Above the bench there is a shelf usually reserved for plants on their way to the house. Underneath is a small storage area for flats, glass plates, labels and other miscellaneous supplies.

Electricity in the Sunpit

Successful management of a Sunpit does not absolutely require the use of electricity. As a precaution, however, provisions were made for both supplementary light and heat. Fluorescent lights were installed the full length of the Sunpit about 2 feet from the ridge. Each fixture is four feet long and all are operated by a switch near the door. I use the top of these fixtures as a shelf for seed-flats once the seeds have germinated. On dull days when the panels are not removed from the front of the Sunpit, the lights are turned on. Also, occasionally during the period of our shortest days, the lights are switched on for a few hours in the late afternoon. In a sunpit without electricity, plant growth would necessarily be slowed down in sunless spells, but the plants could nevertheless be carried over until the brighter, longer days arrive. Some sort of lighting makes evening work possible in the pit, a most pleasant activity, especially in the dead of winter.

Because we did not know how well our Sunpit would perform during the many sub-zero nights of the central New Brunswick winter, we installed a small blown-air electrical space heater on the floor of the north side. It is controlled by an inexpensive but adequately sensitive thermostat set for 40°F. It comes on periodically during days of cold, overcast weather, but with the insulating panels left on and with the heavy insulation throughout the Sunpit, it takes very little supplementary heat to bring the temperature up. In fact, although the heater was unhooked inadvertently on more than one occasion when the outside temperature fell to -20°F, the max/min recording thermometer showed a low of 35°F and there was no damage to any of the plants. There is every reason to believe, therefore, that careful management will prevent a freezeup in the Sunpit greenhouse without the use of electrical power.

The fixtures for heating and lighting are wired into an electrical control box near the spot where the cable comes in from the cellar. The thermostat is located there along with several electrical outlets. I use other small electrical devices for special purposes, such as warming pad to provide bottom heat in a germination chamber, a small fluorescent fixture to provide light for tender seedlings, and a small fan for providing extra ventilation if the pit gets too hot in the spring. These specialty appliances could be dispensed with, although the range of cultural operations might be somewhat less extensive than mine as a result. In any event, none of these devices takes a large amount of electricity, and the total cost for running the electrical apparatus in the pit is less than we have spent in our indoor plant room in previous years. The effective use and conservation of solar energy makes the Sunpit far cheaper to maintain than a conventional greenhouse.

Sunpit Management

In the morning the Sunpit panels are taken off the plastic front as soon as the sun begins to lend its warmth. During our New Brunswick winter this is about 9 a.m. By about 10 or 11 a.m. the door must be opened widely for ventilation and by March the hatch must be opened by noon. This must be watched carefully or the temperature can quickly mount into the 90°'s (F.), a condition that would lead to undesirable soft growth. With proper temperature control, the cool moist atmosphere in the Sunpit eliminates some of the typical problems of indoor gardening. The plants do not become "leggy" or stragglystemmed even though the insulating panels may cover the plastic for one or more stormy days. Furthermore, pest damage is minimal because most of the greenhouse plant pests prefer a hotter and drier environment. Should mould present a problem, a garlic solution used in a sprayer is helpful. Over-crowding of the plants should be rigorously avoided and all dead material should be placed in a small compost area.

By late spring when the Sunpit is bursting with flats of transplanted seedlings, many of the semi-hardy plants and

maturing bulbs can be moved to cold-frames. And when the transplants have been put into the garden after the last spring frost, the Sunpit takes a well-deserved rest. It is not practical to use it during the summer because it would be very difficult to keep it cool enough and also provide enough light for healthy plant growth.

Cost

We whittled the cash outlay to a minimum by using local and recycled materials, by furnishing our own labor, by solving problems with ingenuity rather than hardware and by not rushing the job. We spent roughly $350 on such items as delivery of sand, cement, mixer rental, unplaned lumber, asphalt shingles, plastic sheeting, styrofoam and plywood.

Bibliography

Much of my inspiration and Sunpit planning came from the book, **Winter Flowers in Greenhouse and Sunheated Pit**, by Kathryn S. Taylor and Edith W. Gregg. It is published by Charles Scribner's Sons, New York and I believe the revised edition (1969) is still in print. This is presently the Sunpit enthusiast's bible. Kathryn Taylor also published an article on **Cold Pit Gardening** in Horticulture Magazine, autumn, 1974. Ken Kern, Sierra Route, Oakhurst, CA 93644 has also written about the Pit Greenhouse, chapter 9 in his **The Owner-built Homestead**, Kern's ideas are not entirely practical for north temperate pit greenhouses which must be dug deep into the ground and covered with insulating panels at night. He does provide a good plan for a halfdome Sunpit which could be attached to an existing structure and could actually provide some of the dwelling's heat, if carefully managed. For information on the plants suitable for the Sunpit, Kathryn Taylor's book can be supplemented by G. W. Robinson's **The Cool Greenhouse** (Penguin Books, 1959), out of print, unfortunately, but perhaps available through a library.

Indoor Composter Toilets

by John Shore

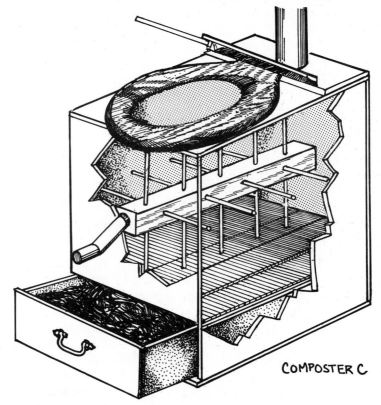

COMPOSTER C

People often wonder how we can go on growing food without putting something back on the land in return. Sure, the solar energy, gases and water needed for plant growth are freely available, but what about mineral trace elements and the humus needed for a good soil structure? If we don't want to find ourselves starving one sunny day, we must make sure that everything we take from the land is returned, and in a form suited to the cycle of decay, uptake, growth, harvest, use and decay once more.

Aerobic composting is one of the most natural ways of converting faeces, urine, plants and organic materials into safe fertilizer. The system is simple, inexpensive to build, uses no water for flushing and is suitable for use on a domestic scale. As with any natural system, many variations are possible, and these toilets are still experimental. Because of widespread ignorance of the role of nature in our lives, fear and prejudice are common attitudes and your local authority may not approve such a system.

Safety

Human and animal faeces and sometimes urine, contain organisms which could harm your health if reasonable precautions are not always taken. No system is perfectly safe, water closets do not prevent contamination of hands. Faeces and diseases are natural to our bodies; we all have to live with them both.

Construction

The toilet must contain the compost safely and provide optimum conditions for decomposition. You will need an insulated container which must be water and air tight. An air inlet and outlet, both screened to keep out flies must be provided for ventilation. Use the finest screen you can get, because some flies are tiny!

The outlet pipe must be insulated and provided with a cap to keep out rainwater. The cross-sectional area of the outlet must be larger than that of the inlet.

You may be able to find a ready-made container. I've been converting a scrapped refrigerator into a toilet. Take care you don't get an eyeful of harmful chemical when you cut away the pipes. You'll need to cut a hole in the top and make an air-tight lid, fit an air vent in the door and an outlet pipe. The shaped panel on the inside of the door can be replaced by a flat plastic sheet. The large door gives a good view of the interior. Inside you will need a number of grids to support the compost. If these are made with wood or metal sides they can be arranged to keep compost and liquids away from the sides of the composter, so that they can only fall into the tray that must be made to collect the finished compost. The grids can be 3/4" (20mm) tube spaced at 3" (80mm) centres. The main problems with fridge conversions are sealing the insulation against moisture penetration and ensuring that liquids flow into the tray, and do not seep out under the door (see Fig. 1). Two of my experimental units have been made from 1/2" (12mm) chipboard, with internal coatings of Bituminous and waterproof paint (the rubber-based paints supplied for roofing or water tanks are ideal). Marine grade plywood will be better than chipboard (which is still going strong after two years), but do use waterproof glue.

COMPOSTER A

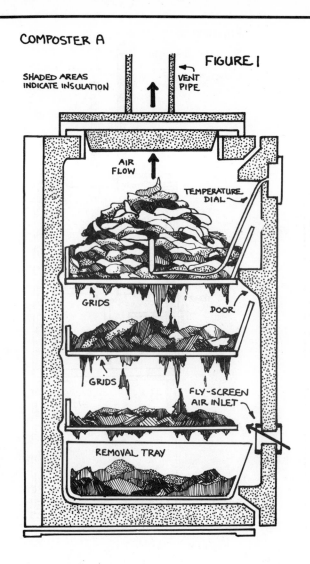

FIGURE I

SHADED AREAS INDICATE INSULATION

VENT PIPE

AIR FLOW

TEMPERATURE DIAL

GRIDS

DOOR

GRIDS

FLY-SCREEN AIR INLET

REMOVAL TRAY

FIGURE 2

COMPOSTER B

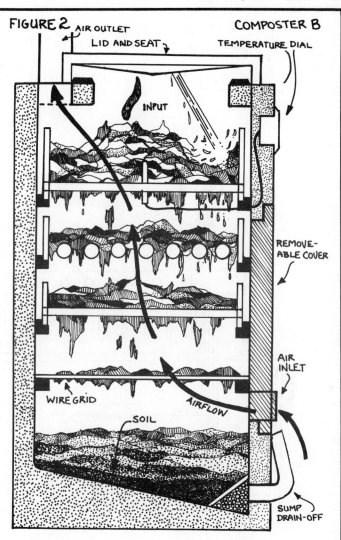

AIR OUTLET

LID AND SEAT

TEMPERATURE DIAL

INPUT

REMOVE-ABLE COVER

AIR INLET

WIRE GRID

SOIL

AIRFLOW

SUMP DRAIN-OFF

Fig. 2 shows a simple toilet which was built of chip-board, and insulated with 1" (25mm) expanded polystyrene sheet. It is 49" (1200mm) tall and 20" (500mm) square, fitted with grids like the fridge has. Before first using the toilet cabbage leaves are laid out on the grids to stop the compost falling through. A layer of soil is placed in the bottom of the toilet to absorb excess moisture.

Another unit has been built incorporating a stirring arm. (Figs. 3 and 4), but is rather complicated to build. It is made of wood and lined internally with 1" (25mm) expanded polystyrene, glued in place.

The stirring arm is turned each time the toilet is used, helping to mix and aerate the compost. A grid of tubes are placed in a curve just below the sweep of the arms. The stir arm is made of 2" x 2" (50 x 50mm) wood and 5/8" (15mm) dowels. Where the arm rotates in the sides of the composter; sleeves, cut from 2-1/8" (55 mm) PVC pipe are fitted to act as bearings. Discs fitted to the stir arm locate it within the toilet and help prevent leakage. The top of the toilet is removable and a deflector of flexible plastic/rubber is fitted below the seat to top urine reaching the front wall. The compost gradually falls through the tubes into the lower grid and eventually into the bottom compartment. The finished compost is scooped out after the cover, which also forms the step, as has been lifted off.

Small toilets like these will be suitable for regular use by one or two people. However, all the urine can not be added at the start, since there will not be sufficient compost to absorb it. The same situation might arise during a party. Fortunately urine is rich in nitrogen and makes a good compost heap activator or can be used direct as a liquid fertilizer. Therefore a separate collection of urine will sometimes be needed. (See the urinal on page 23 of **Cloudburst 1**.)

Figure 5 shows composter D, which is an improved version of composter B (Fig. 2). Since the unit is four feet high, a small staircase will be needed. Figure 6 shows a three-step unit. While this will enable you to use the toilet without much effort, it increases the area of floor covered by the toilet to 57 x 22 inches.

Figure 7 shows how to cut the components from an 8 x 4 foot and a 4 x 4 foot piece of ½ inch thick board. Ensure that the edges of each component are planed flat before gluing and pinning together. The cutaway drawing (Fig. 5) is fairly accurate in terms of dimensions. Think carefully about the design, the materials you can use, and the job they will have to do. If you can improve the design, that's good. Pay particular attention to the waterproofing, especially around the openings for the toilet seat and ventilation pipe. A good seal is also needed where the grid-supports are attached to

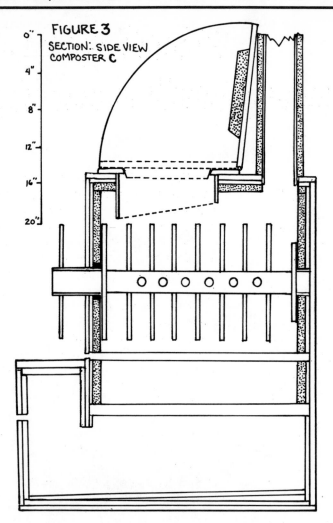

FIGURE 3
SECTION: SIDE VIEW
COMPOSTER C

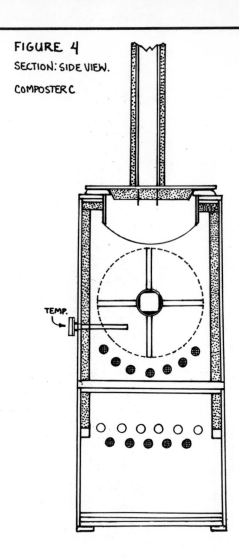

FIGURE 4
SECTION: SIDE VIEW.

COMPOSTER C

TEMP.

the walls and water may accumulate. The top of the toilet and the lid over the finished compost can be lifted off for access. Use a soft plastic or foam strip to keep these joints airtight. Externally the unit can be finished with panels of insulation.

Figure 5 shows the air flow through the toilet. Air entering through the screened inlet can flow through three apertures, which lead to three plastic channels (two-inch square drainpipe cut in half will make fine channels), bolted to the inside front of the toilet. Two inch by ½ inch slots cut in the sides of the channels allow air to escape and circulate underneath the grids. The slots are placed close to the wall, just beneath the grid-supports, so that compost cannot block them up. One channel is longer than the others and allows air into the upper part of the toilet. The lower ends of the channels are blocked off, so that compost cannot force its way up. The grids shown in figure 5 are made from metal or strong plastic angle.

Some people don't seem to care about pathogen survival — they are quite happy to either dig faeces straight into their gardens, or compost it on the garden heap. One simple way of "cooking" the compost before you take it out of the toilet (if you have access to an electricity supply) is to put a very carefully insulated heater element in the toilet, say just under the three air channels in the composter(Fig. 5). A soil-warming cable would be quite good. Then you could switch

on and off whenever you wanted, perhaps just to cook the compost before use, or perhaps only on nights in winter. The cable could also be timeswitch controlled.

Composting

Ventilation of the toilet has to remove odours, water vapour and provide oxygen for aerobic decomposition. The compost must be kept warm and moist, but not too wet, or pore spaces block and anaerobic conditions occur. If too dry, crusts will form, limiting aeration and microbial activity Decomposition is slow at low temperatures.

Micro-organisms (bacteria, fungi and moulds) feed on the materials, transforming them through molecular changes into nutrients suitable for uptake by plant roots. Because living organisms use about 30 parts of carbon to each unit of nitrogen, the amount of carbon to nitrogen (C/N ratio) in the materials change during the process. The carbon is metabolised for energy and the nitrogen is conserved as tissue. By this process materials with high C/N ratios (straw 128:1; potato tops 25:1; grass cuttings 19:1) can be reduced to the 10:1 favoured by plant roots. Plant and organic materials compost best if they have been finely shredded to increase surface area and help mixing. I strongly recommend doing this.

Bacteria such as E.coli are normal inhabitants of the gut or large intestine, but can be harmful given access to other parts of the body. Diseases like typhoid, intestinal worms and the much more common Salmonella food poisoning organism must be destroyed during the composting process. These organisms can be killed by heat coagulation of their proteins or by hostile environmental conditions and bacteriophages. The first method is very quick (E.coli die within 1 hour at 55°C) but the second may take 12 months. Since we are not heating the compost artificially we must retain the compost for at least a year. Weed seeds can be destroyed either by premature germination or by protein coagulation (40-60°C).

The analysis of compost from my first toilet showed a C/N ratio of 9.1:1; 1.82% Nitrogen, 3.94% Phosphate and 1.73% Potash. Compared with other available compost-products this has a very high phosphorus and potash and an average nitrogen content.

These are only suggestions for building experimental units. If you are not able to build a strong, water-tight toilet and look after it carefully, play safe and don't try. The process and the toilets are described in greater detail in my handbook, **Aerobic Composter Recycling Toilets.** If you want more information write to me: 23 Park Street, Taunton, Somerset, England.

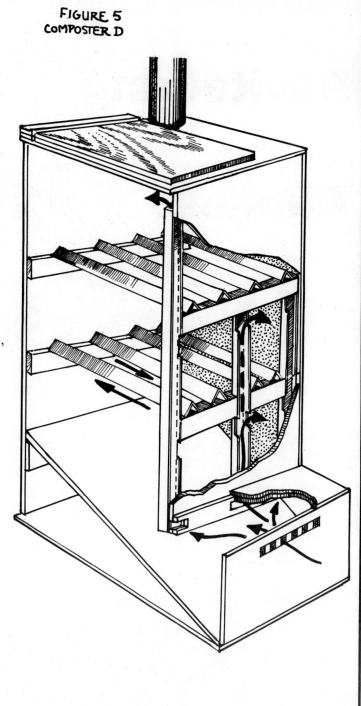

FIGURE 5
COMPOSTER D

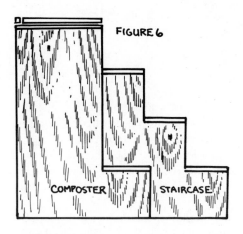

FIGURE 6

COMPOSTER   STAIRCASE

FIGURE 7
CUTTING PATTERN;
DIMENSIONS IN
INCHES.

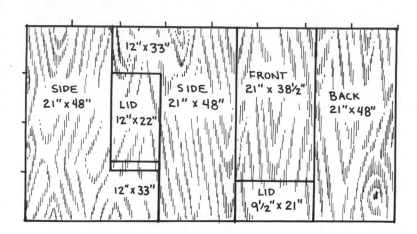

SIDE
21" x 48"

12" x 33"

LID
12" x 22"

SIDE
21" x 48"

FRONT
21" x 38½"

BACK
21" x 48"

12" x 33"

LID
9½" x 21"

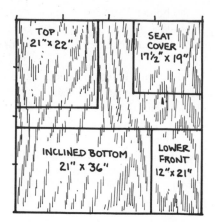

TOP
21" x 22"

SEAT
COVER
17½" x 19"

INCLINED BOTTOM
21" x 36"

LOWER
FRONT
12" x 21"

Revitalizing Wood Ranges

by Kurt Boyer

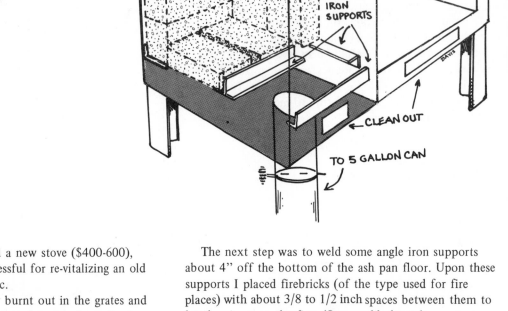

For those who can't afford a new stove ($400-600), here's a method I found successful for re-vitalizing an old one, with burnt out grates, etc.

Most old stoves are usually burnt out in the grates and the cast iron pieces which protect the oven from direct heat of the firebox. We have an old Fawcett stove in which one grate was shot and part of the oven protector was also burnt out. (Many were the cookies burnt on one side and raw on the other.)

I removed the grates and all the supporting iron as well as the oven protectors. Because I wanted a large firebox, I decided to use most of the ash pan space as well. In the bottom, upon which the ash pan used to sit, I cut a 6" hole and through this passed a 6" stovepipe which went through the floor and into the top of a 5 gallon drum under the house. This formed my draft and ashpan. In the pipe I made a tight fitting butterfly valve (like in a carburetor on an automobile) with which the draft can be regulated.

The draft pipe extens outside for two reasons. First is that if a fire burns air from inside the house this air must be replaced and the only way it's going to come into the house is through cracks around windows and doors. This sets up unpleasant drafts within the house. With the pipe coming directly into the firebox, the fire burns this air only. Secondly, this setup makes it easier to clean the ashpan outside rather than walking through the kitchen with a bunch of dusty ashes.

The next step was to weld some angle iron supports about 4" off the bottom of the ash pan floor. Upon these supports I placed firebricks (of the type used for fire places) with about 3/8 to 1/2 inch spaces between them to let the air up to the fire. (One could also take a masonary drill and put many holes in the bricks.) These took the place of grates.

Then I lined the interior of the firebox with more firebrick. Finally I mixed up a "mud" of ½ silica sand and ½ fire clay and used this to plug up the old draft on the side of the stove and all other holes and cracks between metal and bricks.

This firebox loses very little heat and burns with a lot of blue flame, emits very little smoke (smokes only when lighting up or if closed down completely with wet wood) and gives a very hot fire to the top surface. Also the brick now protecting the oven, insulates just to the right amount giving an even temperature throughout the oven. It will also hold fire for 4 hours or so if closed down.

A small hole (should have a cover) below the "grate" bricks allows the ashes to be scraped into the draft pipe and thus to the 5 gallon ashpan (which only needs changing every 2-3 weeks in the winter when using the stove 12 hours/day.)

I think if someone wanted to, they could build a stone or tile cookstove (tile would clean easier) with a brick lining. The simplest method would be to use a surface from an old cookstove and make the rest of brick and tile. A stove pipe oven would simplify matters greatly.

An Outdoor Rock Stove

by Richard Eichenauer

In the summer we spend most of our time outdoors and find it especially convenient to do all cooking, baking, laundering and canning outside the house. The house not only remains cool that way but we are also in fresh air and don't have to be quite so pedantic with water we spill, cherry pits we spit and wood chips that fly. For this we needed an efficient outdoor fire arrangement. Some people put an old kitchen range out and use it until it rusts out. We came up with the rock stove described in the following pages. It is practically built with waste materials, cement and firebrick excepted, although some items may have to be bought from a junk dealer by others. But I would say that in no way would the cash outlay exceed $70 and will probably be as little as $30, while any old stove these days costs at least three times that much and won't do half the job this one will.

I will describe the stove I built and give alternative solutions for parts that may be found in your dump and junk yard. Take all measurements and methods as approximations and keep in mind that you want to build your own stove and not mine. My present one can stand some improvements and they have been considered in the text.

List of Materials:

1. Pile of rocks, angular rather than rounded, and granite or similar hard, sound rock rather than shale.
2. Pile of sifted sand without much silt or other organic materials.
3. Depending on the size of your stove and chimney, and assuming free form construction, about 4 to 6 bags of Portland Cement, type I.
4. Two bags of lime to be mixed into the mortar as needed where you want the mortar more sticky, but go sparingly on it, it weakens your mortar and makes it only stickier to glue the rocks together without much weeping of joints. I don't think much of the ready bag-mixed "Masonry Cement". Portland Cement is far stronger for the purpose. Any surplus lime can go into your compost heap.
5. Twenty firebricks of the 4½" x 9" x 2" size — unless you have really sound rock like basalt.
6. 2' x 4' piece of steel plate ¼" thick or similar for the fire grate. Several other scrap pieces of heavy gauge steel can be used instead, if one solid piece is unavailable.
7. Stove top from an old kitchen range with removable round insert plates. This too can be a solid piece of steel plate, as pots should never be exposed to open fire — they will stay cleaner that way.
8. A few pieces of 2" or 3" angle iron or old leaf springs about 30" long for the rock support of smoke stack above the firebox.
9. Old water tank or 10, 13 or so gallon oil drum for an oven drum. The drum should be at least 2' long and have a diameter of no less than 14". Water tanks and 13 gallon (tall type) oil drum are just fine.
10. Two old oven doors from wood, gas or electric range (as can be found in every dump) for ashpit and firebox doors.
11. One round home-made oven door with hinge to be attached to the opening of the oven drum. An old big enameled lid or a nice wooden one with a metal inside and some insulation in between will do fine.
12. Optional home-made damper of 3/8" rod and piece of heavy gauge sheet metal, like an old lawn mower blade.
13. About five to ten 5 gallon old oil buckets (from any dump, garage or logging work shop) or similar cans to be used as smoke stack inside the chimney. Commercial flue lining can be used too — but will cost a lot of money.

14. One or two square feet of ½" hardware cloth to be used as a spark screen at top of chimney opening.

Materials for the building form if one is being used:

A pile of 4 to 7 or 8 feet long 1" boards, about 12 to 20 stakes about 6' long (scrap 2" x 4" can of course be used), about 1 pound of shake or box nails 2½" long and some old wire for ties (Fig. 1).

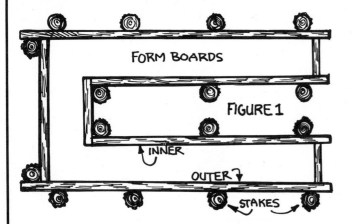

Building Details

Footing and Base: As in Fig. 1, a U-shaped trench about 1½' deep (depending on your ground frost depth) is dug wide enough to accommodate the form for the footing of the walls of about 9" to 12" thickness. If dug into clay, no form for the footing is needed, but the stakes for a form for the walls above ground can be pounded into the ground beside the footing when it is just up and above ground level.

The stove can be built without a form, but I prefered a form to keep the whole structure in line and hold fresh mortar in place. I also like a form to give a structure like this an even shaping and taper, usually concave, broader at the base and narrower towards the top. That makes for stability and eliminates totally the worry about plumbness.

The form can be built quite flimsy and improvised since the rocks lean only lightly against it. This is not a high-pressure commercial "bulge and bust" poured-concrete form. Not all boards (and definitely not each point with a backing stake) have to be nailed, only where the nail is needed to hold the board in place and up. The rocks will press the boards lightly against the stakes and keep them there. This will make it much easier later when the form gets removed, particularly the inside form. Tie wires or short nailed tie boards I use only above the wall. No ties go through the wall or will be incorporated in the rock and mortar — though that could be done. Stakes could also be braced from the outside with another set of stakes pounded slant-wise into the ground, but this kind of thing gets in the way when dancing around it with heavy rocks in one's hands. I usually combine a couple of methods, improvise and wiggle my way through.

As I lay rocks and mortar upon the footing I insert always one more board on all sides as one round of rock is completed. That way a high initial form structure doesn't get into the way of rocks and fingers; needless to say, the heaviest rocks go on the bottom courses. Build this U-

shaped base up to a height of about 18" and then remove the inner form, boards and stakes and place the ashpit floor slab into the centre of the U, curving the floor up at the closed end like in drawing cross-section A. That will make it easier to remove ashes later on. At the open end we can now incorporate a hinge provision for the ashpit door into the soft cement. An old oven door has at the bottom hinge pins to the sides that I inserted into the side walls at the beginning of the wall building, leaving a little gap in the form boards at that point. That was the easiest, but a piece of sheet metal or other suitable door on simple strap hinges will do too. Just insert the strap hinges into the soft cement slab. I made a weak mix concrete batch for that slab with a fairly smooth surface. Ash removal is easier on a flat surface with a square shovel than on uneven rocks, but a rock floor will do also.

Firegrate: We are now at an 18" level all around the U and can lay the firegrate into a bed of mortar on top of the open end of the U walls. Whatever pieces of scrap metal are being used, it suffices to have them supported by about 2" on either side of the wall. Too deep a penetration into the rocks might crack them apart through buckling and expansion during heat. My grate is a solid ¼" steel plate, 2' by 4', scrap from a logging repair shop, without any holes or slats for air intake from below or for ashes to fall through. Our air comes from the front opening, where until now I have not installed a door. We burn a lot of scrap wood from old structures and the woods. They are often oversize pieces and stick out the firebox, being supported at the other end by a nearby bench. We all hop and dance about it with pots of hot stew in our hands. Ashes are shoved to the rear where there is a big gap between the grate and flue down to the ashpit, where they collect until the garden or the compost heap are ready to receive them. There is lots of space underneath the grate for the ashes.

If you make the grate out of several smaller pieces of heavy gauge steel, the gaps between them will provide an air intake if you close the front opening of the firebox with a tight fitting door. You then provide some air holes in the bottom door of the ashpit — just like a regular kitchen range is built. For an outside stove like this, the leakiness of the door fittings are usually enough for air to get in.

Firebox: Now a collapsible box can be made, about 18" to 20" wide and about 30" to 48" long, depending on the size of stove top you have managed to scrounge and on the size of your fire grate. This box is set onto the grate and takes for the time being the space of the future firebox. And between this box and the outside form boards, we have again our form to go on with the rock laying. But on the inside of the wall, we now place the 10 firebricks (or so) on either side, and fill with mortar and rock the remaining 6" to 8" behind them. I placed my bricks right tight to each other without mortar between the bricks themselves. I also used the 1" thin bricks and a couple show cracks, but they are standing up fine, after seven years of hard use. I recommend now 2" thick brick. (This kind of lining can always be replaced after 20 or so years, if necessary.) The mortar around the firebox can be improved through the addition of fire clay, which I did not have and did not do.

If you have very sound rock, that will not shatter in a hot fire, you can use it instead of firebrick. Basalt supposedly is such a stone, a dull black beautiful stone of volcanic origin, but very rare in our area. The advantage of the brick lining is, that if it really wears away someday, it is just those 2" and the lining can be replaced, while rocks usually would penetrate deep into the wall and the whole wall section would have to be done over again.

Oven Column: An easy collapsible box on stilts can now be set between the grate and the enclosed inside U cavern. It again makes with the outside form the space into which rocks and mortar can be laid up towards the point where the drum is going to rest. Such forms can be quite improvised and escape words totally, since you are building in curves and slants and tapers, but unless you have imagination you won't tackle this kind of thing anyway. Just make sure that you remain with about 3" to 4" of open space around the oven drum, when it is set in place; that means drum diameter plus 8" is the lower inside of your smoke stack.

Stovetop: We are now at about a 27" level off the ground all around and are ready to install a bunch of metal items.

Above the grate area goes, again on a nice mortar bed, the stove top from an old kitchen range. Ours is a 32" by 24" cast iron one with four 9" and two 8" holes with removable plates. A special feature on this one is that all crosspieces and bridges, that hold the round plates in place, are also removable and so the whole stove top (except the basic rim) can be removed and the fire openly enjoyed. This has given us many an evening with guitars and drums, kettles and pots giving slowly away to open flames and smoke chasing the mosquitoes. Search a little and you may be just as lucky.

If you can't find an old stove top at all, a solid piece of steel plate will do too. It will have the advantage that the pots and pans will not be exposed to the open fire and so will stay much cleaner, although a frypan or waffle iron will take a little longer to heat up.

This stove top is either going to be the very top of the stove at this point or it can have a shoulder of about 4" on either side, the coping of the rockwall. If you make a shoulder, provide a V-groove between it and the metal-plate, so that the coping won't get disjointed when the metal expands. We have the V-groove and the shoulder, and support on it big canning pots and laundry tubs when some of the stove top is still taken up by kettles and stew pots. This is a great advantage instead of lifting heavy and hot boilers off and on.

Rock Support: Next to the stove top goes the rock support, a few pieces of heavy metal about 30" long, that will support the rock above the fire box where it will form the smoke stack. I used a wornout chainsaw bar and an old leaf spring. The chainsaw bar got soft in the heat and is now drooping in a half-elliptical shape down into the firebox, without doing any harm, in fact prventing sticks of fire wood being shoved down into the ashpit. The

spring is standing up fine. So either old leaf springs or some length of heavy gauge 2" or 3" angle iron will do. These pieces sit in mortar right next to the stove top and lay about 3" to 5" into the rock walls on either side, having firebrick on the inside underneath.

Oven Drum: Our oven drum sits about at the height of the firebox with flames drawing right against the metal. This seems a mistake, for it heats the oven unevenly and one has to watch and tend the fire carefully to get satisfactory results with breads etc. We think now the oven drum should be higher in the smoke stack at about chest height. That will circulate the heat evenly around the drum and the oven can be tended without stooping. Also the need for a damper will probably be eliminated.

Our drum is an old cut-off water heating tank of 14" diameter and about 30" long. We feel that is about minimum size of diameter. Old heavy gauge oil drums of between 10 and 20 gallons will do the job too. There are the 13 imp. gallon tall type oil drums that seem just about ideal for the job; although they're not that heavy a gauge sheet metal, they are of heavier gauge than most commercially fabricated stoves and will last at least as long, especially since they are not directly exposed to very hot flames.

Old oil drums may need a bolt or two at the closed side with it suspended into the rock wall, as the old oven drums from the Hudson's Bay Company used to be, while water tanks come quite long and can be laid right into the wall for about 2" depth. Although they don't pick up much heat in the rocks, the shorter suspended oil drums will be exposed with their back to the hot flue air and smoke.

Whatever drum you use, set it about 4' or about chest height above the firebox, back into the wall or suspended on one or two bolts (one bolt in the exact centre makes them quite easily removable and they can be cleaned or exchanged when rusted out). At the open end extend it right through the rock wall so that it forms the oven opening to which a home-made door can be hinged. The door can be made of a big old enameled lid like the ones that come from leaky old blue canners with a handle attached. But even a wooden round with a metal inside will do the job.

Wherever the drum is surrounded by mortar and rock, wrap around the drum before installation a length of 2" thick fibreglass. It will compact as rock and mortar is packed around it, but will leave a big enough flexible and chinked crack for heat expansion of the drum. This crack will also make the removal or exchange of the drum later on easier. If fibreglass is not available, simple clay, fire clay or rockwool will do. The clay may need chinking anew now and then, but will not cause much smoke leakage.

As you now lay rocks and mortar up and around the drum, be sure to leave at least 2" to 4" of space between the drum and the rocks (or your ingenious little removable form) where the smoke can draw through. Our space is about 3" to 4" wide and can be cleaned with a length of chain on a rope being moved up and down from above the chimney. Always make sure you clean both sides when you do! If your space is below 2", you may do well to have your drum removable for cleaning — as those Hudson's Bay oven drums are built.

About halfway up the drum, I placed a damper on the stove top side of the drum, which when closed, will send most of the smoke around the drum to the other side. I believe with a higher drum position this damper is not needed, unless you build very tight openings and insert two dampers or one big one higher up, which will give you a very controllable fire.

We laid rocks and mortar up above the oven drum for at least ½' on all sides. This brings us at a 5½' to 6' level to a kind of platform with a roughly square hole in the middle. That finishes the lower part of the stove. Whatever pieces of form you have now still inside the stove or smoke stack, take them out — the cleverer you built your form, the easier it will be. But if something remains inside, don't worry — the first few slow fires will char and burn the wood a bit and they will fall out into the ashpit, as pieces or as ashes. Just be sure to have no wood incorporated or penetrating into the rockwall as that would later weaken the structure.

Smoke Stack and Chimney: Over top of this hole in the platform goes the chimney. I placed 5 gallon oil cans over top of each other and built with rocks around them. The cans fit just a little inside each other, being a bit tapered, and are of heavier gauge than regular smoke pipe with about a 11" diameter. Other similar cans, clay tile or regular flue lining can of course be used too. The expansion from heating has caused through seven years of hard use only a few hairline cracks. If one is worried, the cans could be cut open and lapped with their sides, which then would allow them to slide a little past each other.

One could now build an outer form, but at this point I gave up on forms and laid rocks around the cans in a rather free way, interlacing now and then with strips of cut chickenwire doubled-up for reinforcement against cracking or loosening rock sections. A lot of old chimneys are by no means a monolithic block, but an interlocking mass of stone or brick sections, standing up even if the whole house is being put on a flat bed and moved to a different location — as I have experienced myself.

This rock laying can be done with imaginative carefulness, letting some rocks project out to form little shelves onto which thermometers, rennet starter solutions and tooth brushes can be put, or a cup of tea kept warm.

The chimney should go at least 9' high. Ours goes through the roof of the summer kitchen (a roofed over outdoor space) and about 2' over the roof to an overall height of about 11'. It can be topped with a coping of a concrete slab as a weather guard, or some other suitable piece of hardware that won't fly away in a strong wind. A piece of ½" hardware cloth is definitely advisable as a spark screen. Soot and hot sparks catch in it and won't fly into the dry woods (to cause a fire). It now and then needs shaking out to let the smoke through again. Watch the fireworks when burning dry tamarack or cedar. You don't want to do that in "Extreme Fire Hazard" without the spark screen.

After the structure is finished, perhaps some pointing between rocks has to be done, but it is better to do that right when you lay the rocks. Pointing brings structurally no strength, you only fill a crack.

Now: don't start a fire right away. Season the whole thing for at least 5 to 6 weeks with a few buckets of water every day, keeping damp racks and sacks draped over it in the summer time. After that seasoning, let it dry for a while, a week perhaps.

Starting to Use the stove: Your first dozen fires should all be very gentle, rather low and long instead of short and blazing. Some hairline cracks will develop as time goes on but they will not do any harm.

Clean the smoke stack now and then, paying attention to the two sides around the oven drum. When the stove is not in use, wax or grease the stove top against rust in the winter, fall and spring.

The fire: for just a couple of pots we built it mostly to one side, using the three holes in line to each other; for baking, towards the back; and for canning and laundering, mostly all over and of course any combination. The firebox is after all almost 2' wide and goes in deep; it doesn't have to look like a volcano's mouth all the time and any odd size wood can be used. The person who cuts the firewood will be grateful for this detail.

Afterthoughts: Tony built our first stove of this kind just with rocks and clay and it did ok for three seasons. Then the weather started to take it apart dangerously and I replaced it with the above described version. Building such a stove outdoors gives a person lots of play for experimentation and practising, but to build one like it inside the house would be of even more advantage, since one can combine cooking, baking, heating and warmth storage all in one unit.

We find that all customary cooking stoves have too small a firebox to be efficient for heating, as well as being built too drafty to really control a long sustained fire, while most heaters don't provide enough surface area to cook upon and of course never have an oven. This was made up for years ago by what I referred to earlier as the Hudson's Bay drum oven. This was a contraption of sheet metal, one smaller drum set into one bigger one with about 1" to 2" of air space all around between the two drums. The outer drum had stove pipe stubs, top and bottom, to be set in the stove pipe above a heater. There was a door to close the oven. This was a very functional and effective oven and threw out a lot of heat in addition. But being rather flimsily made, they burned out fast. We went through a bought one and two home-made ones within five years in conjunction with an Ashley heater, on which one can cook pretty well (cheap model).

A home built indoor rock stove can have a good size firebox to be used with unsplit rounds of 3' to 4' length (which saves half the sawing) and so functions as a heater. It can have a fair size stove top for cooking and a built-in oven for baking. In addition to this, one can build into such a massive rock stove additional moderately warm and

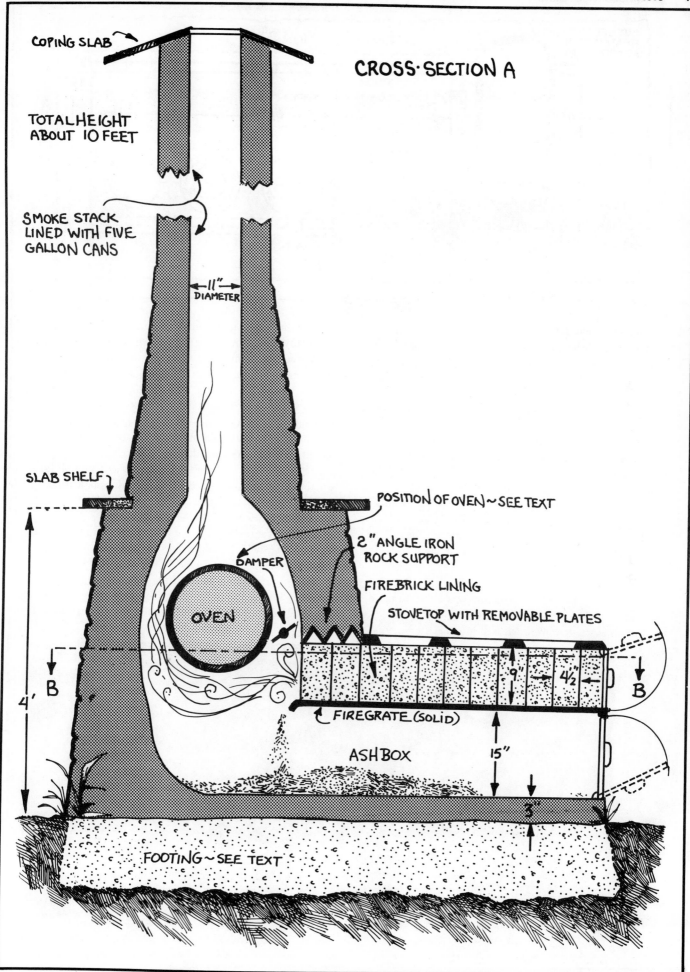

CROSS·SECTION A

COPING SLAB

TOTAL HEIGHT ABOUT 10 FEET

SMOKE STACK LINED WITH FIVE GALLON CANS

11" DIAMETER

SLAB SHELF

POSITION OF OVEN ~ SEE TEXT

DAMPER

OVEN

2" ANGLE IRON ROCK SUPPORT

FIREBRICK LINING

STOVETOP WITH REMOVABLE PLATES

9"   4½"

B   B

4'

FIREGRATE (SOLID)

ASH BOX

15"

3"

FOOTING ~ SEE TEXT

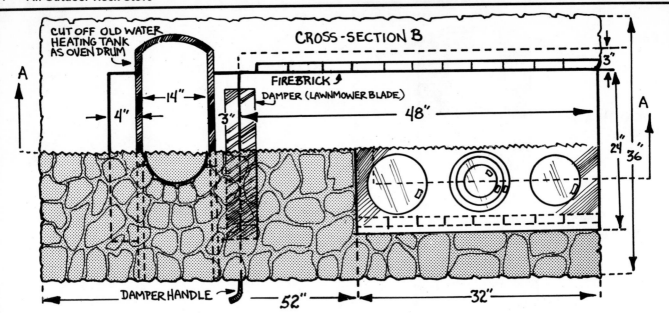

CUT OFF OLD WATER
HEATING TANK
AS OVEN DRUM

CROSS-SECTION B

FIREBRICK
DAMPER (LAWNMOWER BLADE)

A

14"

4"

3"

48"

24" 36"

3"

DAMPER HANDLE

52"

32"

hot drying chambers for drying seeds, herbs or kindling, keeping ceramic dishes warm, or pots with stews and roasts etc. All such chambers, especially if openable on both sides, would circulate warm air into the house and would be very effective in winter. And of course all the massive rock would absorb lots of heat during fire peaks and radiate it out during low fire times or in the night. If such a stove can be made to serve as a backrest to a bench on which you can have your winter breakfast or evening reading-and-writing hours, then I don't have to tell you any longer what I am dreaming of. This would be real economy and wisdom of housekeeping. Russia, China and Korea are known for this kind of stove: in fact, they are built in a way as to provide sleeping area on long broad smoke ducts. (See F. H. King: **Farmers for Fourty Centuries**.)

In Germany in previous centuries the tile stove was used. A massive stone and tile structure was built around a firebox with smoke ducts circulating the hot flue gases many times before they were released into the chimney,

thus making much more use of the fuel being burned. These stoves are now being torn down because they are considered too clumsy and space wasting; just old castles, palaces and such have them preserved as antiques and museum pieces. People don't realize that their little sheet metal gas and electric heaters and cookers absorb a tremendous amount of their time and space, in terms of their having to go to jobs and factories to earn and exploit the earth to keep them going.

A stove of this sort can also be made as a monolithic concrete structure (with rod or wire reinforcing), totally of red brick or even as a transportable unit of sheet metal. The latter kind would lose the warmth storage capacity and would eventually wear out. I believe it to be important that cooking, baking and heating be combined into one unit. It's nonsense for a homesteader to tend two fires in a small house, or even to build two chimneys in a small house (as I keep seeing lately) to accommodate two stoves.

I hope and wish people with time to spend can experiment and come up with some units that work.

A Home Built Insulated Chimney

by Kurt Boyer

Insulated stove pipes are very expensive things if you have to buy them. Here is what a neighbor of mine did.

Take a number of 5 gallon oil cans (logging companies, etc., throw them out) and remove the lid, and with a cold chisel remove the bottom. The bottom barrel should have a hole cut in it the size of your stope pipe (7" diameter). Also cut the bottom of a second barrel to fit over the stovepipe.

To make the flashing where the chimney goes through the roof, lay out on a 20" by 20" piece of 28 gauge or thicker sheet metal the oval hole. Here is how I did it. With a bevel square set to the angle of the roof (or a piece of cardboard or wood cut to the angle), lay your oil barrel at this angle above the sheet and mark the corner touching the sheet (A) and the point projected from the opposite side (B). (See Figs. 1-3.)

This gives you the angle or greater arc of your ellipse. Now place the barrel flat on the sheet, draw around it with point "A" in the line. Then shift the barrel over to point "B". About ½" inside this line draw a second line. This is your cutting line. After cutting out, bend up the remaining metal with pliers and ballpeen hammer, to allow the barrel to slip through. Sand off all the paint from the barrel around the area that the flashing touches until the surface is clean and shiny. Screw or bolt the flashing to the drum. Then solder up the joint between the two. (Do not braze this if the flashing is galvanized – zinc poisoning is terrible.)

If soldering is a hassle, then a good furnace cement could probably be used to "goop" up the seam and bolt heads. I would use furnace cement rather than roofing cement, because if any creosote blew down around the pipe, it might burn the bonding in the roofing cement.

Now we have our barrel with the flashing upon it. Braze-weld (just tack) the rest of the barrels together (top to top, bottom to bottom). The uppermost barrel should have its bottom end up, and the bottom most barrel should have its bottom end down.

Now the chimney should go through the roof, the flashing over and under shakes to allow run off without leaking. Also nail this down on the high side or wherever it's under the shakes far enough.

The stovepipe is next. I used 28 gauge galvanized pipe (15' for $12.64). Don't use the black pipe you find in the hardware. It's thin and not really worth it. Go to a furnace and plumbing outfit and ask what they have. Shop around too. There's quite a range of prices for the same stuff. Don't go under 28 gauge galvanized, and the fewer joints the better. So get long pipes made up — mine are 36" though you can get even longer. And then of course there is always stainless steep pipe if you want it to last forever.

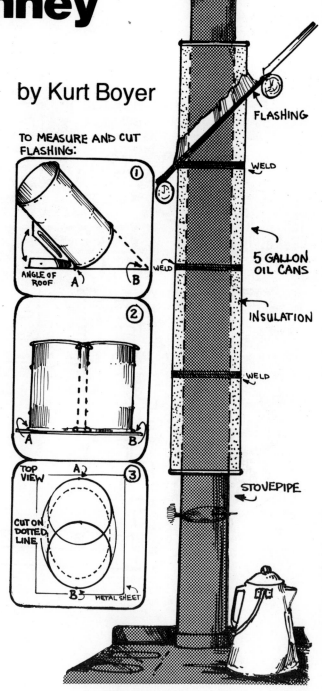

TO MEASURE AND CUT FLASHING:

① ANGLE OF ROOF   A   B   WELD

② A   B

③ TOP VIEW   A   CUT ON DOTTED LINE   B   METAL SHEET

FLASHING
WELD
5 GALLON OIL CANS
INSULATION
WELD
STOVEPIPE

After the stove pipe is in the barrels, pack in fiberglass insulation with a long stick between barrel and pipe. What I did was pack in 4-6" of glass at the bottom and then poured in vermiculite. The fiberglass acts as seal to keep the vermiculite from sifting out around the stove pipe.

Last, take the second barrel with a hole cut to fit the stovepipe, and slide it down over the uppermost barrel on the chimney. Cap the stovepipe and fini.

With the one I made you can put your hand flat upon it — when the stove pipe entering it is "tssp" to a wet finger.

A Large Wood Burning Oven

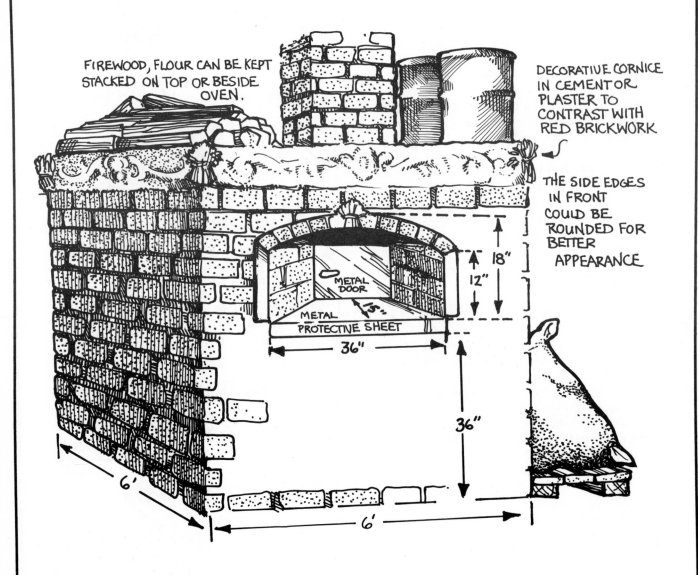

FIREWOOD, FLOUR CAN BE KEPT STACKED ON TOP OR BESIDE OVEN.

DECORATIVE CORNICE IN CEMENT OR PLASTER TO CONTRAST WITH RED BRICKWORK

THE SIDE EDGES IN FRONT COULD BE ROUNDED FOR BETTER APPEARANCE

METAL DOOR

METAL PROTECTIVE SHEET

18"

12"

15"

36"

36"

6'

6'

Our oven is of brick-and-mortar construction, a cube measuring 6 feet in every dimension, on the outside. Inside, the oven proper, where the bread is put to bake, measures 4 ft. x 4 ft. or a trifle more. The roof of the baking space is not a dome but a simple arch, high in the middle and sloping to right and left. From front to back there is no slope. The highest point of the arch is 22 inches above the floor. It could be as low as 18 inches. It is not recommended to make the arch more than 24 inches because the higher the arch is, the more firewood is needed to heat the oven and the further away is the source of radiated heat

that bakes the tops of the loaves.

The floor of the baking space should be of firebrick if available. Ours is of the hardest ordinary building brick we could find. We chose burnt bricks (which are mostly rejected by masons), not just red baked bricks but bricks burnt black at least in part. As far as possible the same kind of bricks should be used for the arch.

Below the layer of firebricks, or burnt building bricks, or ordinary building bricks, we have a 4 inch layer of sand and crushed glass. This, we were told, retains heat very well, better than plain brickwork. I don't believe it. But since we had plenty of broken window panes and old broken bottles we crushed them all up and mixed them in. Below the sand, if you use it, or below the firebrick, is just plain brickwork right down to the floor of the room.

Our chimney is a dream. If you construct your oven well, especially the chimney part, not the faintest wisp of smoke will enter the bakery. After ten years of use the front of our oven is not even the least bit discoloured. The chimney should be constructed outside the oven door and not through the centre of the arch, as some make it. The chimney should have an inside diameter of 9 or 10 inches. Ours rises straight up through the roof. Our bakery is in a one-storeyed building. If yours is not, there should be no difficulty in leading the smoke out by the side wall of the bakery through a metal stovepipe.

Make the door-frame of the oven of 1½" or 2" angle iron with the angle facing the brickwork on all four sides, so that the bricks fit snugly into the angles, and the metal can protect the brick edges from chipping. For the size of opening suit yourself. I recommend 14" wide, so that your 12" baking sheets can fit easily without tilting, and say 12 or 14 inches high. Have four hooks of thin iron rod fixed to the door frame and protruding from it the width of a brick, so as to anchor the frame to the brickwork. Make the door itself of 1/8 inch sheet iron. The bottom of the door frame should be fixed flush with the floor of the oven.

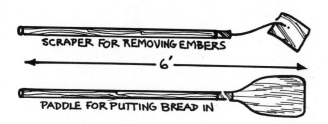

SCRAPER FOR REMOVING EMBERS
6'
PADDLE FOR PUTTING BREAD IN

Just outside the oven door is a ledge. (Immediately above this is the chimney.) The inner dimension of the ledge is the same as the width of the door frame. The outer measurement is 3 ft. This is because sideway manoeuvering room is needed to get at the extreme right and left inside the oven. This ledge is protected with a sheet of galvanized iron which bends down for a couple of inches in front as well. As the floor of the oven, so the surface of the ledge also should be flush with the bottom of the door frame. All three should be quite level. This facilitates the shoving in and pulling out of loaves. You need your hardest bricks right opposite the door where most shoving and scraping takes place.

Our oven has no back wall of its own. We built it against the end wall of the room, and for a special purpose. The room behind our bakery is used as a store room for things that need to be kept dry, things like flour, biscuits, cake mixes, spaghetti. If you want a room like this heated by your oven, dig a hole into the wall at the level of the oven floor, 3 ft. long and 18 inches high, leaving only a thin partition (5 inches thick, the width of a brick) between the oven and the room. The room will get very dry and

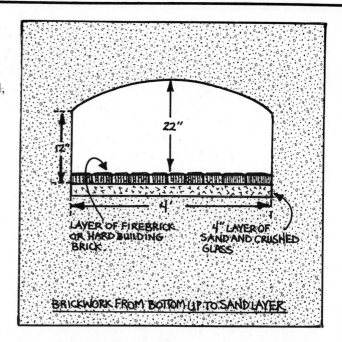

22"
12"
LAYER OF FIREBRICK OR HARD BUILDING BRICK
4'
4" LAYER OF SAND AND CRUSHED GLASS
BRICKWORK FROM BOTTOM UP TO SAND LAYER

pleasantly warm. To control the admission of heat, put a door to the dug-out space. This room is excellent for drying wet clothes during the rains.

Firewood and sacks of flour can be kept dry either on top of the oven or stacked beside it.

How to Operate the Oven

Build a fire inside the oven with a good armful of logs. Light it and leave the door wide open till the wood has all burnt up. Pull out the embers and ashes and put the bread in. Then close the door.

After baking the bread, the oven is still quite hot enough to bake lighter things like cookies, muffins or buns.

The handles for the scraper for removing the embers, and for the paddle for putting in and pulling out the loaves, could be either of light wood or of that light metal tubing used for electric wires. Make them 6 feet long. The paddle blade could be 12 x 8 inches of strong galvanized iron or thin iron sheeting.

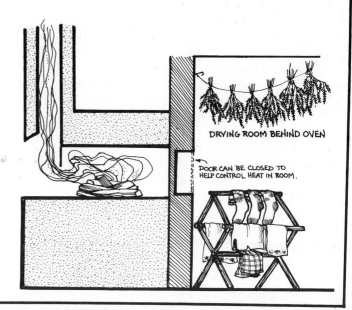

DRYING ROOM BEHIND OVEN

DOOR CAN BE CLOSED TO HELP CONTROL HEAT IN ROOM.

A One Pony Sled

by Greg Bloomberg

Anyone who burns any quantity of wood to keep warm quickly discovers that the biggest part of the work is moving the wood. One of the most primitive devices for moving wood (or anything else) is a sled. Although certainly of prehistoric invention, the sled is still with us, and is still useful. Now something that's been around that long must have something going for it — and it does. No matter where you are, materials can be found to make one. It is easy to construct one with few hand tools. It has no moving parts. The cost to build one is little or nothing. You don't even have to oil it.

This is how I built a sled to haul firewood behind my pony. All the material was scrounged. You can use logs and poles, but it takes much longer. The short lengths of lumber required shouldn't be hard to find. The length and width of the sled are not critical and can be modified to fit the materials you have or find.

The runners are the most important part so it is well to begin with them and build around them. I cut the first runner to shape and drew its outline on the board below to make sure both runners were the same shape. The inside cross pieces were cut all the same length (try to be accurate here) and nailed in place. You may be tempted to quit right there. I was and I did. I want to tell you that even little ponies are plenty strong, and that first sled didn't last more than a couple of trips.

The next thing I did was cut and nail the top cross pieces in place. Then I rooted around until I found some flat steel pieces from an old army cot which were riveted together in the form of an "X". I drilled a hole at each end of the "X" and nailed it in place on top of the runners. This keeps the sled from twisting. To keep the runners tight to the cross pieces, I drilled four holes through each runner just under the front and back inside cross pieces. I looped a wire through these holes and twisted it under the cross pieces, using a nail. After the runners were pulled together tight, I drove the nail into the cross piece.

If you want the runners to last, they must be "shoed" The best thing to use is shoeing steel — the kind used on logging sleighs, bob-sleds, cutters, etc. . . . Next best thing is spring steel. Shod in steel, your sled will last many, many years (if you can keep it from rotting). Steel can be hard to find and hard to work with, however, so I used what was at hand — galvanized sheet metal. I used roofing nails to fasten it to the runners. I expected it to rip off or wear out fast, but it has lasted two seasons so far and is easy to replace should it come apart.

Unless you enjoy restacking a load every few yards, your sled must have some way of holding the load in place. This can be done by tying it on with chains or rope or using side stakes or bolsters. If you're the insecure

type, you can use both. I had a lot of trouble keeping the side stakes from breaking or coming undone. If you use wood stakes, try nailing them well and then lashing them with strong wire passed through holes drilled in the runners. A better way might be to use lengths of pipe driven into holes drilled in the top of the runners.

To hitch the sled to my pony, I first drilled a hole in the front of each runner and then drove a steel pipe through them. A piece of wire cable was run through this pipe and then through the bolt on a single tree. I used two cable clamps to secure the cable to itself at each end.

If you have steep or long hills to go down, consider using some kind of brake. If you have a team, use a pole and breeching so the horses can hold back on the down grade. You can make a brake as illustrated in Fig. 2. The log or plank used as a brake drops in front of the sled runners to keep it from running up on the horse or team.

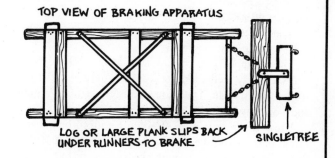

TOP VIEW OF BRAKING APPARATUS

LOG OR LARGE PLANK SLIPS BACK UNDER RUNNERS TO BRAKE   SINGLETREE

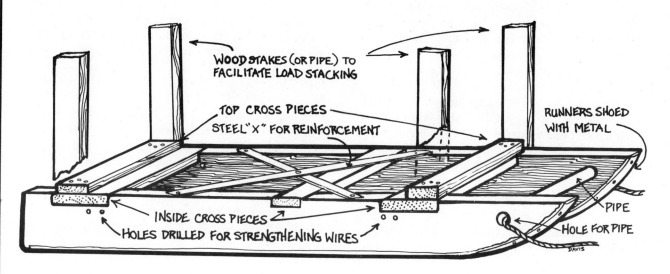

WOOD STAKES (OR PIPE) TO FACILITATE LOAD STACKING

TOP CROSS PIECES
STEEL "X" FOR REINFORCEMENT

RUNNERS SHOED WITH METAL

INSIDE CROSS PIECES
HOLES DRILLED FOR STRENGTHENING WIRES

PIPE
HOLE FOR PIPE

Building a Hydraulic Ram

by Don Marier

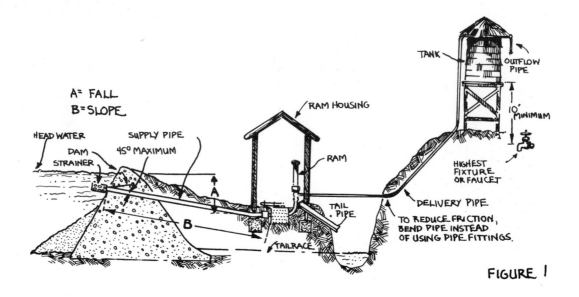

FIGURE 1

I'm always interested in getting something for nothing, so I find hydraulic rams intriguing. They pump water using water — no gas, oil, or electricity is needed. You do need a stream, artesian well, or a spring as a source, though, so not everyone can use one.

The hydraulic ram was invented about 150 years ago and was fairly well widespread in use, until electricity came to the countryside. There are still a few of them around and you may be lucky enough to find one, on an old farm.

I first saw a ram in 1970, when I noticed one in my father-in-law's toolshed in northern Wisconsin. It looked like some type of pump with an octopus- or bulb-shaped chamber on top. My father-in-law still had copies of the sales information on the ram (see references 1 and 2 at end). I was able to get the ram working by reading this information. It's too bad they don't explain how things work anymore.

I took the ram apart, expecting to find a series of chambers and valves inside the bulb, but all I found was one simple leather valve. The leather had lost its zip after 25 years, so I replaced it. With this simple repair done, I installed the ram near a pond with a two-foot dam on it. The ram was irrigating the garden within a few hours.

The ram looked so simple that I began to think of ways to build one out of regular plumbing parts. Two weeks later, I found out that the people at VITA had just put out a manual — **A Hydraulic Ram for Village Use** — on how to do just that (page 52). Since then, I also found a **Popular Science** article on building a ram (page 57). As a future project, I'd like to combine the best of both designs.

I built a ram according to VITA's plans and I'm satisfied with the results. It cost me about $18 worth of parts but that's only about one-tenth the cost of buying a factory-made ram. The parts list calls for regular plumbing parts such as tees, couplings, and bushings. A two-foot section of three-inch pipe with a cap on it serves as the air chamber. The plans are detailed and the parts list is complete.

I made one major modification in VITA's plans that I wouldn't recommend. I used plastic sewer pipe rather than galvanized pipe. I did this because I didn't have the facilities for some of the machining operations called for in the plans and plastic is easier to work with. I got by with this variation, as it turns out, because the ram was operated at very low pressure. If it had operated at higher pressures, chances are it wouldn't have worked. I don't see why plastic **water** pipe wouldn't work, though.

I also modified VITA's plans by using a leather valve from a hand pump rather than the homemade one called for in the plans.

A diagram of a typical ram is shown in Fig. 1. Here's how it works. Water rushes down the drive pipe and escapes out the waste valve until enough pressure is built up to close the waste valve. The amount of this pressure increases as the fall increases. The fall is the vertical distance from the water to the ram.

When the waste valve closes, water is forced through the check valve and into the air chamber. The rushing water compresses the air in the chamber and the compressed air pushes back like a piston. This action closes the check valve and forces water up the delivery pipe to a storage tank.

When the check valve closes, the water in the drive pipe rebounds for a moment. This action created a partial vacuum which allows the waste valve to drop open again. When the waste valve opens, the excess water which was not forced up the delivery pipe flows out of the waste valve. The partial vacuum also draws a small amount of air into the ram through the air valve or "snifter" which is just below the air chamber. This air will be forced into the air chamber when the water starts slowing down the drive pipe again. The air is needed to replenish the air supply in the chamber because some is mixed with the water during each cycle. A small amount of water is lost through the air valve during each cycle but it is very small and it serves to keep the valve clean.

The cycle just described is repeated about 25 to 100 times a minute. How fast it is repeated depends on how much tension is put on the waste valve spring by means of adjusting screws. The slower the ram pumps, the more water it will pump, so the waste valve tension is adjusted for the minimum number of strokes per minute at which the ram will still operate. I had to build the waste valve spring a couple of times so that it lined up properly and had the correct tension. Otherwise, the pressure would not build up properly and the ram would not work.

How much water the ram will pump can be calculated from the following formula:

$$D = \frac{S \times F}{L} \times \frac{2}{3}$$

Where:

D is the amount of water delivered in gal./min.

S is the amount of water supplied to the ram in gal./min.

F is the fall, or the vertical difference in height between the ram and the storage tank

L is the lift, or the vertical distance the water is lifted from the ram to the storage tank

The 2/3 represents the efficiency of the ram. Older rams had efficiences of about 40%

The minimum fall a ram will work with is 18" and this is the fall I had to work with. I measured the supply flow to be 10 gallons per minute by catching the water in a pail and timing how long it took to fill. The lift I used was 10'. Thus the amount of water I should have expected to be delivered was:

$$D = \frac{10 \text{ gal./min.} \times 1\frac{1}{2}'}{10 \text{ ft.}} \times 2 = 1 \text{ gal./min.}$$

I actually measured about .5 gallons per minute.

It sounds "inefficient" to use 10 gallons of water to pump one gallon, but if you figured it out, one gallon per minute adds up to 1440 gallons per day, since the ram pumps constantly, unlike a windmill. Besides, that nine gallons which went out the waste valve isn't really wasted since it can be returned to the stream or can be used for any convenient purpose.

You can't pump the water to an indefinite height since pipe friction slows the water down. Friction is kept to a minimum by using sufficiently large pipe and by keeping connections and bends to a minimum. It is much better to bend a long piece of pipe at a gradual angle than to use sections of pipe which are connected together at a sharp angle. The VITA ram calls for a 1½" drive pipe with a 1" delivery pipe. Garden hose is out of the question because all the bends would produce too much friction.

The drive pipe should be between five and ten times the height of the fall and should not be more than 30 degrees from the horizontal. Audel's book on water supply has a good chapter on hydraulic rams. According to Audel, the delivery pipe should not be more 20 times the lift height in length. Also, according to Audel, if a storage tank is used, it should be at least 20' from the highest plumbing outlet. This is to guarantee a minimum of eight pounds of pressure. Storage tanks must be insulated from freezing in cold climates so a better solution might be to use a pressure tank like those used with electric pumps.

Other precautions are to put a small house around the ram to keep it from freezing and to put a piece of screen over the supply pipe intake to prevent leaves from clogging the ram.

The only company I know of that still makes hydraulic rams is the Rife Company. Their rams cost about $180 and up. This is more than the cost of a regular pump but then there are no electricity costs and, with only two moving parts, a ram should last a lifetime. Rife also sells double-acting rams which allow you to pump pure spring water using water from a nearby stream.

My next project is to build another ram based on the VITA and **Popular Science** designs. My objective is to use only parts that can be bought in a hardware store and to limit machining operations to drilling a couple of holes.

References

1. **Gould's Hydraulic Rams**, Gould Pumps, Inc., Seneca Falls, N.Y. (about 1945). No longer available.

2. **Montgomery Ward Hydraulic Rams for Running Water Without Power**, Montgomery Ward Co., Chicago (about 1945). No longer available.

3. **A Hydraulic Ram for Village Use** by Ersal W. Kindel, Volunteers for International Technical Assistance (VITA), 3706 Rhode Island Ave., Mt. Rainier, MD 20822.

4. "Hydraulic Ram Forces Water to Pump Itself", **Popular Science**, by A. W. Kaufmann, October 1948, pp 231-233.

5. **Domestic Water Supply and Sewage Disposal Guide**, by Edwin P. Anderson. Theodore Audel & Co., New York, 1967. (Chapt. 10 is on hydraulic rams.)

6. **Manual of Information: Rife Hydraulic Water Rams**, Rife Hydraulic Engine Mfg. Co., Box 367, Millburn, NJ 07041. 1968.

A Village Ram

by Ersal Kindel

A hydraulic ram is a simple device, invented about 150 years ago. It uses the power from falling water to force a small portion of the water to a height greater than the source. Water can be forced about as far horizontally as you desire, but greater distances require larger pipe, due to friction. There is no external power needed and the ram has only two working parts. The only maintenance needed is to keep leaves and trash cleaned away from the strainer on the intake and to replace the clack and non-return or delivery valve rubbers if they get worn. The original cost is almost the only cost.

Two things are needed to make the ram work: (a) enough water to run the ram and (b) enough height for water to fall through the drive pipe to work the ram. A small amount of water with plenty of fall will pump as much water as a greater amount of water with only a little fall. The greater the height to which the water must be raised, the less water will be pumped, under a given set of circumstances.

Water may come from a spring on a hillside or from a river. It must be led into a position from which it can pass through a relatively short supply pipe to the ram, at a fairly steep angle (about 30 degrees from the horizontal is good). Often a catch basin or cistern is used as the source for the drive pipe, but an open ditch such as that which supplies a water posho mill could be used. Be sure to put a strainer on the top of the drive pipe to keep trash out of the pipe and ram.

The water starts to run down through the drive pipe, going faster and faster till it forces the automatic valve or clack to close suddenly. The weight of the moving water, suddenly stopped, creates very high pressure and forces some of the water past the non-return or delivery valve and into the air chamber, compressing the air more and more till the energy of the moving water is spent. This compressed air acts as a spring and forces the water up the delivery pipe to the storage tank in a steady stream. It takes a lot of falling water to pump a little water up a hill. Often about one part in ten is delivered to the storage tank at the top of the delivery pipe. The snifter hole wastes a bit of water but takes in a bubble of air with each stroke. This is necessary to keep air in the air dome and it must not get plugged or the air dome will get filled with water and the ram will stop. The small ram works best at about 75 to 90 strokes per minute, depending on the amount of drive water available. The slower it goes, the more water it uses but the more it pumps.

Any working fall from 18" to 100' can be used to work a ram, but in general, the more working fall you obtain, the less the ram will cost and the less drive water it will require to raise a given amount of water. If there is plenty of water, a fall of four feet could be made to raise water 800' but this would be an expensive installation.

Our ram at Kaimosi farm is a very small one and has a small amount of water to run it, but there is plenty of fall and not very much lift.

Head 20', lift 44' uses 8.4 gal./min.

Drive pipe 85', run 690', delivers 1-2/3 gal./min. = 100 gal./hr. or 2400 gal. in 24 hr.

Unless you have practically unlimited water available, measure it exactly by making a temporary dam and putting a large pipe or two through it. Then catch and measure the water for, say, 15 minutes. Next sight along a carpenter's level to the top of a 10 ft. pole set on the ground down the hill at a lower level. Then move the level to the pole's position and sight again to the top of the pole, finding how many levels or fractions you have, and this will give you when added together, the amount of fall for the drive pipe. Do the same for the height to which the water must be raised. This height is measured from the ram level. For a more elaborate method of measuring fall, refer to **Cloudburst 1**, page 43.

A factory-built ram is more efficient but costs more. This small ram you can make up yourself from pipe fittings and you only have to buy or build the clack and delivery valve assemblies.

Building the Ram

Start by building the clack valve. If you do not have a metal lathe, a machine shop will do the work for a small price. Chuck a 3" x 1" pipe bushing in the lathe and turn the inside smooth, where the clack strikes. Turn out the threads and eliminate any sharp edges. Drill two ¼" holes near the end of a piece of strap iron ¼" x 1½" x 2" and, using it as a template, drill and tap holes in the top of the pipe bushing. Grind off the galvanizing, then bolt the clack spring support solidly to the bushing and braze it also. Bend a 36" iron strap, 1½" x 1/8", around a 2" pipe to make the clack spring. Drill two ½" holes through the end and also through both the support and two short pieces to make up the pad as shown in the drawing. Cut pieces of rubber inner tube and assemble the sandwich. This is to keep vibration from breaking the support off the pipe bushing. A brace can be added for additional support but is not absolutely necessary.

The clack valve itself is made up of a rubber disc and metal washer 3/8" smaller than the inside of your bushing and assembled on a 3/8" x 4½" bolt. The best rubber I have found is from an old tractor tire — it shows no wear at all after 8 months' use. I cut it on a band saw and sanded it flat and even on a disc sander with coarse paper. A similar one is used for the check valve. Slip a washer over the bolt and a short length of thin wall steel tube (¾" o.d. conduit) with the ends filed exactly square. Then put it through a hole in the clack spring. Adjust by bending so the rubber clack strikes true and doesn't rub on the sides of the bushing.

Drill a hole for a carriage bolt to adjust the stroke of the spring; also a pair of holes about three inches from the round end of the spring for a tension bolt. If the bottom hole is filed square to fit the under side of the bolt, it will not turn when adjustments are made.

The check valve is similar in construction but a ½" x 2" galvanized bolt is used. Machine the lip true where the valve rests but do not cut it down farther than necessary. This gives

HYDRAULIC RAM IN OPERATION

1. GATE VALVES
2. 1½" STREET BEND
3. 1½" x 3" BUSHING
4. BRACE CLAMP
5. BRACE
6. RUBBER
7. ¼" x 3" CARRIAGE BOLT
8. A SECOND LOCK NUT IS OPTIONAL
9. CLACK SPRING
10. CHECK VALUE

11. 3" x 3" x 1" TEE
12. AIR DOME 3" x 24" PIPE
13. CAP - WELD OR SCREW ON
14. 1" NIPPLE
15. 1" UNION
16. 1" PIPE
17. SNIFTER HOLE - 1/16" WITH WIRE
18. CLACK VALVE
19. 1" STREET BEND
20. 1½" PIPE
21. STRAINER
22. SOURCE
23. STORAGE TANK

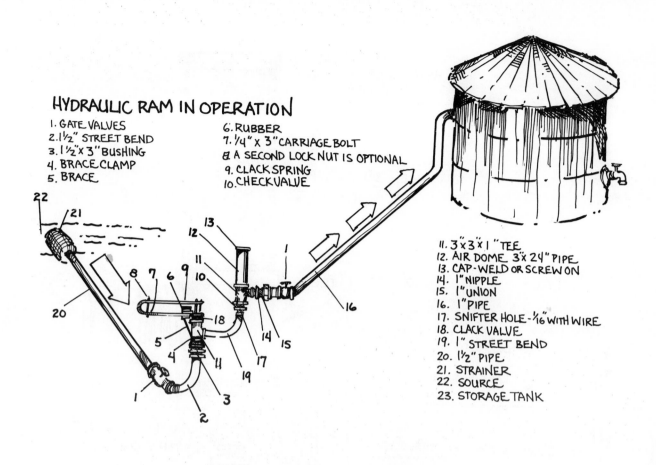

HYDRAULIC RAM - COMPLETE ASSEMBLY

1. GATE VALVES
2. 1½" STREET BEND
3. 1½" x 3" BUSHING
4. BRACE CLAMP
5. BRACE
6. RUBBER
7. ¼" x 3" CARRIAGE BOLT
8. A SECOND LOCK-NUT OPTIONAL
9. CLACK SPRING
10. CHECK VALUE (SEE DETAIL)

11. 3" x 3" x 1" TEE
12. AIR DOME 3" x 24" PIPE
13. CAP WELD OR SCREW ON
14. 1" NIPPLE
15. 1" UNION
16. 1" PIPE
17. SNIFTER HOLE
18. CLACK VALVE
19. 1" STREET BEND
20. 1½" PIPE

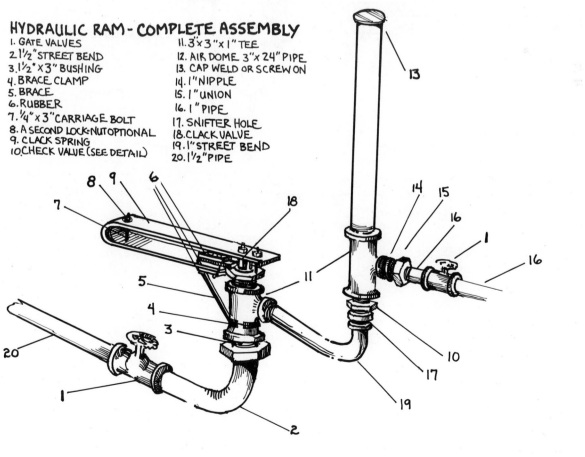

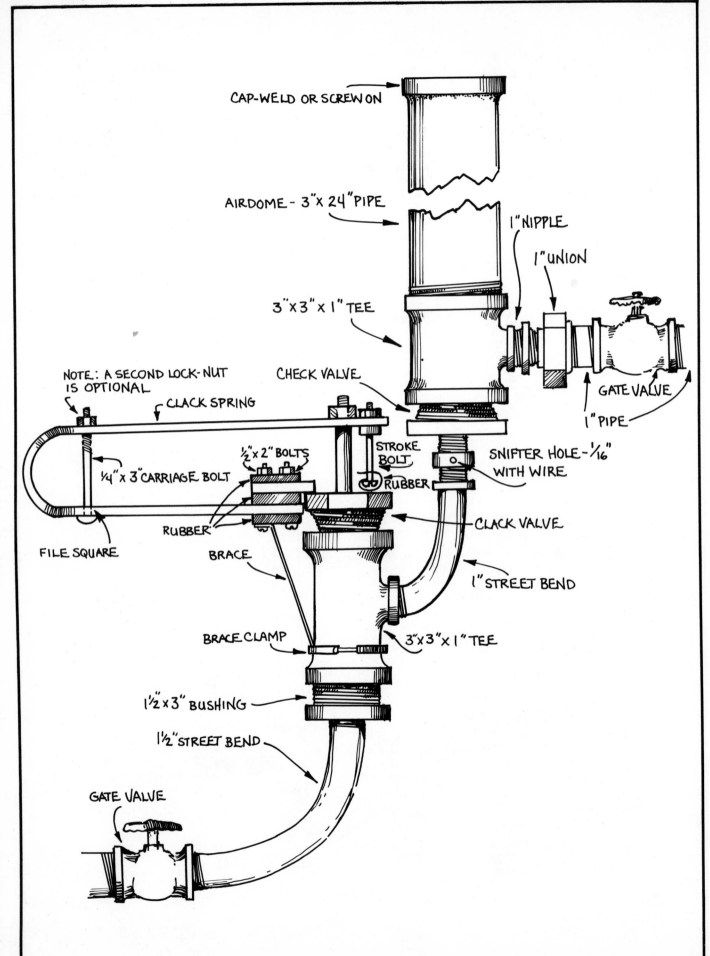

CAP-WELD OR SCREW ON

AIRDOME - 3"x 24"PIPE

1"NIPPLE

1"UNION

3"x3"x1"TEE

GATE VALVE

1"PIPE

NOTE.: A SECOND LOCK-NUT IS OPTIONAL

CLACK SPRING

CHECK VALVE

STROKE BOLT

SNIFTER HOLE-1/16" WITH WIRE

1/2"x2"BOLTS

1/4"x3"CARRIAGE BOLT

RUBBER

CLACK VALVE

RUBBER

FILE SQUARE

BRACE

1"STREET BEND

BRACE CLAMP

3"x3"x1"TEE

1 1/2"x3"BUSHING

1 1/2"STREET BEND

GATE VALVE

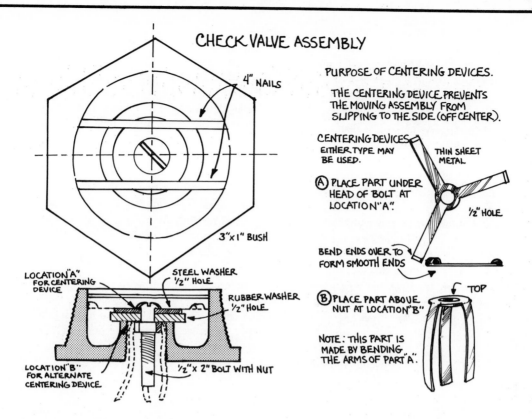

CHECK VALVE ASSEMBLY

4" NAILS

3" x 1" BUSH

LOCATION "A" FOR CENTERING DEVICE

STEEL WASHER ½" HOLE

RUBBER WASHER ½" HOLE

LOCATION "B" FOR ALTERNATE CENTERING DEVICE

½" x 2" BOLT WITH NUT

PURPOSE OF CENTERING DEVICES.

THE CENTERING DEVICE PREVENTS THE MOVING ASSEMBLY FROM SLIPPING TO THE SIDE. (OFF CENTER).

CENTERING DEVICES EITHER TYPE MAY BE USED.

THIN SHEET METAL

(A) PLACE PART UNDER HEAD OF BOLT AT LOCATION "A".

½" HOLE

BEND ENDS OVER TO FORM SMOOTH ENDS

(B) PLACE PART ABOVE NUT AT LOCATION "B"

TOP

NOTE: THIS PART IS MADE BY BENDING THE ARMS OF PART "A".

---

a bit of clearance for the water to pass. Drill two holes on each side of the middle for a 4" common nail to pass just above the valve metal washer, to keep it in place. Leave enough clearance so the valve can open just about 1/16". Spread the bolt with a centre punch just below the nut, so the nut can't work loose. Cut the nails off and file threads across their ends so the bushing will screw into the tee above it.

Just one other small job before assembly: Drill a 1/16" hole in the centre of the 1" nipple just below the check valve and bend a piece of copper wire to the shape of a cotter pin and insert it from the inside of the nipple with long nosed pliers. Spread the outside ends. This copper wire restricts the jet of water coming out, yet moves enough to keep the hole clean, most always.

The air dome can be a 2' length of 3" pipe, threaded on both ends with a cap on the top end, or the top end can have a plate welded over it. It must be airtight at great pressure. I coated the inside of the pipe with asphalt paint to protect it from rust and to seal any small leaks in the weld. Let it dry in the sun while assembling the rest of the ram.

Assembly

Use plenty of good grade pipe joint compound, both on inside and outside threads. Screw things together firmly but not excessively tight, and leave them in the correct position for your installation. Set the ram reasonably level but nothing is demanding in this respect. The snifter hole must be immediately below the air dome so the bubbles will go up into the dome. Clack and check valves must be free from binding and touch evenly all around. The old tractor tire rubber with some fabric on the back seems to be just the right toughness and resiliency to last a long time — much longer than either gasket rubber or live rubber.

I find no reason at all to mount the ram in concrete as has been suggested — in fact it is a convenience to be able to shut off the two valves, loosen the unions, and take the ram to the shop for cleaning and painting. Painting of course doesn't help its working but it does make it look better when visitors go to see it. The cost of a home built ram is about a tenth the manufactured cost and it works on at no cost at all. A bit of rubber stretched over the head of the stroke bolt quiets the ram but isn't essential. Adjust the spring tension bolt and stroke bolt together to get the best period for your particular ram. Support the drive and delivery pipes so they don't bounce and vibrate.

This is a small ram but larger ones can be built — we have built two with 3" drive pipe and correspondingly larger ram parts. One lifts water about 150' and drives it through 3600' of pipe.

Installation & Adjustments

The drive pipe should have a strainer on the top made of ½" coffee tray wire, hardware cloth or anything suitable. This keeps out trash, frogs and leaves, any of which will stop the ram if they get inside. The drive pipe should be 1½" or larger (we use 2" pipe) and, if possible, new, solidly put together, straight, and well supported through its length. A gate valve on the drive pipe about 4' from the ram is a great convenience but not necessary. Another gate valve on the delivery pipe is almost a necessity to avoid draining the entire delivery pipe whenever the ram is cleaned. The ram should be connected to the delivery and drive pipes by unions so it can be removed for cleaning. If it is desirable to use two rams, they must have separate drive pipes, but the delivery pipes can be joined, provided the pipe is large enough to carry the water.

The delivery pipe should start from the ram with about two lengths of 1" galvanized iron pipe. From there ¾" plastic pipe can be used. The iron pipe will give the ram better support, but plastic pipe is smoother inside and can be a size smaller than the iron pipe. Also, plastic pipe is cheaper, but it must be protected from mechanical injury and sunlight. Do not take any branches off the supply line at less than three times the working fall, or when the tap is turned on the ram will stop. (A float valve might be an exception.) Best results will be obtained by putting all the water from the ram directly into a storage tank and using it from there. Use the overflow to irrigate the pasture.

The small bolt at the end of the clack spring controls the length of the stroke of the clack spring. Experiment for the best length of stroke and tension for your set of conditions. Adjust the length of stroke first, then the spring tension. The greater the tension and length of stroke, the slower the ram will work and the more water it will pump, but it will take more water to keep it working.

If Action is Faulty

See that the clack valve closes squarely, evenly and completely. If it does not, the clack spring may have been bent somehow, and it will have to be straightened.

See that the clack valve does not rub on the front, side or back of the valve body.

Check for trash in the ram or delivery valve or snifter hole.

Check to see that the air dome is not filled with water. It must not be full of water or the ram will knock loudly and may break something. The snifter lets in a bit of air between each of the strokes and this keeps the dome full of compressed air.

Check rubber clack and delivery valve for wear or looseness.

If drive water is in small supply, speed up the stroke by loosening spring tension and shorten the stroke by lowering the stroke adjusting bolt. More water is delivered by a faster stroke and continuous running than a slower stroke

that stops every day.

Check for leaks in the drive pipe. If air bubbles come out of the drive pipe after it has been stopped for a while, air is leaking into the drive pipe and the ram action is spoiled.

Clean the ram once in a while. It deserves it after working without rest day and night for weeks and months on end. Protect it from outside injury and inquisitive children.

When the ram runs out of water, it will usually stop, remaining open and losing all the water available until it is closed again. You can listen at the storage tank to hear if it is still running and, if it isn't, go to the ram and close the drive pipe until water has accumulated in the cistern.

Long delivery distances require larger pipe to reduce friction.

A cistern is a good thing to have at the top of the drive pipe to let dirt settle out of the water. The outlet from the cistern to the ram should be a foot or so above the bottom to allow room for dirt to settle out. A cleaning drain in the bottom is good.

Parts List

Quan.	Part		
1	1½" valve	2	4" nails
1	1½" street bend	1	¼" x 3" bolt with 2 nuts
1	1½" x 3" bushing	1	3/8" x 4½" bolt with nut
1	Brace	1	¾" dia. x about 4" long
1	Brace clamp		thinwall tubing
2	3" x 3" x 1" tees	1	Rubber washer, 1¾" dia.,
1	¼" x 3" carriage bolt & nut (2 nuts optional for lock-nut)		3/8" hole
		1	Steel washer, about ¾" dia., 3/8" hole
1	Clack spring	1	Steel washer, about 1¼" dia., 3/8" hole
3	Rectangular pieces of rubber	1	1" valve
2	½" x 2" bolts with nuts	1	1" union
1	3" x 24" pipe	2	1" nipples
1	Cap for air dome	1	Small piece of rubber for stroke bolt
2	3" x 1" bushings		
1	Sheet metal disc about 2¼" in diameter	1	1" street bend
		1	Short piece of 3/32" wire for snifter hole
1	½" x 2" bolt with nut		
1	Rubber washer, 1¾" dia., ½" hole	1	Steel washer, ½" hole

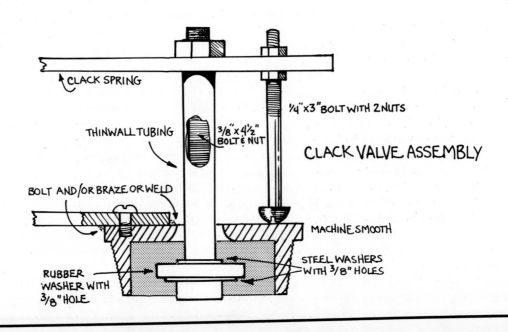

CLACK SPRING

THINWALL TUBING

3/8" x 4½" BOLT & NUT

¼" x 3" BOLT WITH 2 NUTS

CLACK VALVE ASSEMBLY

BOLT AND/OR BRAZE OR WELD

MACHINE SMOOTH

RUBBER WASHER WITH 3/8" HOLE

STEEL WASHERS WITH 3/8" HOLES

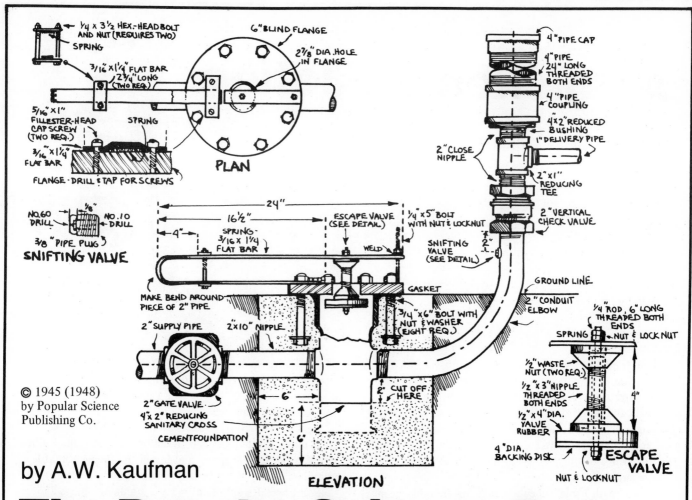

by A.W. Kaufman

The Popular Science Ram

A small but efficient ram may easily be built at home. For the base, use a 2" x 4" cast-iron reducing sanitary cross. Saw off the small 4" end 2" below the threads. Face or dress the bell end flat and true.

Make the spring, strap, and clamp from 3/16" x 1¼" galvanized flat-bar stock. For the escape valve, assemble a ½" x 3" nipple, ½" galvanized waste nuts with the ears cut off, a 4" valve rubber, and a backing disk. A ¼" rod threaded at each end holds the assembly together.

The flange is made from a blind flange for 6" pipe. Drill a 2-7/8" hole in the centre and drill and tap two holes for the 5/16" cap screws that retain the spring. Carefully dress one side of the flange to provide a smooth valve seat.

Assemble the cross with a 2" x 10" nipple and a 2" conduit elbow. Tap the latter for 3/8" pipe about 2" below the threads at one end for the snifting valve.

Invert this assembly on the flange, with the bolts and clamp screws in place. Centre the anchor bolts in the flange holes with tape, and wire the washers in position. Stuff the interior of the cross with crumpled newspaper, topping off the stuffing with a small piece of chicken wire. Also wrap several layers of wire fencing loosely around the cross to reinforce the cement. Then build a wood form to enclose the cross.

The cement block must supply a solidity and mass that absorbs the ramming shocks of the water. Hence it should be carefully made. Thoroughly mix equal parts of sharp coarse plaster sand and lump-free cement. Wet slowly until jellylike and tamp into the mold. When the cement has set, knock off the form, remove the flange and the newspaper stuffing, and fill the interior with cement up to the lower level of the inside of the 2" pipes. Smooth this to reduce friction.

The ram is now ready for installation. Lay a 2" supply pipe of a length equal to the height the water must be raised, keeping it straight and uniformly slanted. The fall should be as great as possible.

Cement the ram in position, connect the supply pipe, fit a gasket to the top of the cross, and bolt on the flange. Then assemble the escape valve and spring. Finally, attach the check valve and the capped 4" x 24" pipe nipple that functions as an air dome.

To start operation, open the gate valve, permitting the water to close the escape valve. Then push the escape valve open and allow the water pressure to close it. Repeat this action several times and the ram should pick up the cycle and operate automatically thereafter.

If you house the ram and use a tail pipe to carry away the waste water that flows out of the ram, be careful to locate the tail pipe high enough so it won't be submerged in times of flood.

A Chicken Guillotine

by Larry McWilliams

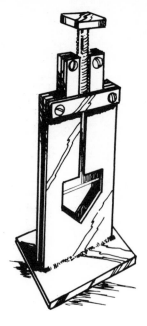

Quite a number of people ask for a poultry killer of this fashion. I hope you won't mind if I go ahead and try to convince people with guineas, turkeys, pigeons, ducks, etc. that they should give it a try too. I've even included a drawing with the dimensions for a guillotine that can be used for rabbits. The latter is the same machine except that the width of the steel plates has been changed to allow a larger hole and blade.

To start with I might mention that this item has been designed for a lifetime of use and maybe even your children's lifetime. It's constructed entirely of ¼ inch plate steel and is designed so that the plunger and blade assembly can easily be removed for sharpening. Probably the easiest way to build this contraption would be to first cut out all the necessary parts. When doing this please note that the vertical slot on side 1 is cut at an angle of 45° to the inside. Note the plan view. Also there are four spacer blocks which can be made of a piece of 1/4 inch plate plus a piece of 1/32 inch metal or you can use four pieces of 9/32 inch thick steel. The purpose of these spacers is to give a space of 1/32 inch inside the slot where the blade is moving. This should promote a smooth operating plunger.

The other critical point will be where the blade is welded to the 1/2 inch plunger rod. The weld must be ground down well until the assembly will move smoothly up and down the slot made for it. When cutting the parts for the base and handle you can round off the corners a bit if you want. Smooth down all rough edges and sharp corners except the opening on side 2. You want a good straight edge on the side which will contact the blade so you will get a good sheer action.

Lastly drill four holes in the base plate so that it can be bolted to a plank or table.

To start assemblying your guillotine clamp one of the uprights to the base in the proper position with a piece of angle iron. Make sure the angle is a true 90° after it is clamped. Weld the first upright to the base with the weld being on the outside. Next use a couple of the spacers which you've made to space the bottom of the uprights apart the proper distance and clamp to the upright which is already welded. Now you can weld the second upright and remove the spacers.

Next you'll have to make sure that you have a proper fit between the plunger and the uprights. When this is done you can put on the spring and install the plunger and blade assembly.

Right here I would like to say a couple of things about this spring. It should be a compression type srping with an inside diameter of 1/2 inch or just slightly larger. It needn't be a real strong spring as all it needs to do is return the plunger and keep it up. If you use a spring that is stronger than necessary then it will just be harder for you to push the plunger down. To put the spring on the rod wrap one end around the rod and then just screw it on like screwing on a jar lid. Put the plunger assembly in between the uprights, insert the spacers and bolt them together. You might want to add lock washers to all of the bolts just to be on the safe side. Before putting on the spring you might want to oil or grease the rod and lubricate the insides of the uprights with a light oil. A light machine oil in a small spray bottle will cover all the parts and protect them from rusting. It would be a good idea to lubricate the guillotine after each washing also.

Well there you have it. The whole thing can be taken apart quite easily to sharpen the blade or for a thorough washing and relubrication. For you rabbit people who raise large breeds or just need a larger opening than the one shown on the drawing for the rabbit guillotine I've also noted the largest possible opening for that machine. By all means try to make a v shape at the bottom of the opening though. This helps the sheer action of the blade when cutting.

After assembling the guillotine you can mount it to a 2"x6" or a 2"x8" plank and use it over a barrel in which you can drop the poultry so they won't thrash around so much.

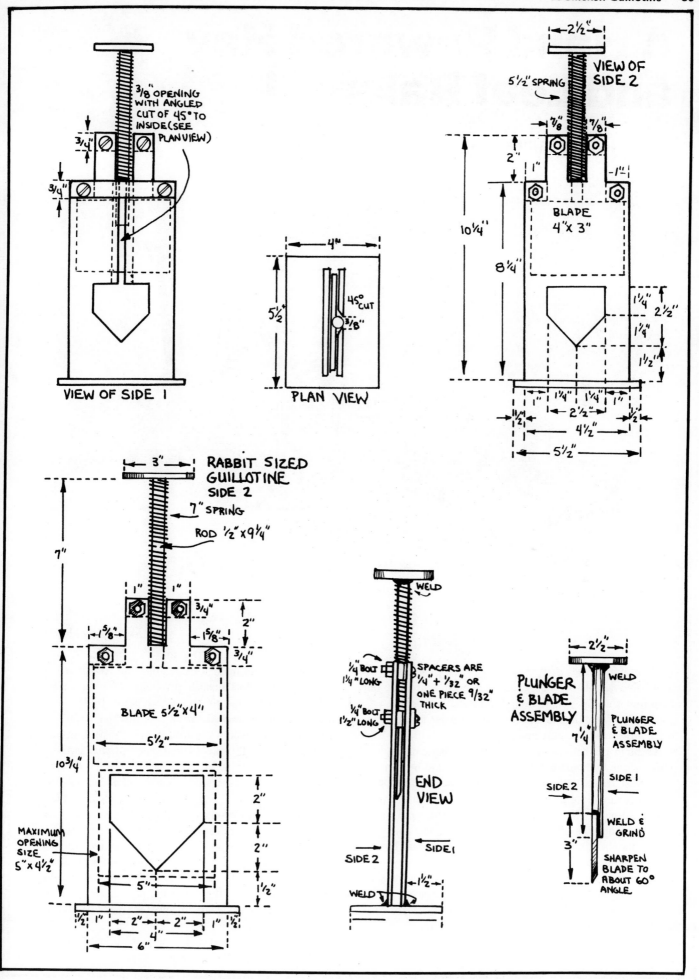

VIEW OF SIDE 1

PLAN VIEW

VIEW OF SIDE 2

RABBIT SIZED GUILLOTINE SIDE 2

END VIEW

PLUNGER & BLADE ASSEMBLY

A Hand Powered Hay and Leaf Baler

by Larry McWilliams

©1974 by Larry McWilliams

Many homesteads of twenty acres or less may have materials available for baling and storing for winter use but until now this has usually been impractical because of machinery costs. Here is a hand-powered baler that can be built with very little cost involved.

To build the baler begin by making the basic crate shape. This is done by constructing the sides, top, and bottom first. Next fasten these together to form the crate shape. All joints should be fastened with a waterproof glue and galvanized nails. The piston is put together the same way and care should be taken to make sure the spaces on the piston line up with the slots in the baling chamber. There are slots indicated on the top and bottom blocks of the piston. This is for a board, cut to fit, which is used while compressing materials into a bale. This piston face is removed when tying the bale together. All of the pivot points are put together with aluminum conduit, washers, and cotter pins. The entire machine should be painted with a good exterior paint.

This baler will make a bale about one foot square and two feet long. Most small homesteads don't use a full sized bale at one time and the hay which is usually left over is more than likely wasted. Anyway, I just don't want to lift a ninety pound bale when I don't have to. If a machine is needed which will make a larger bale just change the size of the whole thing to suit your needs. The levers which operate the piston should remain the same because they just move the piston. Only the size and length of the chambers need to be changed along with the size of the piston. This machine can also be made out of metal. Just use the plans as a guide for sizes and operative portions.

Now to operate this baler you have to first decide what you want to bale. In the summer it will probably be hay or straw. Don't quit there, the fall provides a lot of dry leaves which are excellent for livestock bedding and feed and lots of leaves can give you a great mulch the following summer in your garden. Likewise you can bale crops like comfrey provided it is thoroughly dry.

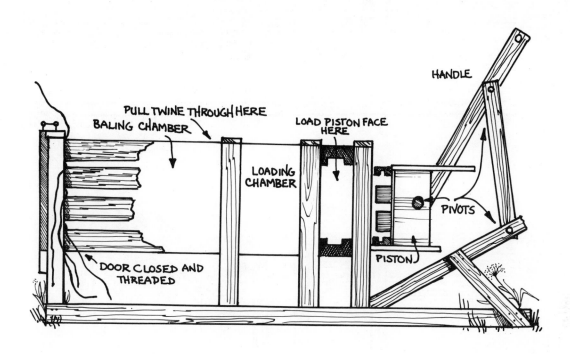

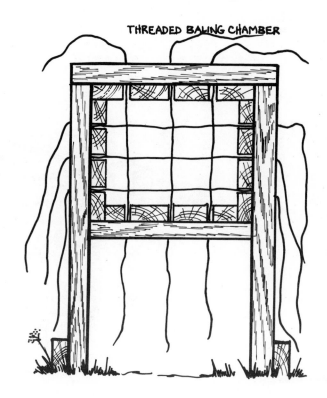

THREADED BALING CHAMBER

   To begin the baling operation thread the baling chamber
with pieces of twine or cord which has a test strength of
sixty to one hundred pounds. Each piece should be about
six feet long and should be threaded through the slots in
baling chamber as shown. You can make a small saw kerf
at the end of each slot to hold the twine. Close the baling
chamber and insert the piston face plate through the side
at the place indicated. If you're baling hay you're ready to
go. If it's leave you need to put a piece of newspaper in
front of the piston face and push it into the chamber first.
Now fill the loading chamber with material and push it into
the baling chamber with the piston. Repeat until you have
a fully compressed bale in the baling chamber. Remove the
piston face plate by pulling it out the side. If it's leaves
you're baling you need to insert another piece of newspaper at this point. This is not necessary with the hay.
Now push the piston in as far as it will go. Using a stiff
piece of wire with a small hook formed at one end pull the
twine through the slot of the baling chamber right in front
of the piston. Tie off that piece and repeat with the rest
of the threads of twine until they are all tied. Then drop
the door and push the bale out of the chamber with the
piston. Now you can grab the bale and remove it from the
chamber and you're finished. It may sound complicated
but one man can make a bale in about six minutes from
start to finish. It goes faster if there are two people working at it. One person can load while the other operates the
piston.

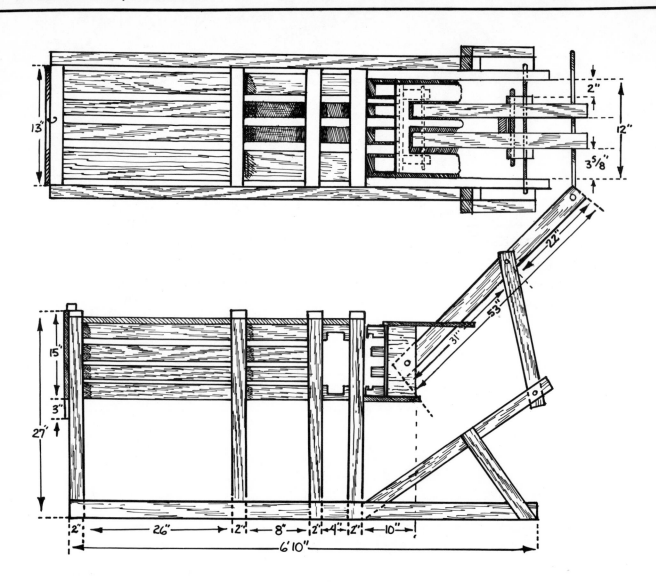

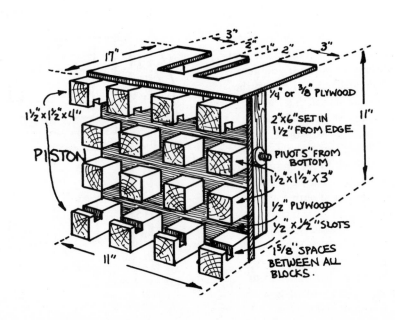

A Hand Operated Drill Press

by Arthur Howe

There's no need to place work on the floor or climb up on the bench to put enough pressure on the drill if you have a hand-operated drill press. This particular one, Fig. 1, is made from a ½ inch, 2-speed breast drill, although other sizes may be substituted. Either wood or metal is used for the base. The column is a 36 inch length of 1½ inch pipe. One end is threaded for a floor flange and the other end is notched for the operating lever. The pipe should be dressed so the two tees will be a smooth fit. These tees are reamed also and the backs are drilled and tapped for a ½ inch thread. Nuts are brazed in place in the following manner: thread them onto ½ inch bolts and turn the bolts into the tees until the nuts are flush against the tees. Then braze and remove the bolts. This will align the threads. Bend and thread short lengths of rod to make the adjusting screws.

The drill-press table is assembled as shown in Fig. 2 A short length of 1½ inch pipe is screwed to the tee on the column and an identical tee is fastened to the free end. A short nipple screws to this tee and connects to a floor flange and the table. For the upper assembly, bush the tee down for ¾ inch pipe. The nipple and tee here should centre over the drill-press table. The upper left-hand detail shows how the ¾ inch tee is assembled with the 5/8 inch rod. If you have a drill with a removable handle, you may be able to insert the rod and lock it with a setscrew, or you may have to braze it to the drill. The lever is a length of flat iron with a wooden handle riveted on. A linkage connecting the lever to the rod is held with locked nuts and washers. Fig. 3 shows an easy way to make a foot-feed drill.

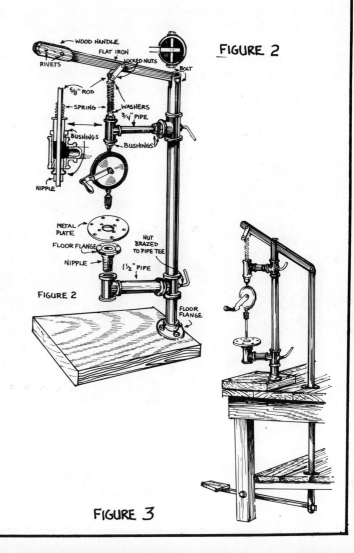

FIGURE 2

FIGURE 2

FIGURE 3

A Foot Powered Scroll Saw

by Wayne Lecky

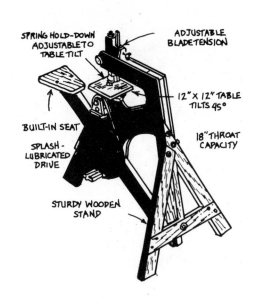

SPRING HOLD-DOWN ADJUSTABLE TO TABLE TILT

ADJUSTABLE BLADE TENSION

12" X 12" TABLE TILTS 45°

BUILT-IN SEAT

SPLASH-LUBRICATED DRIVE

18" THROAT CAPACITY

STURDY WOODEN STAND

Aside from the bolts and bushings required, this scroll saw can be constructed mostly of wood. The few other pieces of metal needed can be salvaged, in most cases, from odds and ends found in the junk box. If you prefer not to use plywood, you can use solid stock by gluing up panels of sufficient width. The crankshaft mechanism of the drive head operates in a bath of oil and is sealed inside an ordinary 1 qt. paint can of the type having a press-fit lid. Fig. 4 will give you an ide of how it works. A crankshaft, entering the side of the can, engages a bar, which slides back and forth in a channel clamped to a vertical shaft. This produces a smooth reciprocating motion of the shaft much like a piston, the stroke being 1 in. Oil in the bottom of the can is splashed by the crankshaft to keep the mechanism well lubricated.

The complete drive unit is shown in fig. 1, partly cutaway so that you can get a better idea of its assembly. Bronze bushings are used as sleeves for the vertical shaft

and also as a bearing for the crankshaft. Fig. 3 shows how the channel is clamped to flattened places on the shaft, and how the lower bushing is mounted in a flatiron bracket. Note from fig. 4 that the bolts in the latter fasten both it and the can to the wooden base. You can work the channel to shape by hand using a hacksaw, chisel and file, or you can have the channel and crankshaft made. Thick felt washers prevent leakage of oil at points where the two shafts pass through the can. The oil level, of course, should be kept below the hole in the side of the can, as shown in fig. 4. It is important that the block holding the crankshaft bearing be rigid. Fig. 2 shows a way of bolting this, which allows it to be retightened easily if it should work loose. When installing the crankshaft there must be no end play, as the face of the disk, bearing slightly against the channel, keeps the bar engaged in the latter. It also prevents twisting of the shaft and saw blade, which would cause the latter to break. So, see that the setscrews in the pulley and the

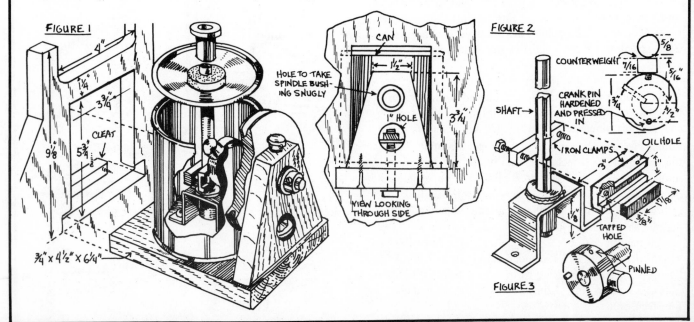

FIGURE 1

4"

1/4"

3/4"

CLEAT

9/8"

5 3/4"

3/4" X 4 1/2" X 6 1/4"

CAN

1 1/2"

HOLE TO TAKE SPINDLE BUSHING SNUGLY

1" HOLE

3/4"

VIEW LOOKING THROUGH SIDE

FIGURE 2

COUNTERWEIGHT

5/8"

7/16"

5/16"

CRANK PIN HARDENED AND PRESSED IN

1 3/4"

1/2"

SHAFT

IRON CLAMPS

OIL HOLE

3"

1"

1/8"

3/8"

TAPPED HOLE

1 1/4"

PINNED

FIGURE 3

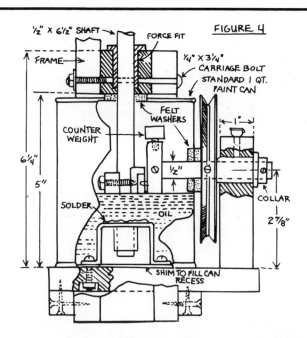

FIGURE 4

1/2" X 6 1/2" SHAFT

FORCE FIT

FRAME

1/4" X 3 1/4" CARRIAGE BOLT

STANDARD 1 QT. PAINT CAN

FELT WASHERS

COUNTER WEIGHT

6 1/4"

5"

1/2"

1"

COLLAR

2 7/8"

SOLDER

OIL

SHIM TO FILL CAN RECESS

but solid stock can be used. Fig. 9 shows how both side pieces can be laid out economically on a panel, after which the two can be cut apart roughly with a compass saw and then trimmed to exact size. The size of the opening in which the drive head fits is given in fig. 1. Note that the left-hand side has projections above the opening, which serve as stops for the tilting table. The frame or core to which the side pieces are glued and bolted is made up of common 2 by 4 in. material. Fig. 6 shows the arrangement of the pieces, while figs. 5 and 8 detail how the rear legs are fastened rigidly with bolts and screws. The member which extends to form a seat is bolted to the front and rear legs in the same way as used in the drive head. As individual leg reach varies, the length of this piece will have to be determined by trial. This is likewise true in locating the bearing hole for the large drive pulley. For some persons it may be satisfactory if centred in the seat member as in fig. 8; for others it may be necessary to fit an extra block as indicated to permit lowering the position of the pulley to a point where it is easy to pedal.

collar are tightened securely to the shaft on each side of the bushing, without side play. If desired, you can make the pulley of wood and pin it to the shaft. Before the lid can be pressed on the can, the upper end of the shaft must be threaded and slotted, so that a blade chuck like the one detailed in fig. 7 can be fitted to it after the upper bushing and the filler block in which it fits, have been slipped over the end.

You can set the drive-head unit aside for the time being, and proceed to make the wood stand. Plywood is preferred

Assemble the stand as far as shown in fig. 6 and then slip the drive unit into the opening provided for it before putting the opposite plywood side on the frame. This, of course, will necessitate removing the pulley and the wood bearing block. In doing this, be careful that the pin in the crankshaft does not disengage the bar. Cleats are used in the manner shown in figs. 1 and 4 to fasten the drive unit in place, after which the filler block containing the upper bushing of the shaft is bolted flush with the top of the plywood sides. With this filler block in place, you

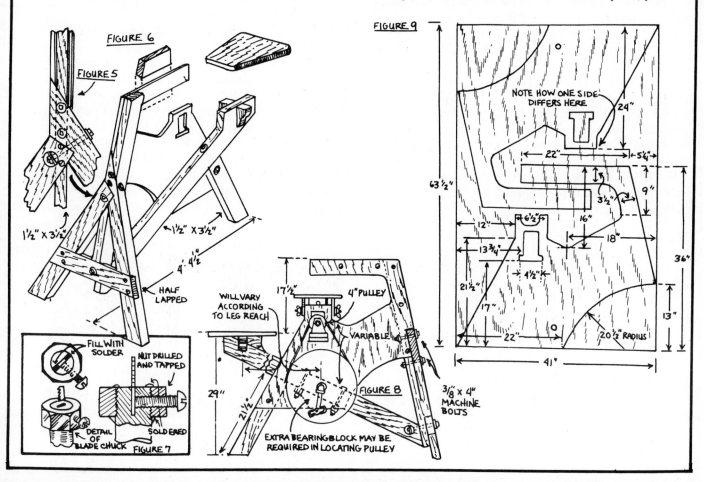

FIGURE 6

FIGURE 5

1 1/2" X 3 1/2"

1 1/2" X 3 1/2"

4' 4 1/2"

HALF LAPPED

FILL WITH SOLDER

NUT DRILLED AND TAPPED

SOLDERED

DETAIL OF BLADE CHUCK   FIGURE 7

WILL VARY ACCORDING TO LEG REACH

17 1/2"

4" PULLEY

VARIABLE

29"

21 1/2"

FIGURE 8

EXTRA BEARING BLOCK MAY BE REQUIRED IN LOCATING PULLEY

3/8" X 4" MACHINE BOLTS

FIGURE 9

NOTE HOW ONE SIDE DIFFERS HERE

24"

22"

5 1/4"

63 1/2"

9"

3 1/2"

12"

6 1/2"

16"

18"

13 3/4"

21 1/2"

17"

4 1/2"

22"

36"

13"

20 1/2" RADIUS

41"

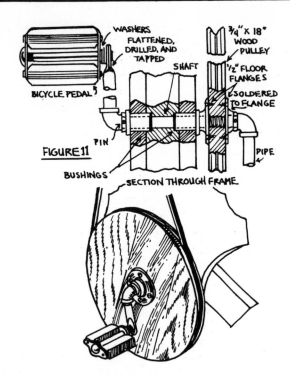

FIGURE 11

SECTION THROUGH FRAME

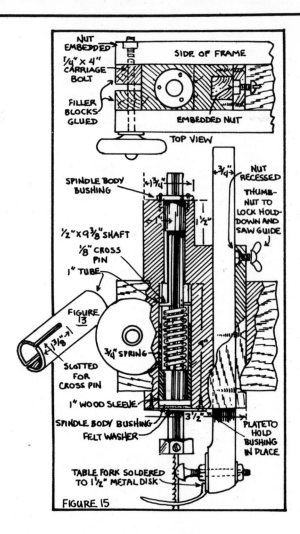

FIGURE 15

can go ahead and add the blade chuck to the slotted end of the shaft. This consists of a hexagon nut screwed and soldered to the end and then drilled and tapped crosswise for a setscrew to clamp the blade as shown in fig. 7. The blade can be made self-centreing in the chuck by filling the slot with solder on each side of a piece of wood that is the same width as the blade.

The sectional view in fig. 11 shows how the large drive pulley is held to a ½ in. pipe shaft by two floor flanges which are centred and screwed opposite each other. One end of the shaft is threaded to pass through the flanges far enough to permit a ½ in. elbow to be pinned to the projecting end and soldered to the flange. If you are unable to have the bushings turned of metal to fit the pipe shaft, satisfactory ones can be turned of hard maple and replaced at signs of wear. If metal bushings are used, they should be a press fit in the stand. Bicycle pedals, which can be picked up at a repair shop, attached to flattened ends of short pipe arms make a neat job. Owing to the size of the plywood drive pulley, you'll have to true it on the outer end of the lathe.

You make the blade-tension unit, fig. 12, next. This is adjustable up and down in the arm so that the tension on the blade can be varied to suit the size being used and thereby reduce breakage. A record of the tension found best for each blade can be indicated on the side of the unit by marking on it across the top of the frame. These calibrations will tell you how much to raise or lower the unit when changing to a finer or coarser blade. Fig. 14 gives the steps in making the wooden housing of the unit. You begin with a hardwood block 1½ by 3 by 7 in. A line is drawn down one side and across both ends to mark the points for boring. As it is important that the holes be in

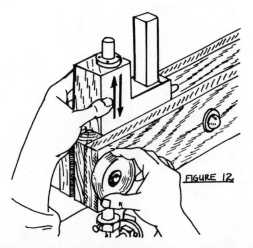

FIGURE 12

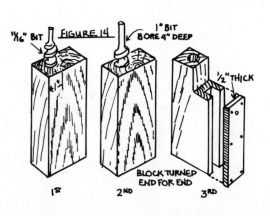

FIGURE 14

line centrally through the block, a drill press is preferred to boring them by hand, although the latter can be done fairly accurately if you are careful to keep the bit running as straight as possible. Bore the top hole 3 in. deep, then turn the block end for end, and with a 1 in. bit, bore through to meet the first hole. Next, groove the rear edge of the block to take the hold-down, after which the upper corner is notched according to the dimensions given in fig. 15.

The cutaway sectional view in fig. 15 shows what the tension mechanism looks like when installed in the counterbored housing. Bronze bushings of the type that were used in the drive head are used here to carry the shaft; the upper bushing being pinned to the block through the flange and the lower one bushed centrally in the hole with a turned wooden sleeve. Fitting the lower bushing is done after the large hole is lined with a 1 by 2¾ in metal or Bakelite tube, slotted like the one shown in fig. 13. This tube, besides forming a well for grease to lubricate the spring and lower bushing, keeps the shaft tracking without twist by engaging a cross pin in the shaft in slots in the tube. Needless to say, the slots in the tube must be cut down each side exactly in the centre, otherwise the pin is apt to bind or prevent assembly. The shaft, with the cross pin either threaded or pressed into it, must be slipped inside the tube and both inserted in the hole at the same time,

after which the spring is added and the lower bushing and its sleeve are pressed in the end to hold the tube in place. The width of the slots in the tube should equal the diameter of the cross pin. Note that a thick felt washer is provided between the bushing and the metal plate which holds the former in place, to prevent oil from being thrown out through the shaft clearance in the plate. The upper blade chuck is made the same way as the lower one, which was described previously, the end of the shaft being threaded for the nut before the shaft is installed in the housing.

A turn of a handwheel clamps the unit securely in the arm. This can be made of wood and fitted with a carriage bolt to engage an embedded nut in the opposite side as shown in the top view of fig. 15. The completed unit must be mounted in the arm so that the upper chuck will be directly in line with the lower one. You can do this best by clamping the unit temporarily in place with a C-clamp or a handscrew and checking it for alignment with a square held along the underside of the arm. When centred, the frame core piece along the top of the arm is fitted and bolted in place behind the unit and filler blocks or stops are glued between the sides at the front. See top view, fig. 15.

The work hold-down, figs. 15 and 16, is improvised from an old table fork having the two centre tines removed.

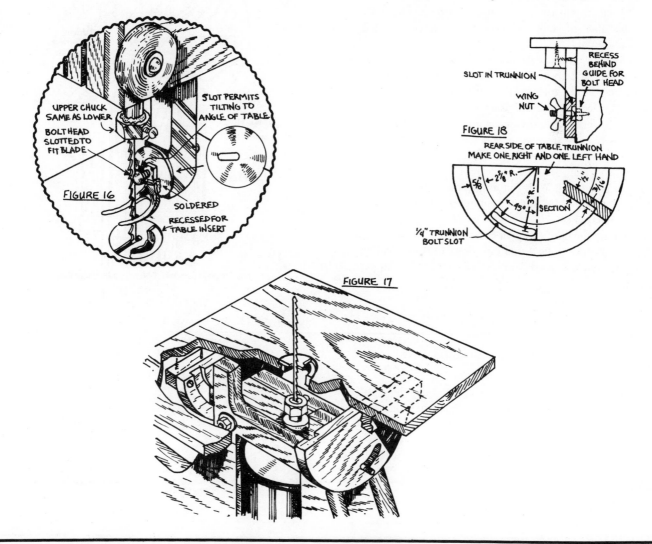

FIGURE 16
UPPER CHUCK SAME AS LOWER
BOLT HEAD SLOTTED TO FIT BLADE
SLOT PERMITS TILTING TO ANGLE OF TABLE
SOLDERED
RECESSED FOR TABLE INSERT

FIGURE 18
SLOT IN TRUNNION
RECESS BEHIND GUIDE FOR BOLT HEAD
WING NUT
REAR SIDE OF TABLE TRUNNION MAKE ONE RIGHT AND ONE LEFT HAND
¼" TRUNNION BOLT SLOT
SECTION

FIGURE 17

It is soldered to a 1½ in. disk slotted crosswise, to permit the hold-down to be adjusted to whatever slant the table may be tilted. The fork and disk are held to a wood shaft by a bolt blade guide. Several of these guides will be needed to accommodate blades of various thicknesses. You can make them easily from ¼ in. carriage bolts by slotting the heads the required depth with a hacksaw and then closing the slot slightly by peening it to suit the blade thickness. A thumbnut fitted as shown in fig. 15 serves to lock the hold-down at the desired height, and wax applied to both the shaft and the channel in which it moves will make it slide easily.

Making the **trunnions** for the tilting table will require the use of a lathe, as a groove must be turned in them to take guides on which they move. Both trunnions can be had from one plywood disk by sawing it carefully in half after turning to size. Note in fig. 18 that the bolt slots through the trunnions must be cut on opposite sides of the centreline to obtain right and left-hand units. Use hard-pressed board from which to turn a ring to fit the trunnion grooves nicely and then screw 3 in. segments of the ring flush with the top of the frame at the front and back as shown in figs. 19 and 20. Notice that the square heads of the trunnion bolts are embedded under the guides before screwing the latter in place. A wing nut and washer are provided on each bolt to lock the trunnions in position. Wax applied to the trunnion grooves and the guides will make the table tilt smoothly. Plywood is preferred to solid stock for the table, as it will stay flat. It is attached to the trunnions with cleats as shown in the upper detail in fig. 18. You will have to do this, of course, while the trunnions are in place on the guides. The recess for the metal table insert is formed easily by pressing a turned ring in the hole as shown in fig. 17. Here you can also see how the frame extensions provide stops to permit returning the table quickly to a horizontal position. Where it is desired to have the table so it can be tilted 45 degrees to the left also, the stops can be cut off. With this arrangement, the clamping-bolt slots are extended and the trunnion indexed 90 degrees for rapid setting.

If you are unable to buy an endless V-belt long enough to reach the drive pulley, you can resort to round leather belting or even sash cord, applying belt dressing if slippage develops.

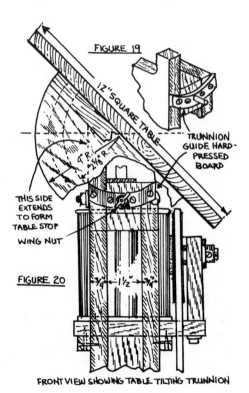

FRONT VIEW SHOWING TABLE TILTING TRUNNION

Cotter Pins Hold Bandsaw Blade in Vise While Brazing

Instead of making up a special jig to hold the ends of broken bandsaw blades in perfect alignment while brazing, just slip a couple of cotter pins over the blade and clamp them in a vise as shown. To protect vise jaws against excessive heat from the torch, a piece of asbestos paper can be held in place under the blade by forcing both cotter pins through the centre of the paper before clamping them in the vise.

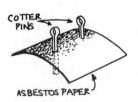

Sprouting Trays

by Larry McWilliams

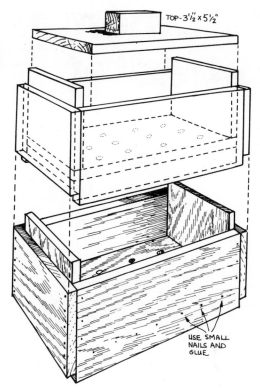

TOP-3½" x 5½"

USE SMALL NAILS AND GLUE

© 1974 by Larry McWilliams

There's a lot of interest in sprouting devices for livestock and feed and a request came through for a simple but effectively designed system for stacked sprouting trays. The ones shown here will stack as tall as is practical for your own situation and will provide excellent drainage. There is no need for a special tray for the bottom since all the trays can be used as a bottom tray.

To make the trays use ¼ inch plywood and cut the parts as shown. The only point I might make is that you might taper the top ½ inch of the inner end pieces slightly. This will assure an easy fit after painting. After you have all of the parts cut for as many trays as you want and the one for the top, you can assemble them.

To do this put together the inner ends and the sides. You should use a good glue and small nails for the construction. After the inner ends and sides are put together put on the bottoms. Next you can attach the other ends. For a handle on the top, any type can be used from a thread spool to a regular handle or a simple block of wood.

After drilling your drainage holes in each tray, you then need to completely paint the trays. Since they are going to be used in constant connection with water, you should use a good waterproof paint. Do not use a lead-based paint, as the lead is toxic. My recommendations would be a good epoxy-type paint.

You will probably want to make five or six trays for each stack. Remember that it is easier to make several of these trays at one time than it is to make a few now and then have to make more later. I won't try to tell you about sprouting or its virtues here, but I would like to say that I've tried it and the results are fantastic to say the least. So if you haven't tried sprouting, build these trays and join us in some great eating.

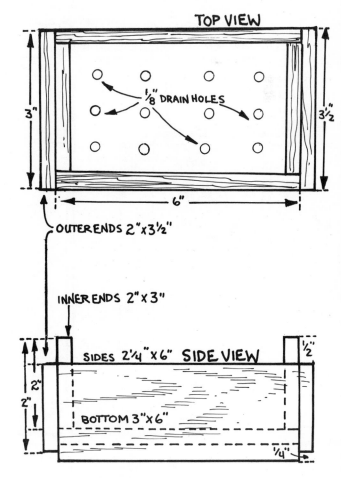

TOP VIEW

⅛" DRAIN HOLES

3"   3½"

6"

OUTER ENDS 2" x 3½"

INNER ENDS 2" x 3"

SIDES 2¼" x 6"   SIDE VIEW   ½"

BOTTOM 3" x 6"

2"   2"

¼"

A Homemade Honey Extractor

by Larry McWilliams

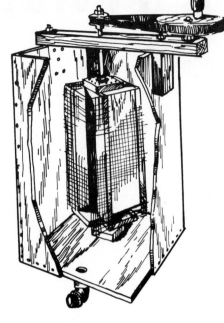

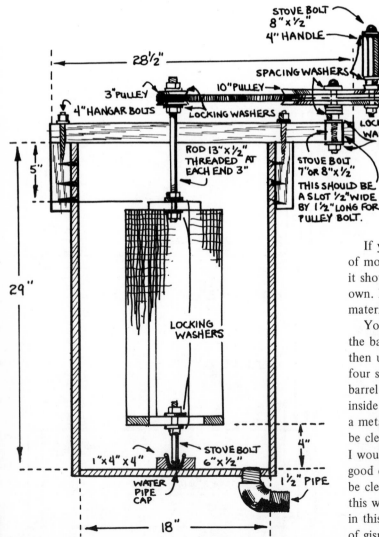

STOVE BOLT
8" x ½"
4" HANDLE

SPACING WASHERS

28½"

3" PULLEY   10" PULLEY

4" HANGAR BOLTS   LOCKING WASHERS

LOCKING WASHERS

ROD 13" x ½"
THREADED AT
EACH END 3"

STOVE BOLT
7" OR 8" x ½"

THIS SHOULD BE
A SLOT ½" WIDE
BY 1½" LONG FOR
PULLEY BOLT.

© 1974 by Larry McWilliams

5"

29"

LOCKING
WASHERS

4"

1"x 4" x 4"   STOVE BOLT
6" x ½"

WATER
PIPE
CAP   1½" PIPE

18"

If you have only two or three hives then spending a lot of money on a honey extractor may seem ridiculous and so it should when for just a few dollars you can build your own. In fact most homesteads probably have the required materials just lying around waiting to be put to a good use.

You'll need some kind of large barrel or tank to use for the basis of this whole operation. If you don't have one then use the method shown in the sketches which is just a four sided box made of plywood. If you use a drum or barrel the minimum size should be 29 inches high with an inside diameter of at least 18 inches. You may even find a metal garbage can of that size. Whatever you use it should be cleaned thoroughly and if you use wood or bare metal I would suggest you paint it with two or three coats of good epoxy paint inside. Since the whole extractor should be cleaned thoroughly with hot soapy water after each use, this would give a very duable coating. The bushings used in this extractor are very basic. You can purchase all types of gismos which will substitute for the ones shown. This design is for someone who wants to keep the cost down and still end up with a good machine. The pulleys can also be purchased but two pieces of plywood cut in a circle at an angle of about 45 degrees then glued and screwed together will make a pulley just as well.

The baskets which hold the frames for extracting are very simple and easy to make. You can make both baskets or just the one that you would need the most. The parts of the baskets should be glued and screwed together and then finished with epoxy paint. The wire mesh can be stapled or nailed to the wood. The wire should be only on the sides. Leave the bottoms open so the ends of the frames will fit into them where the holes are located. The sketches will do a better job of explaining the actual construction than I can put into words. Even if you buy all of your materials you should be able to put it together for $20 to $25. But then again materials may cost more than that by the time this article is printed. Enjoy your sweet tooth.

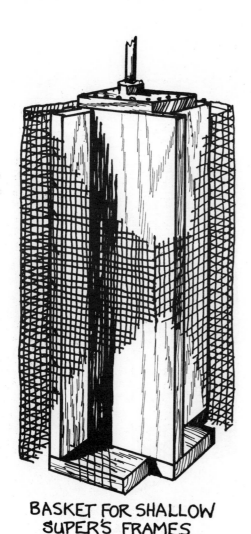

BASKET FOR SHALLOW
SUPER'S FRAMES

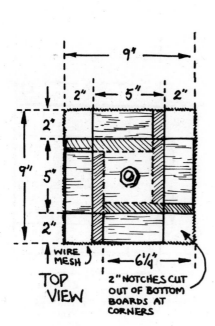

TOP VIEW

WIRE MESH

2" NOTCHES CUT OUT OF BOTTOM BOARDS AT CORNERS

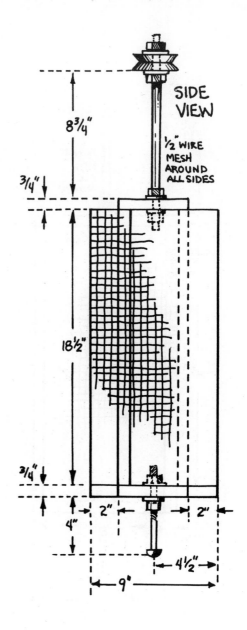

SIDE VIEW

½" WIRE MESH AROUND ALL SIDES

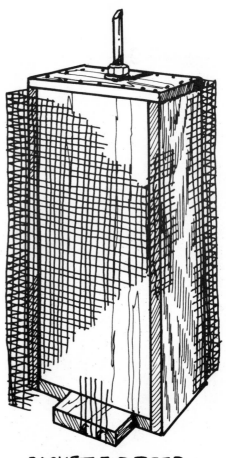

BASKET FOR DEEP
SUPER'S FRAMES

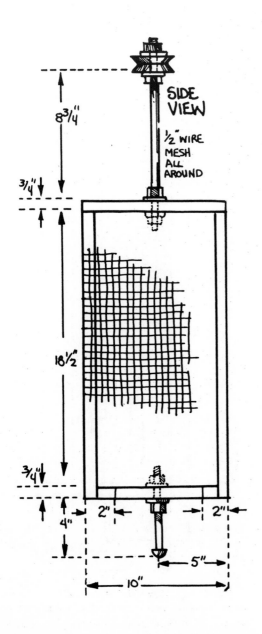

SIDE
VIEW

½" WIRE
MESH
ALL
AROUND

8¾"

¾"

18½"

¾"

4"

2"   2"

5"

10"

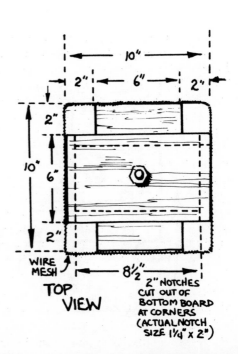

10"

2"   6"   2"

2"

10"   6"

2"

8½"

WIRE
MESH

TOP
VIEW

2" NOTCHES
CUT OUT OF
BOTTOM BOARD
AT CORNERS
(ACTUAL NOTCH
SIZE 1¼" X 2")

A Controlled Smokehouse

by Iola Berg

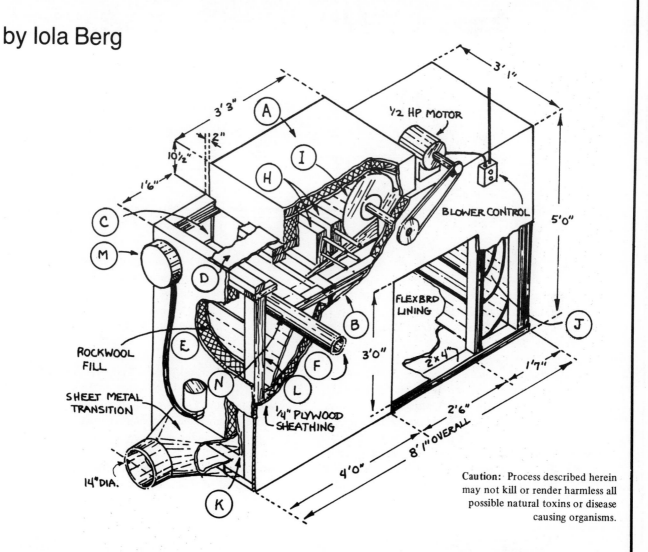

Caution: Process described herein may not kill or render harmless all possible natural toxins or disease causing organisms.

This unit was approximately 8 feet long, 6 feet high and 3 feet wide. The box (A) situated above and fitted tightly into the main housing is removable and necessary only to enclose the volume blower and to allow access to the blower and radiator heating units. Lots of from 150 to 250 pounds of fish can be cured in this smokehouse.

The framework is of 2 inch x 4 inch lumber with an inner lining of 1/8 inch flexboard (cement-asbestos) and an outer covering of 1/4-inch plywood. Rock wool is used for insulation. Flexboard was used for the inner lining since this material will not corrode and may be easily cleaned. A section of flexboard (B) was installed to divide the smokehouse into two sections; that is, to separate the radiators and blowers from the smoke chamber itself. This merely completes and separates the smoking chamber to permit accurate control during the smoking process.

Air enters the house proper through a square hole (C) as indicated in figure 1 and may be seen in figure 2. The air intake is controlled by a sliding panel (D) that fits snugly over the opening. The air intake leads into a long box (E),

which extends horizontally across the house and acts as a mixing chamber for the smoke and air. Smoke enters this box at the opposite end from the air intake at the point (F). This box has an opening near the centre, and facing the radiator heaters (H). The air-smoke mixture is drawn through this opening by the blower (I) and is simultaneously mixed and heated. The heaters are two steam radiators of the "colonial wall" type, held in position by ordinary "U" bolts supported from angle irons. These angle irons rest on the framework proper. The temperature of the radiators is controlled by a thermostat connected to a magnetic steam valve on a by-pass steam line.

The smoke is distributed through the smoking trays on the racks located in the smoking chamber by means of the volume blower and the baffle arrangement (J). The particular blower used has a capacity of 2100 to 2750 cubic feet per minute and is operated by a 1/2 h.p. electric motor. The smoke, after being deflected by the baffles, is either exhausted through the outlet damper (K) or is recirculated back through the radiators and blower after being deflected

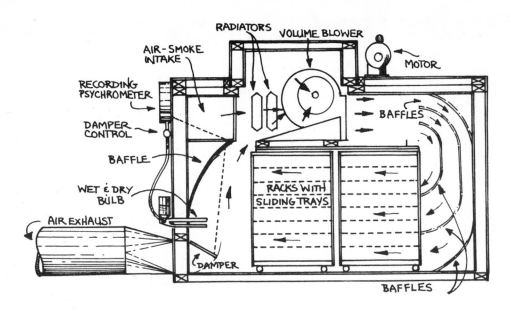

by baffle (L). A sectional view of this arrangement and the direction of air-smoke flow may be seen in figure 2.

The baffles are constructed of pliable light metal sheeting. Considerable manipulation was necessary to locate the exact position of the baffles in order to insure a uniform air distribution. This is accomplished by hanging long narrow strips of cloth across the direction of air flow in the smokehouse chamber. Several sets of these strips placed parallel to each other are set up. When the air blower is turned on, the baffles are then adjusted until uniform deflection of the cloth strips is obtained. The upper portion or inlet of the baffle is spaced evenly and is stationary, while only the lower portions are adjustable. As an aid to obtaining proper circulation in this type of unit, the area of the blower outlet, the air intake, and the air exhaust should be of equal dimensions.

A recording psychrometer (M) was installed to the rear of of the house, with the bulbs and thermostat situated just above the damper. At this location, they are exposed to direct air circulation and are in a safe place away from the "working" parts of the smokehouse.

The smoking racks are constructed of angle iron and mounted on metal casters. These racks are of such height so as to fit flush against the top of the smokehouse chamber when in place. This is necessary to take full advantage of the entire chamber and to permit a more uniform circulation of smoke by eliminating unused spaces. These racks are equipped with a series of angle iron guides along two parallel sides for holding fish trays or rods and are so constructed as to allow 3½ to 4 inches of air space between each tray

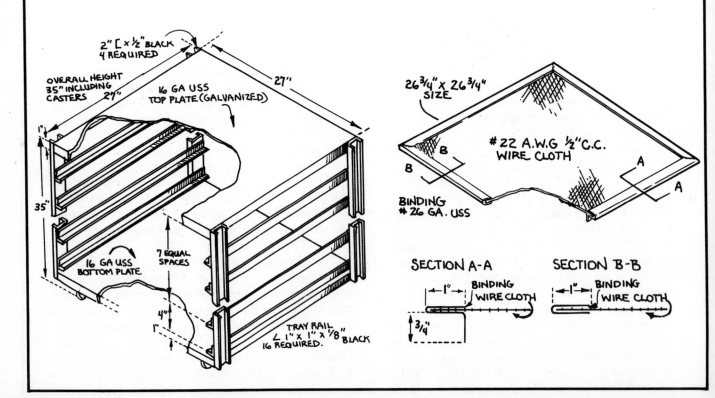

when in place. The trays consist merely of 1/2-inch mesh screen trimmed with a light metal band to make them sturdy and durable. During the smoking process, the racks are placed in such a position that the angle iron guides run parallel to the length of the house, so as to permit an unobstructed flow of air over the trays. The racks are so designed that the trays can be easily removed and rods inserted in their place for hanging fish or fillets. The construction of the racks and trays is shown in figure 3.

The smoke generator consists of a metal oil drum placed horizontally on a metal frame. A door and draft are cut in one end; through the top part of the other end is located the smoke pipe outlet. This outlet pipe leads into a "T" pipe joint equipped with suitable dampers. One part of the "T" joint leads to the smokehouse, while the other leads to the outside atmosphere. The dampers (N) are used to direct the smoke into the smokehouse and to aid in the control of the smoke volume. When the smoking process is completed, the dampers are adjusted so that the smoke is directed to the outside atmosphere.

The smoke generator is located about 20 feet from the smokehouse proper and connected by the 5 inch pipe. In this particular case, locating the generator a great distance from the smokehouse served to minimize any fire hazard. A drain valve was located in the pipe about midway between the generator and smokehouse inlet to allow for removal of the tar and resinous material that condensed in the pipeline.

In general, this design was adopted utilizing the equipment most suitable for pilot plant operation and adaptable for commercial operations. Other individual pieces of equipment may be substituted. For this pilot plant model, steam heat was used. Suitably designed oil burner units or electric heaters may be substituted. Other minor changes could be made, depending upon the materials available in any particular location. For commercial operations the design may be altered slightly, but actually all that would need to be done would be to enlarge the dimensions and increase the unit capacities.

SMOKE CURING PROCESSES

It is emphasized that only good quality fish or shellfish should be used for smoke curing. Smoking will not cover up or conceal the poor flavour and quality of inferior fish. The strictest sanitation at all points in the procedure should be practised. Smoked fish is a perishable product and should be handled as such. Careless handling will result in a poor quality product of short keeping time. Clean utensils, as well as clean, pure salt and water, should be used in brining and washing processes.

For making up the proper brine concentrations, a salinometer should be used. If one is not available, the proper salt concentration can be prepared from the data shown in Table 1.

The smoking procedures given below are **applicable only for use with the preceding type controlled smokehouse.**

Kippered Salmon

1. Any species of salmon may be used; however, the king or chum is preferred. Commercially, the white king salmon is used almost exclusively. Dress the fish into fillets. These whole fillets may be cured, but the usual practice is to cut the fillets into approximately one-pound pieces.

2. Soak the fish for one-half to three hours in 90° to 95° salinometer brine, the length of the fish and the degree of salting or salt flavouring desired. Rinse the pieces and allow to drain slightly.

3. Arrange the fish on screens. New screens or freshly-cleaned screens should be rubbed with a cloth soaked with a vegetable oil. This "oiling" prevents the fish from sticking to the metal screens during the smoking process. Mineral oil or any good quality edible vegetable oil such as cottonseed, corn, or soya oils may be used. The thinner pieces of fillets should be segregated so that they may be removed during the smoking process, since these sections require a shorter curing time. Place the racks in the smokehouse chamber preheated to 100°F. Dry the fish for 1 to 1½ hours at 100°F, using the volume blower, and with both the intake and exhaust dampers fully open. At the end of this time, adjust the dampers to one-half open and begin the smoking operation. Maintain the temperature of 100°F and continue smoking for one hour. Raise the temperature gradually to 170°F - 175°F and smoke for an additional hour, after which time the thinner pieces of fish are removed. The thicker pieces are smoked and cooked for an additional hour at 170°F - 175°F. After this cure, the smoke is by-passed from the smokehouse, the dampers opened full, and the fish allowed to cool to room temperature. Kippered salmon may be consumed immediately or may be wrapped in cellophane and refrigerated for later use. The product is quite perishable, but for longer storage periods the fish may be quick-frozen and held in storage for later use as desired.

Cold Smoked Salmon

1. Mild-cured or hard-salted salmon is used. Soak the fish fillets for 18 to 24 hours in fresh running water. Trim off any ragged edges and drain thoroughly. Draining may be accomplished by hanging the sides on rods or by a procedure known as "water horsing" in which the fish are piled flesh side down and weighted down to press out the water.

2. After the fish have drained thoroughly, arrange the sides on the wire-mesh smoking screens which have been previously rubbed with vegetable oil. The fillets may also be strung on rods or racks. Allow sufficient space for smoke circulation.

3. The curing procedure is varied in accordance with the type of cure and degree of preservation desired. If the product is to be consumed immediately or within a short period or if it is to be quick-frozen for later use, only a light cure is desirable. For a product of good keeping quality, a longer drying and curing process is necessary.

   (a) **Light cure.** The racks are placed in the smoking chamber maintained at 85°F, with the volume blower on. With the dampers fully open, continue this drying process for 3 to 4 hours. After this time, close the air intake damper, readjust the exhaust damper, and begin the smoking operation. Continue the smoking process for 8 to 10 hours, maintaining the temperature at 85°F or slightly lower.

(b) **Heavy cure.** Place the fish racks in the smoking chamber and dry for 2 hours at 85°F. After this time, adjust the intake and exhaust dampers to the one-third open position and begin the smoking. Smoke at 85°F for 5 to 6 days.

This type of cure produces a firm, dark brown product of reasonably good keeping quality. Refrigeration is not necessary, but is desirable if extended periods of storage are contemplated.

Hot Smoked Smelt

1. Only strictly fresh smelt should be used. Medium or large-sized fish are more suitable for smoking. The fish may be headed and eviscerated or may be left in the round. The dressed fish represent approximately 75% of the weight of the whole fish. Wash the fish thoroughly and drain slightly.
2. Soak the smelt for 45 minutes in a 60° salinometer brine. Rinse thoroughly and spread the fish on oiled wire screens and allow to drain. If desired, the round fish may be strung on rods by inserting the rod through the gills and mouth. These rods are then placed on the smoking racks.
3. Place the racks in the smoking chamber preheated to 220°F. Dry the fish for three hours at this temperature, with the intake and exhaust dampers fully open. After this time, set the dampers at the one-third open position and allow smoke to enter the smoking chamber. Gradually raise the temperature of the smokehouse to 130° to 140°F and continue the smoking process for 7 to 8 hours. In this process, the fish lose approximately 25% of their weight due to shrinkage.
4. Exhaust the smoke from the chamber and cool the fish to room temperature. The fish may be consumed immediately or packaged in cellophane and held under refrigeration for short periods of storage.

This cure produces a very fine-flavoured product with a delicate golden brown colour. The smoked smelt may be eaten whole, inasmuch as the process is sufficient to render the bones friable, while the natural oil present prevents the fish from becoming dry and tough.

Smoke Curing Prior to Canning

Fish are smoke cured prior to canning in order to give the canned fish an additional flavouring and colouring and in many cases to improve the texture of the product. Subsequent canning and storage of smoked fishery products tend to enhance the smoke flavour and colour and for this reason the fish should not be oversmoked.

The smoked fishery products may be hermetically sealed in cans by either of two methods: by vacuum sealing or by steam exhausting and sealing. The former method is accomplished by sealing with a vacuum closing machine. In the latter process, the filled cans are first partially sealed; that is, the lids are placed in position and given the first clinch.

These cans are then exposed to live steam in a steam box for 12 to 15 minutes. The steam box is merely a wooden or metal container with a loose-fitting lid and equipped with a steam inlet. After steaming, the seal is completed by giving the lids the second and final clinch.

Anchovies

1. Only strictly fresh anchovies should be used, preferably those not more than 3 or 4 hours out of water. Dress the fish; that is, remove head and viscera and wash in fresh water or dilute salt solution (3%). The fish should be agitated gently during the washing process to remove any blood and loose scales. There is a loss of about 30% of the total weight of the fish in dressing.
2. Allow the fish to drain a few minutes. Then soak them in a 60° salinometer brine for 11 to 15 minutes. After this time, the fish have absorbed a sufficient amount of salt. Place the fish on screens and wash under a fine water spray. Allow to drain for 15 minutes.
3. Arrange the fish, without overlapping, on the oiled wire mesh trays and place the trays in the smokehouse preheated to 110°F. Dry at this temperature for one hour.
4. After this drying period, smoke for two hours; during this time, raise the temperature of the smokehouse to 150°F. This represents a rise in temperature of 5°F for each 15 minutes of smoking.
5. Cool the fish to room temperature. Pack in ½ pound tuna cans or ¼ flat cans. The latter, if available, are preferable. For the ½ tuna flats, add one ounce of vegetable oil (cottonseed, corn, or soya) to the can before packing. Pack the fish in rows, alternating the heads and tails, with their back sides down. Place the second layer of fish on their sides and continue the third layer in the same manner as the first. Add an additional ½ ounce of vegetable oil. Vacuum seal or steam exhaust for 12 to 15 minutes, then seal.
6. Process for 75 minutes at 100 pounds pressure (240°F) and then water cool immediately.

Hot Smoked Salmon

1. Fresh or fresh-frozen salmon may be used. The frozen fish should first be thawed by immersing in cold running water for 8 to 10 hours. Dress the whole fish and wash thoroughly in fresh water or weak brine. Cut the fish into pieces of sufficient thickness to exact fit into the particular can size used. Remove the backbone section from each piece. Do not remove the skin at this time.
2. Wash the sections under a fresh water spray and drain slightly. Soak the fish in a 95° salinometer brine for 2 hours. Drain and wash in a fresh water spray. Drain again for 15 minutes.
3. Place fish skin side down on the screen trays and place the trays in the smokehouse at room temperature. Dry at room temperature for ½ hour.
4. After this drying process, smoke for 3 hours; during this time, raise the temperature of the smokehouse to 170°F. This time and temperature is sufficient to produce a suitable pellicle. Continue the smoking process for 2½

hours. This additional curing is necessary to produce a fine flavour and to cook the fish sufficiently to allow removal of the skin.

5. Cool the fish. Remove the skins and pack the meats solidly in the cans. One-half pound salmon cans are preferred. Add one ounce of vegetable oil. Vacuum seal or steam exhaust and seal. Process for 75 minutes at 240°F (10 pounds pressure).

Smelt

1. Dress the fish by removing the heads and viscera and wash thoroughly. Smaller smelt are more suitable for canning.
2. Soak the dressed fish for 45 minutes in a 60° salinometer brine solution. Use brine in the proportion of two parts brine to one part fish.
3. After brining, rinse the fish thoroughly in fresh water and allow to drain thoroughly. Arrange the fish evenly without stacking on the oiled wire screens.
4. Place the racks in the smokehouse preheated to 110°F. Dry the fish at this temperature for one hour. At the end of this time, close the air intake damper, adjust the exhaust damper, and begin the smoking process. Raise the temperature of the smokehouse to 130° - 149°F and continue smoking at this temperature for 3 hours.
5. Cool the fish and pack in cans. The smelt are packed in the same manner as described for anchovies. For the ½ pound tuna flat, add 1½ ounces of vegetable oil.
6. Vacuum seal or steam exhaust and seal. Process for 75 minutes at 240°F (10 pounds pressure). Water cool immediately.

Oysters

1. Only fresh live oysters should be used. Wash the shells thoroughly to remove any adhering sand or dirt. Steam the oysters in a steam box for 15 minutes at atmospheric pressure or in a retort for 5 minutes at one pound pressure. This procedure is preferable to shucking the oysters fresh, since in the steaming process the oysters become firm and develop a texture more suitable for smoking and for absorbing the smoke flavour. Remove the meats from the shells and wash thoroughly.
2. Soak the oyster meats for 5 minutes in a 60° salinometer brine. Large oysters, less than 200 per gallon, should be cut in halves or thirds before brining. Rinse and allow to drain thoroughly for 15 minutes.
3. Arrange the oyster meats on the oiled screens. Place the racks in the smoking chamber preheated to 100°F. Smoke for one hour, with both the intake and exhaust dampers fully open. At the end of this period, close both dampers and continue smoking for an additional ½ hour. Raise the temperature for a final ½ hour period. The last smoking operation tends to produce the desirable colour in the oysters.
4. Exhaust the smoke from the smokehouse and cool the oysters to room temperature.
5. Pack the meats tightly in cans, preferably ¼ pound flats. The cans must be well filled prior to closing and sealing. Add one ounce of vegetable oil. Vacuum seal or steam exhaust and seal.

6. Process for 60 minutes at 240°F (10 pounds pressure). Water cool the cans immedately after processing.

Cured in this manner, oysters develop a very delicate smoke flavour, which does not obscure but supplements their normal piquant taste.

Razor Clams

1. The clams are opened by exposing them for several minutes to steam in a steam box at atmospheric pressure. Shake out the meats and clean the clams by removing the stomach and splitting open the neck. Wash thoroughly in fresh water. Cut each clam in three sections: neck, foot, and mantle.
2. Soak the clam meats in a 60° salinometer brine for 5 minutes. Rinse thoroughly and drain for 15 minutes. Arrange the meats on oiled wire screens.
3. Place the racks in the smokehouse preheated to 105°F. Smoke for ½ hour with all dampers open full. After this time, close the air intake, adjust the exhaust damper, and continue smoking for 2½ hours, but allow the temperature to rise to 140°F during the last ½ hour. Weight loss of the clam meats during this smoking process is approximately 25 to 30%.
4 Exhaust the smoke and cool the clams to room temperature.
5. The product may be consumed immediately or may be packed in cellophane bags and refrigerated for later use. For canning, pack the meats in ½ pound tuna flats. Add 1½ ounces of vegetable oil. Process at 240°F (10 pounds pressure) for 75 minutes.

Rock Clams

Rock clams are handled in about the same manner as the razor clams, except that the smoking procedure is varied slightly. The prepared meats are placed in the smoking chamber preheated to 105°F. Smoke at this temperature for ½ hour, with all dampers fully open. At the end of this period, close the intake damper, adjust the exhaust damper, and continue smoking at 105°F for 1½ to 2 hours, allowing the temperature to rise to 120°F during the last ½ hour. Complete the packing and canning procedure in the same manner as that for razor clams.

Table 1. SALT TABLE

Salinometer Degrees	Ounces of Salt per Gallon of Water	Salinometer Degrees	Ounces of Salt per Gallon of Water
3.8	1.3	52.8	20.8
7.6	2.6	56.6	22.6
11.3	4.0	60.4	24.4
15.1	5.3	64.2	26.2
18.9	6.7	68.0	28.1
22.6	8.1	71.7	30.0
26.4	9.6	75.5	32.0
30.2	11.1	79.2	34.0
34.0	12.7	83.0	36.1
37.7	14.2	86.8	38.2
40.5	15.8	90.6	40.4
45.3	17.5	94.3	42.7
49.1	19.1	100.0	46.1

Constructing a Large Fruit Dryer & How to Use It

by Lee & Robert McPhadyen

The Dryer Construction

We were called on to construct and operate a fruit drying unit as a pilot project on very short notice. We did not have an opportunity to accumulate a supply of recycled material and (regretfully) had to buy fairly expensive new lumber.

The materials used in the construction of our structure cost approximately one thousand dollars but this we are convinced could be reduced by 1/2 to 2/3 by someone with the time and access to good used wood.

The structure we decided on had base dimensions of 12' x 24'. We felt a dryer this size would allow the processing of enough fruit to provide a reasonable supplement to the income of a small family farm or survival collective. The size or dimensions of the structure are not as important as consideration of its function.

First, we chose a location where prevailing wind or breezes (which carry off the moisture) would blow along the longest dimension of the building (Fig. 1).

The second consideration was to locate the building where it would benefit from the longest period of sunshine not only during each day but during the drying season.

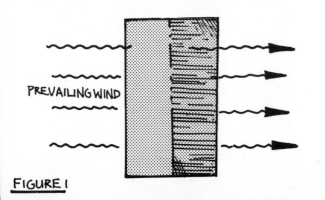

FIGURE I

PREVAILING WIND

Thirdly, we chose a slight elevation, and then used foundation posts or cribbing to elevate the structure even more. This meant a free flow of air around the entire structure. A frame 12' x 24' was constructed of 2" x 6" planks and floor joists (2" x 6") were fitted into the frame on 2' centres. These were cross-braced with scrap materials for strength (Fig. 2). We managed to locate a load of cheap

FIGURE 2

2" x 6" planks and decided to use these for the floor decking instead of more expensive ¾" plywood. Anything sturdy could be used. By this time, we were ready to raise the walls. Our floor was good and level so we fabricated the walls flat on the deck using 2" x 4" lumber. The studs were cut to 7' lengths; this could be shortened by a few inches but should not be shorter than 6½'. There is no advantage of studs longer than 7'. The studs were placed on 24" centres which would allow simple application of standard fly screen of 24" or 28" widths later on. A provision was made in one end wall for a 36" door frame for unloading fruit from a truck plus one space between studs on a side wall for alternative access to the structure. As each wall was assembled it was raised into place and braced to secure it in position. When all four walls were raised 2" x 6" planks were cut into 12' lengths and placed in position on the upper **plate** off the walls. Two inch by four inch lumber spacers were spiked to the plate between each plank and the plank in turn was spiked (3" nails) to the

FIGURE 3

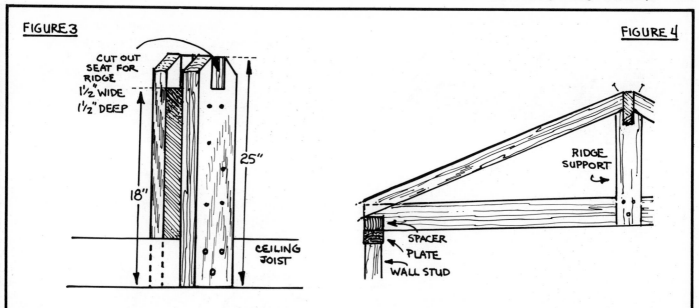

FIGURE 4

CUT OUT SEAT FOR RIDGE 1½" WIDE 1½" DEEP

25"

18"

CEILING JOIST

RIDGE SUPPORT

SPACER PLATE

WALL STUD

ends of the spacers to provide 2' centres for the 2" x 6" planks (Fig. 4). Walls are plumbed and squared as the planks are spiked to the spacers. We planned the roof to provide extended eaves to prevent direct sunlight from hitting the drying fruit at any time. On the other hand the eaves should not extend to a point that might inhibit the flow of air through the structure. The roof was constructed by mounting a ridge board of 2" x 6" plank mounted on supports fastened to the ceiling joists as in Fig. 3.

To make the support, cut two pieces 2" x 6" plank 25" long and one piece 18" long. Nail them together with a shorter piece sandwiched in between the longer two. This creates a slot at one end 5½" deep allowing you to set the support over the ceiling joist to form centre of roof. Cut

a slot on the opposite end 1½" wide x 1½" deep to carry the roof ridge. For a strong roof, one support should be made for each ceiling joist. Our roof withstood a 70 m.p.h. windstorm last December. Next we took 12' long 2" x 4"s and cut the ends to fit to the roof ridge, using the first one as a pattern to mark the rest. Nail the top end of each 2" x 4" to the roof ridge, and the bottom ends to the 2" x 6". The bottom ends will be resting on the spacers. This will provide an adequate overhang for shade.

We then applied an overall roof of 5/16" unsanded sheathing plywood followed by the cheapest 50 lb. rolled roofing (using plenty of lap cement and allowing a fairly generous overlap for a little extra strength). If the budget hasn't been exhausted the walls can be closed in with fly

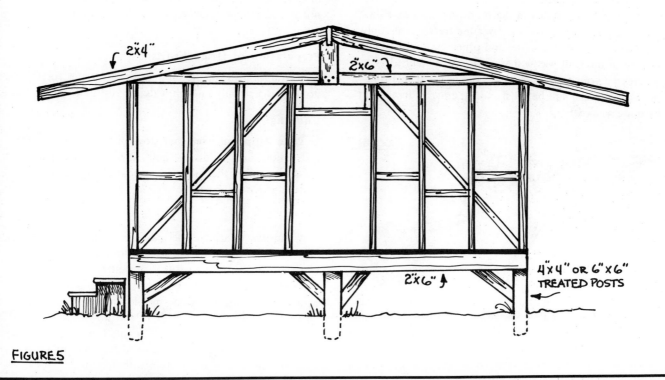

2x4"

2x6"

2x6"

4"x4" OR 6"x6" TREATED POSTS

FIGURE 5

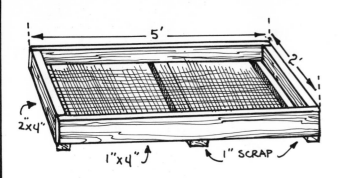

<u>FIGURE 6</u>

screen stapled to the studs and then further secured with plaster lath. Screen doors can be made for the two entrances. For drying racks, we made frames 2' x 5' using 1" x 4" strapping lumber on the sides and 2" x 4" scrap on the ends. Fly screen was stapled to the bottom with end runners and the centre support was made from 1" scrap (Fig. 6)

Spaces between studs should be cross-braced for extra rigidity and overall strength.

Drying Fruits

In the drying of fruits, we used only the natural elements, providing the previosuly described shed to protect the fruit from the direct rays of the sun, as these destroy the vitamin A content. The shed also provided a cover from rain. We had some rain while certain fruits were drying, and while the high humidity slowed the drying process, so long as the fruit was not wetted by the rain, we could detect no ill effects from the wet weather. We used no sulphur and found that with the exception of very ripe pears, the colour remained very good for all fruits. We were drying large quantities and were not able to harvest the fruit as I have stated in the following recipies. However, each day we would pick over the trees, taking only the ripest fruit. With cherries and prunes, we were able to wait until the fruit was withering from the stems. If you are buying your fruit, it is impossible to get it this ripe, but the fruit can still be satisfactorily dried; it just won't be quite as sweet.

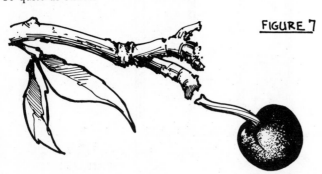

<u>FIGURE 7</u>

When picking your fruit (pears, apricots, peaches, nectarines) the stem should come off the tree when you touch it. If you have to pull to get fruit off, I do not feel that this is ripe enough for proper development of nutritional factors in fruit, and for the flavour potential to be realized.

If fruit is too green when picked, and stored to colour, as is the case with most commercial fruit sales, then you sadly miss out on flavour and can end up with a bitter taste. When picked too green, the fruit does not really ripen; it simply changes colour. The sugar content does not increase from the time it is picked; just what little sugar that was there concentrates.

If you are buying a large quantity from a fruit grower, then demand that the fruit be left on the trees for a longer period than is customary. Most growers are scared by this, as risk of damage because of wind, hail, birds or too much rain increases, but I have managed to convince growers that I must have ripe fruit.

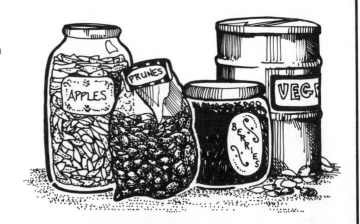

Packing & Storing Dried Products

Once dry, pack your fruit immediately in containers such as tins, jars, plastic bags, etc., that will not allow the reabsorption of moisture and contamination by eggs of insects etc.

Dried fruits are not readily susceptible to spoilage by moisture absorption, but will deteriorate more quickly if not stored properly. Once packed, store in a dark cool place.

Preparation of Dried Fruits

Restoration: Soak the product in cold water for 1-3 hrs.; no longer. Use only enough water to restore to original size.

Cooking

Place the product on your stove in the water used for restoration; simmer, do not boil. As soon as it is tender cease cooking as the fruit will overcook quickly and the texture and flavour will be spoiled.

Eat As Is

Wonderful candy for the kids! Use home dried fruits in place of commercial ones usually called for in recipes. Cherries substitute for raisins very well.

Occasionally concentrations of sugar in the fruit will carmalize, or burn. This does not happen very often but when it does you end up with a dark brown mark on dried fruit. It seems to occur when very ripe fruit has been badly bruised. I prefer to put aside bruised fruit and make juice from it. This occurs most often with apricots.

Grapes — Method 1:   If you can buy or produce a type of grape that will stay on the stems, pick the bunches and hang them to dry under eaves on a string.

Method 2:   Submerse ripe fruit in boiling water for 2 minutes to check *the skin. Place it on racks and dry.

Method 3:   Remove the grapes from their stems, place them on racks and dry. This method takes longer than method 2.

Sun Cooked Preserves: Wash and hull strawberries, raspberries or other berry fruits. Place them in shallow enamelled pans. Drizzle honey over the fruit and mix well. Cover the pans with sheets of glass and place in the sun. Let stand for several days until fruit is a jelly-like consistency, stirring several times each day. Pack in hot clean jars and sterilize in hot water bath 2-3 minutes. Enjoy them on cold snowy days. Open a jar of summer and eat.

Apricots: For small quantities, if you are fortunate enough to have your own trees, let the grass grow as apricots ripen and dry the fruit as it falls to the ground. The grass is a perfect cushion and very little fruit is damaged. This degree of ripeness creates the perfect dried apricot. Collect the fruit as it falls, split, place on racks open side up and allow moisture to escape. If the weather is very hot, they should be ready in 2-5 days. When adequately dry they will separate from each other when several are balled together in your hand. If they overdry, no harm is done, they keep very well but may need some moisture before being eaten. Better to overdry than leave too much moisture in them as they mould if too wet.

Honey Apricots: Prepare solution of 1 part honey to 2 parts water. Bring to 200° F. Split the apricots, place them in a wire basket, submerge in honey mixture and count to 20. Take out and place apricots on racks and let dry. A more extravagant method is to drizzle some pure honey over the apricots once they are on the racks. It's time consuming but gives some very special eating for winter. Fruit done this way will be a little more tacky when dry. There is no need to turn aprictos while drying.

Cherries: Best picked when the fruit is beginning to shrivel from the stem.

Method 1:   Dip whole cherries into boiling water for 2 minutes. The same water can be used several times. It may have honey added to it if desired. Place on racks and dry.

Method 2:   Pit the cherries. It's time consuming and tedious, but it's nice to have no pits in some fruit. I have not found this method allows the fruit to dry any quicker. Place pitted cherries on racks, let dry. There is no need to turn.

Method 3:   Wash whole fresh fruit, put on racks and let dry 3 to 5 days and longer if needed (up to 4 weeks).

Pears — Method 1:   Pick ripe but firm fruit. Wash, stem and cut unpeeled and uncored into very thin slices. You can purchase machines that do this chore quickly and

*check means to cage or make small breaks in the skin, by shrivelling it a little. This allows moisture to escape more readily.

evenly. Place slices on racks but do not turn. They will be dry in 24 to 36 hours.

Method 2:   For a darker but very sweet treat, allow your fruit to ripen till ready to fall or let it fall on thick grass. Wash, stem, cut in quarters, remove core if desired, and place the skin on racks. This method takes longer to dry and fruit oxidizes more but makes delicious eating. If you wish, fruit may be peeled but if very ripe, is likely to stick to the screens.

Peaches: Harvest peaches as late in the ripening process as allows them to be handled without becoming badly bruised. I did not peel mine. However, if you have a slip skin type available to you, do so. The skin once dry, is reduced, and is hardly noticeable. Halve the peaches, pit, and place in racks. They may take up to 7 days to dry.

Nectarines: Do the same as for peaches.

Plums & Prunes: Harvest when the fruit begins to wither from the stems.

Method 1:   Dip the whole fruit into boiling water for 2 minutes, to check the rather tough skins. Do not immerse too many at once as the water must boil around the fruit to achieve desired checking. Place on racks and dry. They may take up to 3 weeks to dry as these fruit are late in the season. I found this method not as satisfactory as the 2nd method. The fruit skins did not check evenly and some fruit simply did not dry as moisture could not escape.

Method 2:   Split the fruit, remove pip or stone, lay open side up on racks, do not turn, and let dry. They can take up to 2 or 3 weeks to dry.

We were able to do all of our drying with the sun's heat and the breeze evaporating. Some geographic areas may have to supplement this with artificial heating etc. — but this would be a whole other subject.

In this past season all fruit took much longer to dry, but with equally good results. However, with the longer time on racks, the racks need rotating and checking, as some pieces of fruit are more likely to mould. Discard any of these. Allow a lot of space, 18" between racks and as much space as possible between stacks of racks, to allow a really good air flow. This is particularly important during periods of cool, cloudy, or rainy weather. Fruit is also more likely to collect dust during extra time on the racks. If desired, this can satisfactorily be removed before storing your fruit. Fill a large pot with water, allowing a 2" headspace. Bring the water to a boil. Place your fruit in a wire basket that will fit in the pot and not allow the fruit to escape through the holes in it. Submerse the fruit in boiling water for 10-15 seconds, shaking it up and down as you do so. Remove the basket from the water and tip the fruit, one layer deep, onto racks to dry off. A warm sunny day with a breeze is the ideal day for this procedure. Within 2 hours the fruit is quite dry, soft, clean and ready for immediate storage before further dust can settle on the fruit. This process does not cook the fruit in any way. The plunge is too short in time. In 2½ hours, you can process at least one hundred pounds of dry fruit.

A Home Built Kick Wheel

by Barry Barnes

The first step in building this wheel is to cut 2" x 6" stock into these sizes: 2 - 36" seat supports, 2 - 28½" front leg supports, 1 - 36" bottom support for back, 1 - 33" bearing base support, 1-36" top support for front, 1-9" top bearing support, 2 - 30" bottom support for sides (inside), 2 - 19" bottom support for sides (outside). 1-36" seat. Next, cut a 60 inch - 2" x 4' stock into 2 - 30" pieces for the foot supports. Now rip a piece of 2" x 4" x 18" in half long-ways, then cut these two 18" pieces 3 times into 6" pieces. These will be your seat support pieces.

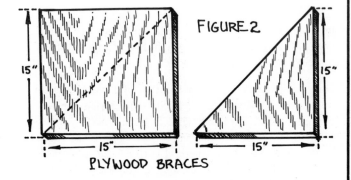

FIGURE 2

PLYWOOD BRACES

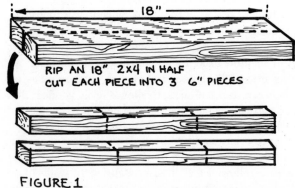

RIP AN 18" 2x4 IN HALF
CUT EACH PIECE INTO 3   6" PIECES

FIGURE 1

Cut 4 squares of either ½" or ¾" exterior plywood into 15" squares. Cut these pieces from corner to corner so you have 8 pieces that are shaped as illustrated in figure 2.

Place the two 36" seat supports on the floor. Glue and nail or pre-drill and screw the 36" bottom support ½" from the bottom of the posts. Then glue and nail (or screw) two of the plywood braces on as shown in figure 3, being sure to square up all the parts.

Stand the 2 - 28½" front leg supports on the floor and glue and nail (or screw) the 39" top support on the top.

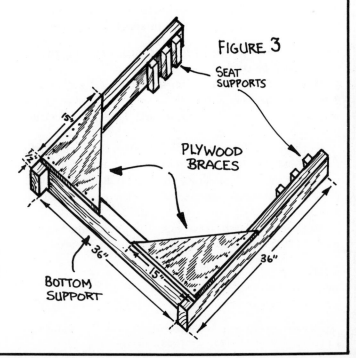

FIGURE 3

SEAT SUPPORTS

PLYWOOD BRACES

BOTTOM SUPPORT

Then add two braces and bring to square.

Place the 2 - 30" bottom side supports on the floor and measuring 5½" from each end secure* the 2 - 19" bottom supports to each one.

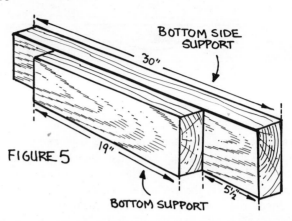

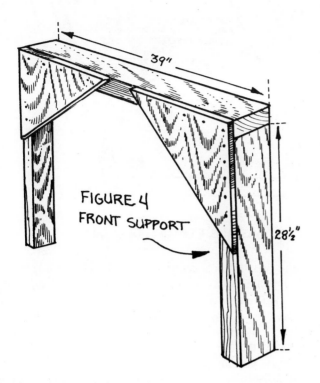

FIGURE 4
FRONT SUPPORT

39"

28½"

FIGURE 5

BOTTOM SIDE SUPPORT

30"

19"

5½"

BOTTOM SUPPORT

Stand the front and back supports on their sides and secure* the bottom side supports with the 30" length on the inside. Nail these temporarily and then attach the plywood supports (bringing to square). When you are satisfied that the pieces are all true drill through the plywood supports and the 2" x 6" supports and attach permanently using at least ½" x 5" bolts with large washers on both sides (Fig. 6).

Your bottom bearing should be bolted to the bearing base support after centering. Mount the bearing base support with the centre of the bearing 7¾" from the front of the front supports.

* Glue and nail or screw.

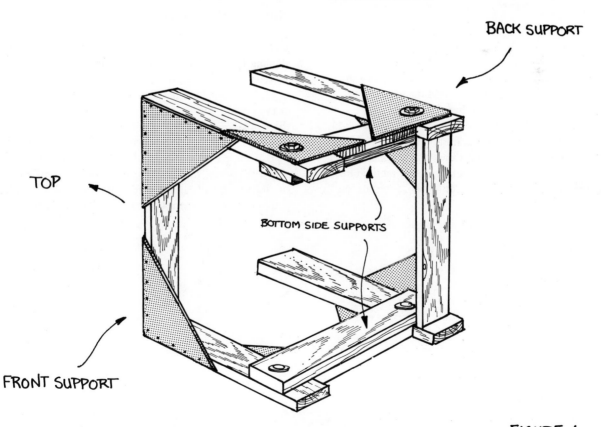

BACK SUPPORT

TOP

BOTTOM SIDE SUPPORTS

FRONT SUPPORT

FIGURE 6

FIGURE 7

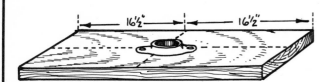

Taking the piece of 2" x 6" x 9" stock cut earlier, drill 3 mounting holes as noted, the top bearing holes and the shaft hole. This mount is turned over and mounted bearing side down (to keep clay out) in the centre of the front top support. Note that the top bearing and the bottom should be directly over each other. Use a level to do this. After you place the shaft with flywheel attached in the bottom bearing, you should have enough adjustability to align and then bore your mounting holes through the front top support.

FIGURE 9

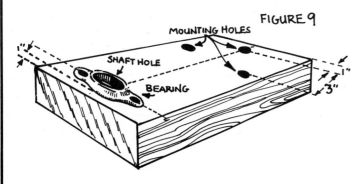

MOUNTING HOLES

SHAFT HOLE

BEARING

One method of constructing the flywheel is to pour using concrete. If you can find an old belt wheel about 30" in diameter you should have the bearing hole **shimmed** or **sleeved** and some method devised to hold the wheel to the shaft, e.g., set screws. You could then fill the open spaces with chicken wire and concrete. Another method you could use if you do not have any luck in finding the old belt wheel is to take two plywood discs, some flanges and concrete and again pour the wheel. I will outline this second method but the basic principal is the same and could be adapted to the belt wheel.

FIGURE 8

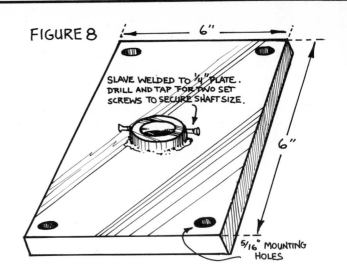

SLAVE WELDED TO ¼" PLATE. DRILL AND TAP FOR TWO SET SCREWS TO SECURE SHAFT SIZE.

5/16" MOUNTING HOLES

A POSSIBLE FLANGE DESIGN

Cut two 30" diameter discs using ½" or ¾" exterior plywood. Drill 6 evenly spaced ¼" holes through both discs at least 3" from the edge. Attach a flange to both discs.

Take one plywood disc and turn it with the mounted flange side down and set it on a bed of wet sand. Wrap the outside of this disc with a piece of linoleum 4½" high and secure the bottom edge at 3" intervals using no. 6 box nails. Place 6 - ¼" x 6" bolts through the holes you drilled in the bottom disc and insert your shaft through the hole and into flange. Using a 5-1 mix, pour your form full of concrete and level. Now place the top disc down over your bolts and shaft, and let harden at least 1 week.

Drop your top bearing and support over the top of the shaft and tighten. Your bearings should be of the self-aligning type so no need to worry that the shaft will be straight. The last step is to mount your wheel head on your shaft. You can construct a wheel head out of ¼" plate steel or even wood, but best to purchase an aluminum one from the many sources listed in such magazines as "Ceramics Monthly."

Using a spacer of at least 2", mount the two foot supports above the wheel by attaching them to the front and back supports with nails and or screws. You may want a splash pan but I'll leave that up to you — happy bolting.

FIGURE 10

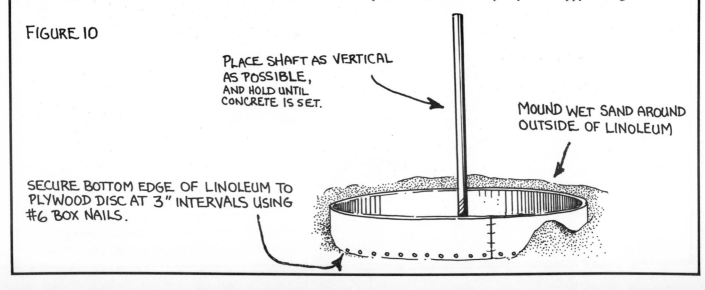

PLACE SHAFT AS VERTICAL AS POSSIBLE, AND HOLD UNTIL CONCRETE IS SET.

MOUND WET SAND AROUND OUTSIDE OF LINOLEUM

SECURE BOTTOM EDGE OF LINOLEUM TO PLYWOOD DISC AT 3" INTERVALS USING #6 BOX NAILS.

A High Temperature Wood Burning Kiln

by Ivan McMeekin

The wood-burning kiln was built at Bagot, Australia, for a number of reasons, and though most of them relate to that particular situation, I feel that this kiln, which may be fired to 1300°C with ease, may be of interest to artist-potters and students elsewhere.

Having decided to build a wood-burning kiln, the next decision was the question of size. The kiln was to be a training kiln, not a production kiln, and had to be small enough to necessitate frequent firings to give trainees adequate opportunities to get to know the setting, firing, cooling, and drawing routine and to develop the judgment and skills required. Firing is at least as important a part of pottery as throwing, and I feel that trainees or students must be taught to fire while they are being taught to throw. So the kiln had to be small enough for frequent firings and small enough for the firing not to be an upheaval, slowing down, or dislocation of the workshop routine. On the other hand, it had to be big enough for full-sized pots to be made and for trainees to feel that the number of finished pots drawn from a firing was adequate reward for their labours. A setting space of ten cubic feet seemed to meet these requirements, and from this I proceeded to the actual design of the kiln.

Though wood-firing was to be a feature of the design, the kiln was not to be an anachronism and was designed in the light of as much contemporary fuel technology as I have been able to acquire. The best and most up-to-date materials and a good pyrometer was used.

The design will be described in terms of the following concepts:

The Chamber or Setting Space: The main or central part of the kiln in which the pots are set for firing.

The Furnace or Fire Box: The part of the kiln in which the heat is generated. This is a traditional concept, and mainly applicable to kilns burning solid fuels like wood, coal, or coke. Many contemporary kilns do not have a separate space for the generation of heat; most electric kilns, LP gas kilns, and some oil-burning kilns generate the heat in the actual **chamber or setting space**.

The Chimney: This needs no definition, but it may be worth mentioning the three main functions of a chimney: it generates draught so that (a) sufficient air may be drawn in through the fuel to burn it; (b) the stream of burning gases may be drawn into the setting to transfer the heat to the pots; and (c) to carry away the burnt-out waste gases.

The Throat: This is the part of the kiln which is used to feed the heat and burning gases generated in the **furnace** through into the **chamber**, and usually consists of a space within the central area of the kiln, separated from the **chamber or setting space** by a low wall called a **bag-wall** or **baffle**.

The Flue: This is the passage which connects the **chamber** to the **chimney** and conveys the waste gases to the chimney. It is also an important link transmitting the pressure generated in the **chimney** to the **furnace**, enabling air to be drawn into the fuel.

The Flameways: These are spaces between and around the bungs of saggars or the setting of bats and props, which enable the flame and gases to circulate in the chamber transmitting the heat to the setting. Setting the chamber too full, so that the flameways are too small for their job, is sometimes a cause of failure to achieve the required temperature. The pattern of the flameways is also important; they should be arranged so that they draw the heat into the cooler parts of the setting.

In addition, kilns need to have a **door** providing entry to the chamber, and a **damper** to control the strength of the draught generated in the chimney.

In the arrangement or disposition of these parts the kiln is a down-draught, or in this case more accurately a cross-draught kiln, in that the burning gases are fed into the bottom of the throat on one side, pass into the chamber over the top of the bag-wall and through bleeding holes at the side of the bag, and are then drawn downward and across the setting to the flues, which are at the bottom of the chamber on the opposite side of the throat. The gases then pass into the chimney, which is a separate structure. This disposition is nearer to Oriental cross-draught tradition than to European down-draught tradition. This applies particularly to the relative levels of the parts; the inlet from the firebox, for example, being below both the chamber floor and the outlet flue. This gives a better draught from cold and enables the chimney to be shorter. Some kiln designers maintain that to lower the outlet in relation to the inlet improved temperature distribution at the end of the firing, but in this kiln there is only 30° to 40°C difference between the hottest and coolest parts of the setting, which to my mind is satisfactory and could not perhaps be lessened by changing the relative levels in any case.

The relative size of the various parts of the kiln is based firstly on the study of proportions of other kilns, both down-draught and cross-draught, and secondly on experience gained in designing, building, and firing the round down-draught kiln at Sturt and the oil-drip kiln at the University of New South Wales. In describing these sizes, the cross-section area of the chamber floor is taken as 100, and the other sizes described as percentages of this area, i.e.:

Area of chamber floor	702 sq. ins.	100
Area of grate	281 sq. ins.	40%
Area of throat	129 sq. ins.	18½%
Area of exit flues	50 sq. ins.	7%
Area of main flue	85 sq. ins.	12%
Capacity of setting space	36" x 24" x 20"	10 cu. ft.

These are proportions that have been found to work well in this context, but it is essential to remember in kiln design that each particular design must be worked out in relation to its unique features. For example, the relative sizes of kiln parts change with scale; a chimney cross section area of 1% in a 30 ft. diameter coal-burning down-draught kiln may work excellently, but in a tiny 3 cu. ft. test kiln would be ridiculously small. However it is possible to generalise to some extent: (a) A wood burning fire-box (40% in this kiln) is better too big rather than too small; it can always be partially blocked in if it proves too powerful a heat source and too expensive in fuel (and this incidentailly is a good general principal — design all openings so that they will prove too big rather than too small. It is much easier to partially block them in than to pull down the whole structure so that they may be enlarged). (b) The throat should be adequate and larger than the outlet flue. In this kiln, it is more than double the outlet, and contains a vertical pillar, which is there to spread the flame toward the sides of

the setting space. Once generated, the heat is not much use in the firebox; it must be passed into the chamber as easily as possible, subjected to maximum turbulence there, and as far as possible bottled up by an outlet which is as small as draught consideration will allow, so that as much heat as possible is transmitted to the setting. (c) The chimney should again be too big rather than too small and fitted with a damper, so that in the event of the draught being too strong, it may be decreased by pushing the damper in. Like the other areas, the size of the chimney is influenced by the size of a brick — 9" x 4½" x 3". In this case, a brick by a brick plus two joints was the nearest size suitable.

The firebox or furnace is a type that Michael Cardew first introduced me to at his Wenford Bridge pottery. It is basically a French design and has been described both in **A Treatise on the Ceramic Industries** by Emil Bourry and in **A Potter's Book** by Bernard Leach. I understand that the Sevres porcelain factory still fires with wood and still uses this type of firebox. I have modified it so that it acts more like a gas producer, adding a cover to the box and a side stoke-hole, providing three inlets for primary air, an inlet for an ember air supply, and fitting all inlets with sliding metal shutters. I have also increased the depth of the box in relation to its width, with the idea of making it easier to produce the carbon monoxide required for reduction by having a deep fuel bed.

The height of the chimney was worked out in accordance with the formula suggested by Baker on p. 191 of **A Potter's Book**, i.e.:

3 ft. of chimney for every 1 ft. of downward pull.
1 ft. of chimney for every 3½ ft. of horizontal pull.

Effective chimney height is taken to be the difference in level between the mean inlet at the firebox end of the kiln and the chimney top. In this case, the mean inlet level was considered to be about halfway between the level of the primary air inlets and that of the secondary air. This is obviously something not amenable to exact calculation. In firing, the draught proved to be adequate in that the damper was never pulled right out.

The kiln was built on an already existing concrete floor. The structure consists of an inner lining of hot-face insulation brick: Morlite 28 is used in the upper part of the throat, where the highest temperatures are likely to be met; Morlite 25 is used for the arch, to line the remaining three walls, for the chamber floor, the flue, and to back the high-alumina brick in the lower bag-wall; Morlite 23 is used to insulate the ash-pit floor, and for the door and stoke-hole blocks.

High-alumina dense firebrick was used where conditions were likely to be most severe — i.e., for the fire-arch and the lower part of the bag-wall. It is important to leave dry joints at either end of the lower bag, to allow for expansion. These bricks will be the first to get hot and will expand before the main structure expands. The upper part of the bag-wall should be set dry. The remainder of the structure — the firebox, the outer shell of the kiln, and the chimney — are all of a medium-grade dense firebrick. The door is of Morlite 23 squares, stuck together to make up 9" x 9" x 9" blocks. The damper is cast in a suitable grade of refractory concrete,

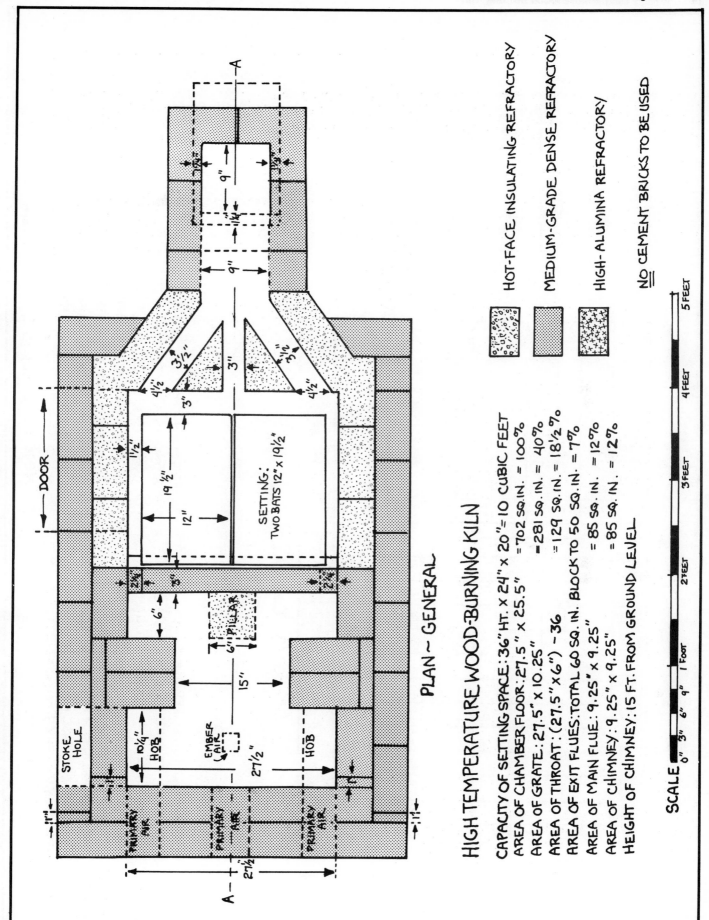

PLAN ~ GENERAL

HIGH TEMPERATURE WOOD-BURNING KILN

CAPACITY OF SETTING SPACE: 36" HT. x 24" x 20" = 10 CUBIC FEET
AREA OF CHAMBER FLOOR: 27.5" x 25.5"   = 702 SQ.IN. = 100%
AREA OF GRATE: 27.5" x 10.25"   = 281 SQ.IN. = 40%
AREA OF THROAT: (27.5" x 6") - 36   = 129 SQ.IN. = 18½%
AREA OF EXIT FLUES: TOTAL 60 SQ.IN. BLOCK TO 50 SQ. IN. = 7%
AREA OF MAIN FLUE: 9.25" x 9.25"   = 85 SQ. IN. = 12%
AREA OF CHIMNEY: 9.25" x 9.25"   = 85 SQ. IN. = 12%
HEIGHT OF CHIMNEY: 15 FT. FROM GROUND LEVEL

HOT-FACE INSULATING REFRACTORY

MEDIUM-GRADE DENSE REFRACTORY

HIGH-ALUMINA REFRACTORY

NO CEMENT BRICKS TO BE USED

SCALE   0" 3" 6" 9" 1 FOOT 2 FEET 3 FEET 4 FEET 5 FEET

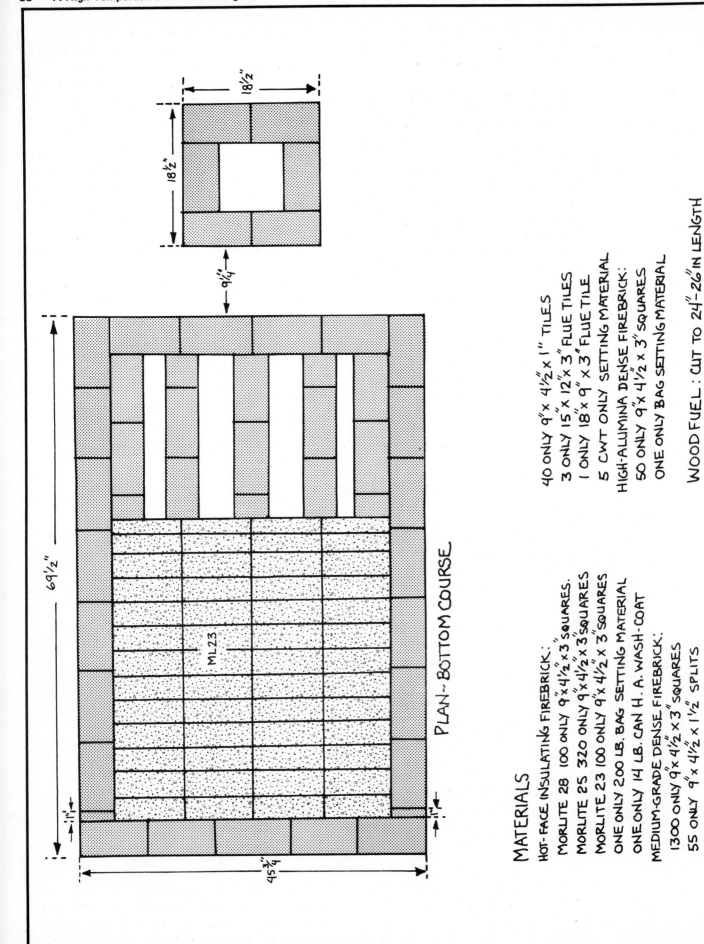

PLAN ~ BOTTOM COURSE

ML 23

18½"

18½"

9¼"

69½"

45¾"

1½"

1½"

MATERIALS

HOT-FACE INSULATING FIREBRICK:

MORLITE 28   100 ONLY 9"x 4½"x 3" SQUARES.

MORLITE 25   320 ONLY 9"x 4½"x 3" SQUARES

MORLITE 23   100 ONLY 9"x 4½"x 3" SQUARES

ONE ONLY 200 LB. BAG SETTING MATERIAL

ONE ONLY 14 LB. CAN H.A. WASH-COAT

MEDIUM-GRADE DENSE FIREBRICK:

1300 ONLY 9"x 4½"x 3" SQUARES

55 ONLY 9"x 4½"x 1½" SPLITS

40 ONLY 9"x 4½"x 1" TILES

3 ONLY 15"x 12"x 3" FLUE TILES

1 ONLY 18"x 9"x 3" FLUE TILE

5 CWT ONLY SETTING MATERIAL

HIGH-ALUMINA DENSE FIREBRICK:

50 ONLY 9"x 4½"x 3" SQUARES

ONE ONLY BAG SETTING MATERIAL

WOOD FUEL: CUT TO 24"-26" IN LENGTH

or made of a high-alumina dense firebrick tile, and should be graduated so that it may be set accurately.

The kiln and chimney must be adequately strapped with buckstays at the corners and horizontal strapping consisting of 2" x ¼" angle iron and ½" diameter reinforcing rod, threaded and fitted so that the strapping may be screwed up to hand-tight when the finishing temperature is reached at the end of the first firing. No further adjustment should be necessary after this. The strapping should be set up before the main arch is built, so that there is no tendency to spring the freshly-laid walls as the arch is worked in.

The three primary air inlets, the secondary air inlet, and the ember air inlet are all fitted with sliding shutters, so that the amount of air admitted may be controlled accurately.

Fuel

Suitable fuel is essential with a wood burning kiln. It must be dry, and with this kiln, hardwood. The timber must be felled, cut to length, split, and then seasoned for at least a year or two before it will be dry enough to use. With green fuel, you simply cannot get the temperature, and with half-green fuel combustion is a little too intense, giving short flames and uneven temperature distribution. The size to split to must be learnt by experience. Toward the end of the firing, the pieces must be big or they will burn too quickly. The length of the firebox is 27½", and the wood **must** be cut 24" to 26" in length. If it is too short, it will fall through the ash pit; if too long, it will not go into the box.

If you are felling your own timber, trunk wood is preferable to branches, and the fuel must be reasonably straight and must be barked. City dwellers can use old telegraph poles, which are usually excellent fuel. Off cuts from timber mills may be suitable, provided they are not too light and small in section and do not contain bark. The bark accelerates the burning so that control over the kiln is lost.

Firing the Kiln

At the start of the firing, a small fire is lit on the ash pit floor, the stoke-hole and all the metal shutters on the primary and secondary air inlets being closed. The opening at the base of the ash-pit slab is left open. The damper is adjusted to give sufficient draught to burn the fuel and draw off the steam from the setting. The size of the ash-pit fire is gradually increased as the temperature rises, and at about red heat (600°C) the burning fuel will be found to half fill the lower part of the firebox. At this stage, the upper part of the firebox is brought into use, a single deck of wood being laid on the hobs. This will ignite in a few seconds and the box will be starting to operate as it was designed to do — i.e., the fuel is now being stoked through the opening at the top of the box, and the primary air is being drawn in through the three inlets above the deck of fuel. Secondary air is now admitted through the inlet just beneath the deck of fuel, and the ash-pit slab is sealed into place, only a small amount of air being admitted at the bottom inlet to consume the ember. In the upper part of the box, now the main heat source, it should be noted that the fire burns up-side-down — the flame is drawn **down** through the burning logs and then

through into the fire-arch and throat. As a log burns through, it falls into the ash-pit, and must be replaced by another, so that there is always a continuous layer or deck of fuel on the hobs.

As the temperature rises toward 1000°C, the number of logs in the top of the box is gradually increased, so that by the time the temperature approaches 1000°C the box is kept at least half-full of fiercely burning logs. With this type of firing, the combustion is taking place in two stages. The primary combustion takes place in the upper part of the box, where the fuel is brought to ignition temperature, the volatile part is driven off in the form of unburnt gas, and part of the fixed carbon (charcoal) is burnt, before the remainder falls into the ash-pit to be burnt more slowly by the ember air supply. Between the deck of burning logs and heap of burning ember, the secondary air is drawn in, and by the time it reaches the throat it has become hot enough to initiate the second stage of the combustion: the burning of the volatile, gaseous part of the fuel. This should take place partly in the throat, but mainly in the chamber itself, where sufficient turbulence should be promoted for the volatile fuel and the hot secondary air to mix and burn as completely as possible. The advantages of this two-stage firing are considerable; the fuel is fully burnt, excessively high temperatures in the firebox and throat are avoided, and because the secondary combustion takes place in the setting itself, uneven temperature distribution is avoided.

If the ware is to be matured under reducing conditions, then at about 1000°C the shutter on the secondary air inlet should be partially closed, so that the total amount of air admitted is less than before. This increases the tendency for air to be drawn in through the primary inlets and through the fuel bed. Because the inlets are obstructed by the fuel itself, it will be necessary to increase the draught by withdrawing the damper off a little more: otherwise, the effect of the construction will simply be to slow down the whole process, so that neither reduction nor temperature rise is achieved. Because every 1% of carbon monoxide used in reduction represents a 7% loss in calorific value of the fuel burnt, it becomes necessary to increase the quantity of wood introduced into the box and the level of logs will probably now have to be up to the bottom of the primary air inlets. It should be possible to continue to the end of the firing with these settings, though it may be necessary to decrease draught a little over the last 30° to 40°C. At this stage, it does not matter whether conditions are oxidising or reducing as far as glaze colour is concerned. Provided that the kiln is properly handled, no raking of ember either in the top of the box or the ash-pit is necessary. At the end of the firing, the fuel should be allowed to burn down and the kiln allowed to cool rapidly to between 1200° to 1100°C. It should then be clammed up and allowed to cool slowly to room temperature.

Handled properly, and with suitable fuel, this kiln will achieve 1300°C under reducing conditions with ease, and has the advantage of wide versatility, in that both firing and cooling conditions can be controlled as far as both speed and atmosphere are concerned; so far it seems to have adequately met the demands made on it as a training kiln.

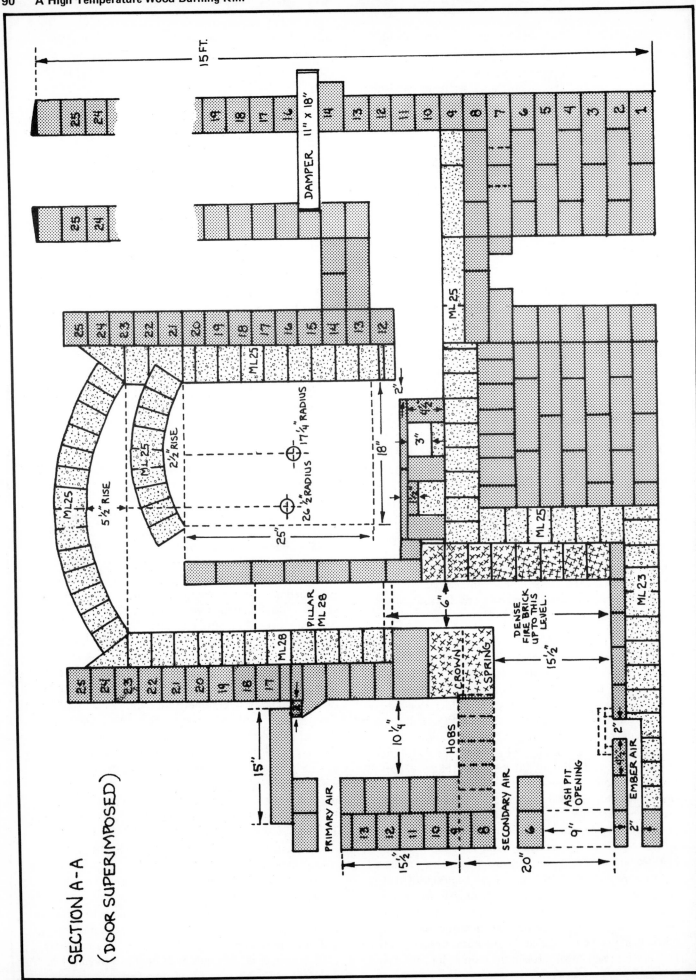

SECTION A-A
(DOOR SUPERIMPOSED)

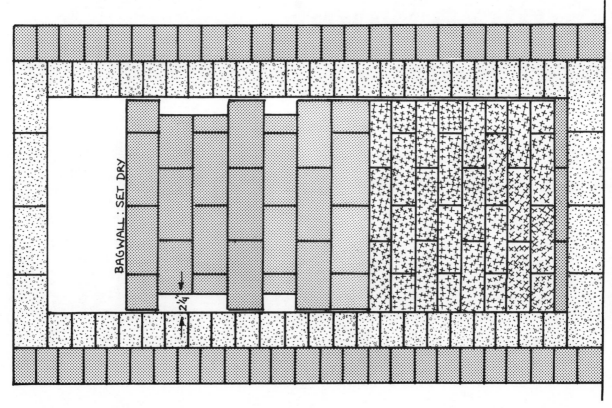

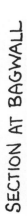

SECTION AT BAGWALL

BAGWALL : SET DRY

2¼"

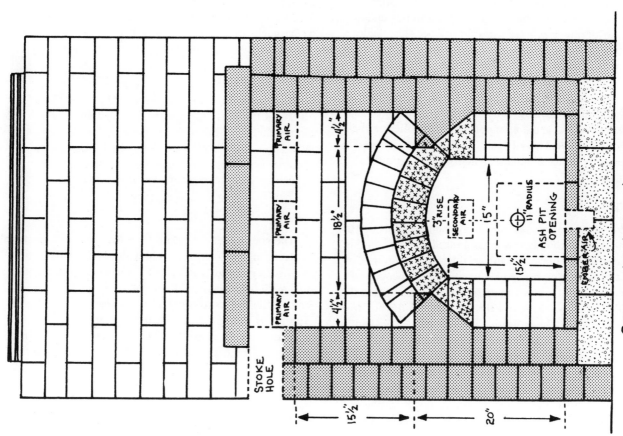

SECTION THROUGH FIREBOX

STOKE HOLE

PRIMARY AIR

PRIMARY AIR

PRIMARY AIR

PRIMARY AIR

1—4½"

18½"

4½"

3" RISE

SECONDARY AIR

15"

11" RADIUS

ASH PIT OPENING

15½"

EMBER AIR

15½"

20"

A Simple Wood Fired Kiln

by Ivan Englund

Pottery can be made by students and potters without expensive electric kilns in a simple wood-fire kiln which is cheap, easy to build, and which will fire without undue effort to glazing temperature in a short time. The kiln described here needs only 100 bricks and these can be firebricks, commons, second-hand, or even broken ones. It can be erected in about an hour. It will fire biscuit in about three hours and glaze in two hours, burning wood in the form of packing cases, timber off-cuts, broken furniture, etc. The results will be real and honest pots of the low-fired earthenware or raku type. This kiln and the glaze have been used as a basis of teaching at summer schools as well as during normal classes.

The Kiln

The kiln is a simple updraught type and needs about 100 bricks. A flat section is selected and raked level and on this a solid square of bricks, 2½ bricks square, is laid on the flat, with two projecting arms to the front. A second course of bricks on the flat is now laid on the projecting arms and the outside of the square, leaving the passage from fire box to kiln open. Across the projecting arms, metal rods are laid to act as fire bars. Around the edge of the square, bricks are laid on edge to a height of seven bricks, using clay slurry as a bond, making sure that the bricks are tapped down to give thin joints. The fire box is built to the front on the projecting arms, two bricks long by two bricks high, still leaving an opening between fire box and kiln. A fire box cover is placed over this space. This could be a clay slab of some sort, if available, but a sheet of steel plate will be easier to get and is just as good. Even a piece of galvanized iron will do temporarily for a few firings, if you can't wait. Underneath the fire bars, the earth should be excavated to a depth of at least six inches, for there is a big build-up of charcoal and this will save some raking. Inside the kiln chamber are two bricks on edge and upon these rests the first or lower shelf.

The Kiln Furniture

All firing is done on open shelves. These are 9" x 9" and can be of fire brick, silicon carbide, clay floor tiles, or brick simply sliced through with a bolster. In this case, two halves make up a shelf. Shelves can be made by the potter with grogged clay. The shelf supports can be pieces of cut brick, or little clay cylinders thrown or hand rolled.

Setting

The pots are set in the kiln from the top. The lowest shelf is placed in position and packed with pots. The next shelf is arranged on supports and packed, and so on until the kiln is full. With the sizes given, there will be about 3" of space all around the shelves to allow plenty of space for the flames. The top is partly closed in with loose bricks across the corners, leaving a space about 4" x 7" for smoke and flames to emerge. If more space is needed to accommodate a few more pots, a couple of extra courses of bricks can be added with no effect on the performance of the kiln.

Firing

In firing pottery, there is one rule that cannot be broken — and that is **fire slowly**. At the start, a very small fire is lit at the very entrance of the fire box and is kept small until the water is driven off the pots, taking about an hour. Do not allow the flames to impinge on the ware at this stage; if an ominous "pop" is heard, the fire must be raked out quickly and continued slowly. When possible, the fire is gradually increased until the firebox is two-thirds full of brightly burning wood and the flames are perhaps 9" out of the top. Very exciting!!! A bright fire is maintained until an even red temperature is achieved all through the kiln. This can be checked by sight, for it is possible to look into the kiln – but watch the eyebrows. Cones 015A (820°C) and 010A (900°C) may prove useful. When the right temperature is reached, the fire is allowed to burn out; the front of the firebox and the top of the kiln are closed with loose bricks to exclude cold air, and the kiln is allowed to cool naturally. While the kiln is firing, the ash pit should be kept clear of ash to allow a good flow of air through the fuel. The only difference in glaze firing is that the early slow fire can be eliminated and the glazes can be checked for melting at the top. Light, quick-burning wood such as packing cases, etc., must be used. Large and heavy pieces of timber should be avoided, since what is required is a quick fire, especially in the closing stages. The fire should be clean and bright at all times.

Because the kiln is bonded only with clay, it should be covered from the weather.

The Clay

In this type of firing, the clay is subject to considerably thermal shocks and while almost any clay can be fired with care, it is better to prepare special clay for this purpose. The addition of about 25% to 33% of grog or sand to the clay will make a suitable open body for this firing technique.

Conclusion

This kiln and glaze works very well at 900°C and there is a terrific amount of sheer fun to be had learning about pots in this basic and fundamental way, but let me conclude on a note of warning. All your expert and non-expert friends will tell you that this kiln can't work because it is too simple, or that you can improve it by dripping oil, or it will be better fired with coke – or coal – or bottled gas, or that if you keep the fire going long enough you will get stoneware, or you must have this or that, and so on and so on. Don't take any notice of any of them. Have a little faith in me and try it **exactly** as outlined here. I guarantee it!

Further experiments have been made: By overflowing the fire-box with wood, the atmosphere in the kiln became smoky and deficient of oxygen. This **reducing atmosphere** on glaze painted with copper oxide gave good pinks and reds. Salt glaze: Pots were placed in the kiln and brought to full heat in the normal way. Common salt was then thrown into the fire-box in small handfuls with the flues closed. After a minute or so, the flues were opened, the fire built up, and further salt thrown in. About 2 lbs. of salt was used and the salting was kept up for about one hour. Results were very encouraging and no doubt further experience with this kiln could give more uniform results.

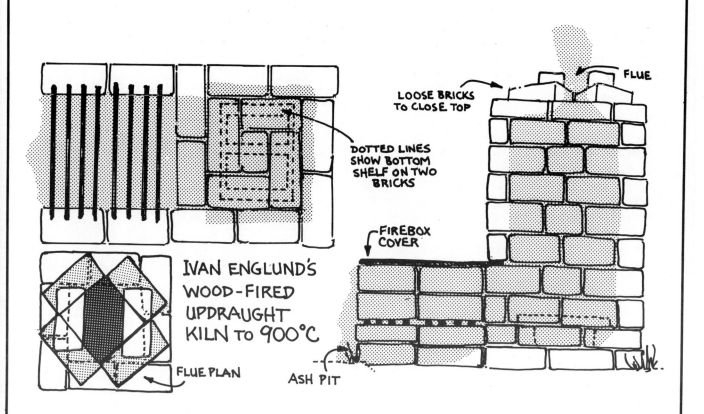

FLUE

LOOSE BRICKS TO CLOSE TOP

DOTTED LINES SHOW BOTTOM SHELF ON TWO BRICKS

FIREBOX COVER

IVAN ENGLUND'S WOOD-FIRED UPDRAUGHT KILN TO 900°C

FLUE PLAN

ASH PIT

A Carding Machine

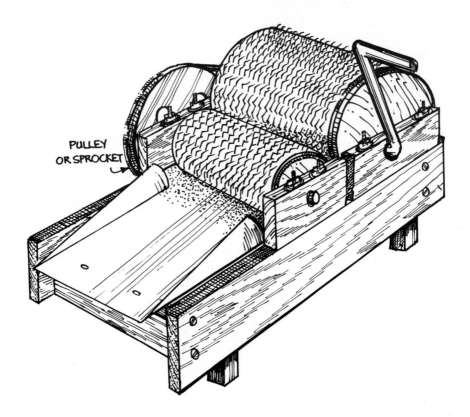

PULLEY OR SPROCKET

This portable device permits carding wool or cotton in a manner which is not only far faster and more efficient than hand carding, but also much easier — a child can operate the machine. The capacity of this device is approximately three pounds of wool per hour.

Tools & Materials

Wood saw
Screwdriver
Metal drill 1/8" diameter
Wood drill ½" and ¾" diameter

Soft wood, leather, wire, metal rods, ¼" bolts and nuts, tacks, flat head wood screws and 16 gauge sheet metal. The exact amount of each is not mentioned due to the fact that many substitutes are available. Look over the plans and develop a list of materials based on your own resources.

Construction

Frame assembly — The frame is really a rectangle as shown in Fig. 1. Drill the holes as straight as possible where indicated.

Outlet tray — The outlet tray is made of heavy gauge sheet metal (12-16 gauge) and is cut to the dimensions shown in Fig. 2. The lower part of Fig. 2 shows where and by how much the tray is bent to shape. The two 1/8" dia. holes are for subsequent mounting to the frame. Bevel the corners 45° and to about 3/8" across the face of the bevel.

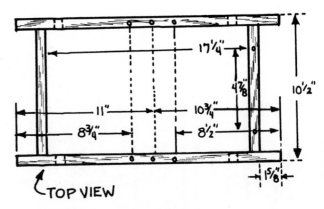

TOP VIEW

FIGURE 1   FRAME
¾" THICK STOCK
3 CENTRE HOLES — ¼" DIA.
2 END HOLES — 1/8" DIA.

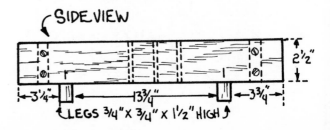

SIDE VIEW

LEGS ¾" X ¾" X 1½" HIGH

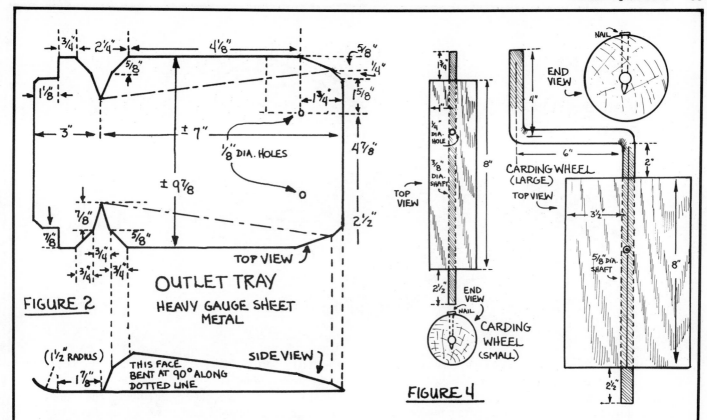

FIGURE 2

OUTLET TRAY

HEAVY GAUGE SHEET METAL

TOP VIEW

1/8" DIA. HOLES

(1 1/2" RADIUS)

THIS FACE BENT AT 90° ALONG DOTTED LINE

SIDE VIEW

FIGURE 4

TOP VIEW

CARDING WHEEL (SMALL)

END VIEW

CARDING WHEEL (LARGE)

TOP VIEW

END VIEW

NAIL

Bearing supports (Fig. 3) — Of the two sets of hardwood bearing supports, the larger is slotted to permit eventual adjustment of the gap between larger and smaller carding wheel. If you have the material handy, the bearing supports can be made a good deal more durable by providing bushings for the 3/8" and 5/8" shaft holes. Take care to fit the bushing (brass tube, G.I. pipe section or other) tightly into the holes in bearing supports.

Large and small carding wheels — These are soft wood cylinders of the radii indicated. The 1/4" hole shown is for securing the wood cylinder to the wheel shaft. Drill the hole deep enough to pass through the cylinder and the shaft, then tap a nail of suitable length to permit a secure anchor in the cylinder. Cylinders are then wrapped with wire studded leather strips (i.e. cards) which are tacked in place with 3/4" - 1" nails. These nails should be about 1"

apart and located along all edges of each leather strip. Note that the metal shafts for the two wheels are of different lengths and diameters and the larger shaft should be long enough to permit the forming of a crank at one end as in Fig. 4.

In making the leather cards the wire studs are inserted into the leather strip through perforations made with a small nail. The wire studs are to be set in from the inside of the leather "tube" at 1/8 spacings. This is accomplished by overlapping successive rows. The teeth should all be bent in the same direction. Make the card for the larger wheel 7 x 3.14 or 21.98" long and the smaller card 6.28" in length.*

*These wire studded leather cards are quite difficult and tedius to make. An alternative is to order a replacement belt from a company such as Made-Well Manufacturing Company, Sifton, Manitoba, Canada

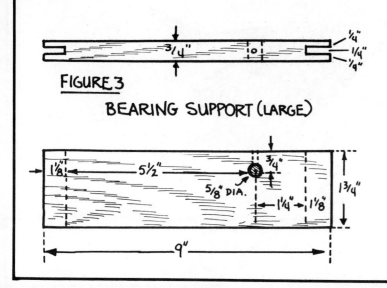

FIGURE 3

BEARING SUPPORT (LARGE)

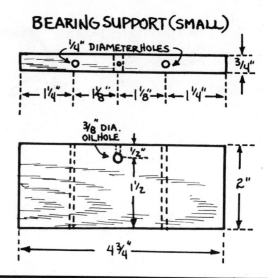

BEARING SUPPORT (SMALL)

1/4" DIAMETER HOLES

3/8" DIA. OIL HOLE

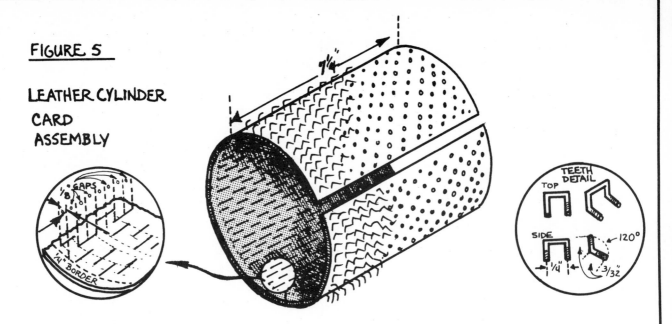

FIGURE 5

LEATHER CYLINDER
CARD
ASSEMBLY

Adjustment bolts, drive mechanism and final assembly — The drive mechanism of the assembly is attached to the longer straight protrusion of both carding wheel shafts. Note the direction of the teeth. General variations of drive mechanisms could be used but one of the best would be a non-slip arrangement utilizing bicycle chain and sprockets. See Fig. 7 for details of the bicycle chain drive. The ratio between the pulleys is to be 1 to 6, with the large carding wheel turning six times for every one revolution of the small carding wheel.

The carding wheels are adjusted by means of two brackets as shown in Fig. 6. Flatten the head of a ¼" bolt, bend it off to one side and drill the flattened head out for the result shown. The adjustment bolts are mounted with two 1" wood screws in the approximate position shown. The sheet metal outlet tray is as shown in Fig. 2, provided with two tabs which are to be fitted between the bearing supports for the small carding wheel and the frame.

The curved portion fits under and around the lower portion of the small carding wheel. Note that this curved portion should not come into contact with either of the carding wheels. In assembling the carding wheels, use flat washers as necessary to insure good alignment and prevention of sideways play of the shafts with respect to the frame.

Chain drive mechanism details — Mount sprockets to shaft by any means available. Weld sprocket directly onto shaft or bolt sprocket onto a mounting collar (hardwood or metal) which could be fixed onto shaft in a manner similar to the method used for fixing the wood cylinders to their shafts (see Fig. 4). If a standard large bicylce sprocket is used for the small wheel it may be necessary to make your own small sprocket. To do this, first determine the required diameter of the smaller sprocket by dividing the diameter of the larger sprocket by six. Bear in mind that the spacing of the teeth will have to be the

ADJUSTMENT BOLTS
AND DRIVE
MECHANISM

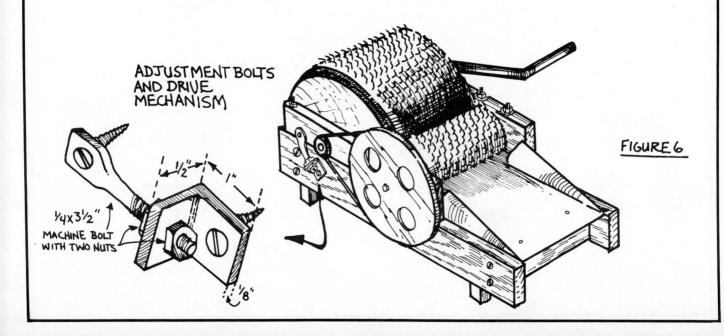

FIGURE 6

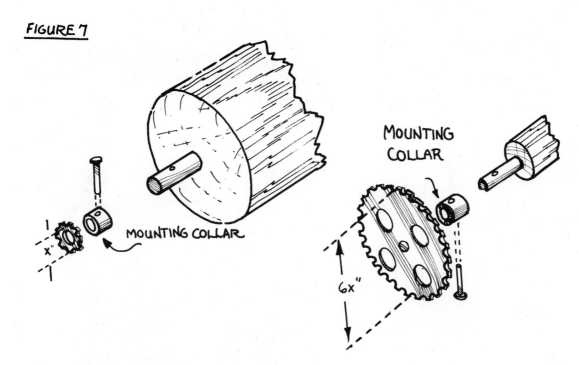

FIGURE 7

MOUNTING COLLAR

MOUNTING COLLAR

same on both sprockets. If this spacing cannot be maintained with the 1 to 6 ratio, it will be necessary to in-increase or decrease the diameter of the smaller sprocket. Increasing or decreasing the diameter one unit will increase or decrease the circumference 3.14 units.

The best way to make such a sprocket is to draw the full size sprocket on paper with a compass etc. Cut out the finished drawing and fix it onto the 1/8" thick metal plate, then proceed to cut the form out of metal. Finish the task by filing the teeth to the shape of those on the large sprocket. Presuming that you've gotten over this hurdle, the final step is to attach the bicycle chain of suitable length.

Operation and Maintenance

To card with the machine, the greatest of care must be taken not to put in tangled or matted wool caused by improper washing, as this will bend the wires so that the carding material will be unfit for use. If wool is matted it should be teased. If it is washed properly it does not need to be teased.

Washing of Wool — Wool fibre is covered with scales; heat opens them, cold closes them. Causes of matting: sudden opening and closing of the scales, caused by varying temperatures, also rubbing and twisting will cause matting. Select a bright sunny day. Set up several containers of warm, **soft** water. Use good soap flakes, and half as much washing soda. Divide a fleece into about ten parts. Put one of these parts into the first container. Press it up and down gently with a hand vacuum paddle, plunger, or with the hands, and then squeeze out the water. A loose wringer may be used. Then do the same in the other waters, rinsing the last. **Do not twist, pound, rub or pack the wool and do not wash too much at one time.** Wool must not be washed in a washing machine or it will mat. The wool

should come out of the water in one piece, the same as it was before washing.

Another method is to place a fleece of wool in a tub of **soft** water. Make good suds with warm soft water. Put the wool through several waters, using a little wool at a time. Use a quarter of a cup of coal oil in the last water soaking. This will make the wool fluffy. Many persons living near streams wash wool there with good results. Some remove the bulk of the dirt at the stream and then finish washing with warm water. Dipping the sheep before shearing is a good custom. The wool is cleaned and the oil retained. When the wool is to be used at home this should be done when possible.

Operation of carding machine — Feed the wool in lengthwise so that it will not get broken up while cranking the large wheel in a direction away from the feeder tray. Do not feed too much at one time. When the wires are about full, cut through with scissors, take a piece of cardboard about 1" wide and 8" long and commence to roll the wool on the cardboard strip away from the feeder, while turning the drum backwards toward the feeder trays, until the wool is all on the cardboard. The wheels should barely touch, but exact clearance will have to be determined by experiment with the type of wool or cotton in your locale.

Adjustment and maintenance — After the carding machine has been used for some time it may be necessary to move the drums a little closer together. You will notice two small slots on each side. Loosen the nuts in these slots and slide the big drum closer by adjusting the tighteners (adjustment bolts) which are located on each side near the front of the machine. The tighteners each have two nuts which can be tightened. Lubrication with a heavy oil and cleaning of the bearings of cotton or wool fibers is all that will be necessary to maintain the machine for long service.

A Parlor Spinning Wheel

by Mike Nickerson

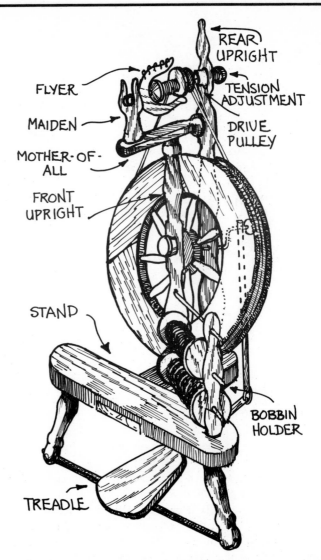

Confronted with many needs that must be filled in order to survive, the majority of us find ourselves dependent on a system that is beyond our control. The problems which are ailing that system seem likely to grow. If we are not to suffer with this ailment we must develop the tools and skills to provide directly for our needs. Such was the inspiration that led to the translation of a sketch in **The Joy of Spinning** into a working parlor spinning wheel. I will attempt here to describe the procedure by which one of these wheels can be made.

The Wheel

The first step in this procedure was to cut a template out of **masonite** with an 18" outer diameter and a 12" inner diameter. The wood used to make the rim was finished 1" x 6" maple. The finished measurements were ¾" x 5½". Two 6' pieces were cut into eight pieces 13½" long (save the ends for making **bobbins** and **hub**). The eight boards were then glued and clamped to make two pieces (Fig. 1) which fit together to make a square. Be sure to remove dried glue that would interfere with the boards fitting snugly. The closer the fit, the less patching later. With the two halves ready and fitted together, the wheel was drawn using the template, and it was cut out on a band saw. The hub was made by laminating two four inch

by four inch pieces of the finished maple and cutting out a 3½" circle from it. It is necessary to have a lathe that can turn an 18" wheel off its end or, as I ended up with, a 5/8" shaft held over the edge of the table by two mounted bearings and a large pulley to attach to a smaller one on a power source (Fig. 2). A suitable **face plate** is then attached to the hub and the circumference rounded, trying to keep the edge 90° to the face. Before

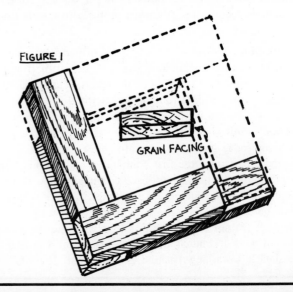

FIGURE 1

GRAIN FACING

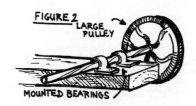

FIGURE 2
LARGE PULLEY

MOUNTED BEARINGS

taking the hub off the lathe, mark the true centre for
drilling. Also mark the hub so that the faceplate can be
replaced in the same position. Drill the centre hole with a
3/8" bit making sure that the press is working at 90 degrees
to the supporting surface. I decided to use seven spokes
and marked the piece of masonite from the centre of the
rim template off into 51.4 degree sections. These don't
have to be exact, just as close as possible. Concentric circles
on this template will help centre the hub for marking.

Once the holes are located, marked, and a starting hole
made, a jig (Fig. 3) can be constructed by cutting in a 2"
x 2" (with a band saw) a semi-circle the same diameter as
the hub. The jig is then clamped to the drill stand so that
when a spoke hole marker is directly up it is right under
the centre of a 7/16" drill. Drill the seven holes an inch
deep or so and return the hub to the lathe to round the
corners and finish with sandpaper.

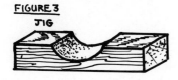

FIGURE 3
JIG

The Spokes

The spokes are the next step, but first some general
procedure for preparing a piece of wood to be turned.
Both ends need to be marked for their centres. On a
square piece this can be done by drawing two lines crossing
from the corners. On one end, lines at right angles to each
other should be cut 1/8" into the wood. This is to ensure
a solid grip on the turning end of the lathe. Both ends
should then be drilled with a **bit** slightly smaller than the
points on the lathe. Finally the corners should be taken off,
leaving a roughly eight sided piece. This final step can be
done either with a chisel or by setting a table saw at 45
degrees and adjusting the guide so that just the right amount
is removed (Fig. 4). The spokes can be made from a piece
of rough 1" x 6" maple. Start with a piece 2' long. The
extra will be used for the flyer later. Prepare seven pieces
6½" long and turn to the dimensions shown (Fig. 5).

Measurements can be made consistent by using **calipers**
or thin open-end wrenches. After trimming the ends,
assemble the spokes with the grain perpendicular to the
hub. If they do not fit tightly, glue them in. The rim is
then prepared by clamping it together in a **vise**, (If using
a metal vise, use pieces of wood to protect the wheel
surface.) Shape and smooth the inside rim with files and
sandpaper.

To assemble, the rim was laid out as one piece and the
hub with spokes was positioned so that none of the spoke
holes corresponded with the joints yet to be glued. The
rim was marked where each spoke touched. One spoke and
mark were identified so that it could be realigned. The rim
was centre punched where these marks, when extended,
crossed the centre of the wheel. They were drilled with a ½"
bit to receive the spoke ends. Fit it to make sure the
holes are deep enough. With all well, glue and clamp the
rim (not the spoke ends).

Wheel Alignment

After drying, the wheel can be aligned by putting it on
the lathe and turning slowly by hand. Compare the rim with
a stationary object. Where the rim moves too far in, out or
side to side, adjust the spokes where they meet the rim.
Sometimes this requires whittling the hole or the spoke,
sometimes it requires **shims**. Work at it until a minimum of
movement is achieved. An eighth of an inch is not critical
but perfection is desirable. Finally, glue is carefully worked
into the joints so as not to disturb the alignment. When
the glue is dry, the wheel is ready to turn. Since the outer
rim of the wheel is almost 5' in circumference and turns a
couple of times a second, the cutting must be done very
carefully. If chisel movements are not very slow the point
can get caught in end grain. When this happens the grain
pulls out, making a rough portion that is more likely to
catch the chisel again.

The entire rim must first be evened and then two grooves
cut as in Fig. 6. Use files and sandpaper to smooth the
surfaces and to round the corners. To finish the wheel, use
a mixture of white glue and the sawdust of the wood used.
This mixture can be worked into joints, gouges and the
screw holes from the face plate. When the glue dries it can
be sanded to a smooth continuous surface.

The Stand

This piece starts out with two lengths of 2" x 4", one
16" and one 14" long. I used B.C. fir for the grain, but
any wood that is unlikely to warp can be used (Fig. 7).

CUT OFF CORNERS

FIGURE 4

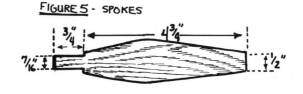

FIGURE 5 - SPOKES

FIGURE 6

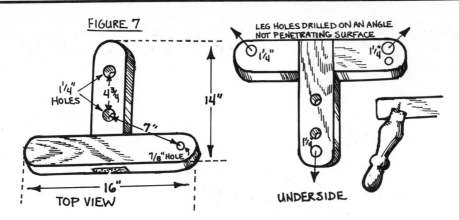

FIGURE 7

LEG HOLES DRILLED ON AN ANGLE NOT PENETRATING SURFACE

1¼"   1¼"   HOLES   4¾"   7"   14"   7/8" HOLE   16"   TOP VIEW

UNDERSIDE

The Legs and Frame

The next eight pieces are all made from 2" x 2" or the same wood as the stand. The pieces needed are:

Legs	3 pieces	10" long
Front upright	1 piece	24" long
Back upright	1 piece	33" long
Mother of all	1 piece	13" long
Bobbin holder	1 piece	13" long
Maiden	1 piece	7" long

All pieces are prepared as in the section on spokes.

Legs (Fig. 8) — All dowels should be slightly larger than the holes so they can be shaped for a tight fit. The end of the legs should be round so that they fit the floor and so that the treadle can be attached conviently. Other shaping is arbitrary.

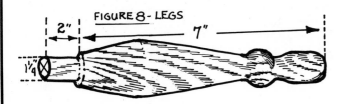

FIGURE 8 - LEGS

2"   7"   1¼"

Front Upright (Fig. 9) — The hole for the axle is perpendicular to the grain. The 7/8" section ¼" to 3/8" deep is for a bearing made of bone. The rest of the hole should be large enough that the axle will turn freely.

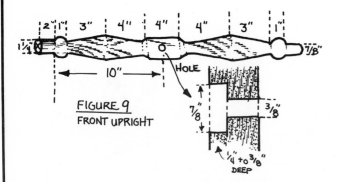

2" 1"   3"   4"   4"   4"   3"   1"
1¼"   10"   HOLE   7/8"
FIGURE 9   7/8"   3/8"
FRONT UPRIGHT   ¼" to 3/8" DEEP

Rear Upright (Fig. 10) — The 7/8" hole for the mother of all should not penetrate the back of the piece. The tension adjustment slot is made by drilling a row of holes

slightly larger than ¼" and then joining them together with a chisel and finishing with a file.

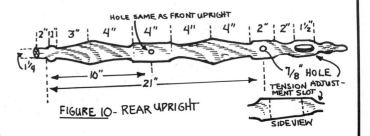

HOLE SAME AS FRONT UPRIGHT

2" 1" 3"   4"   4"   4"   4"   2"   2"   1½"
1¼"   10"   21"   7/8" HOLE
FIGURE 10- REAR UPRIGHT   TENSION ADJUSTMENT SLOT
SIDE VIEW

Mother of All (Fig. 11) — The top portion of the long section needs to be cut flat on a band saw or with a chisel.

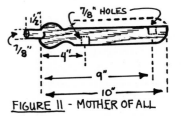

7/8" HOLES
½"
7/8"   4"   9"   10"
FIGURE 11 - MOTHER OF ALL

Maiden (Fig 12) — Both sides of the top want to be cut flat with the grain. Then a 5/8" hole is drilled perpendicular to the grain and is cut on a band saw so that a 5/8" pipe can be lowered in.

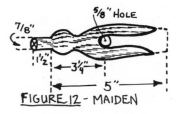

7/8"   5/8" HOLE
1½"   3¼"   5"
FIGURE 12 - MAIDEN

Bobbin Holder (Fig. 13) — The holes should be big enough for a coat hanger wire to slide easily into. When assembled, the lengths of coat hanger, bent at one end for a handle, go through the holes and across to the front upright, to support extra bobbins.

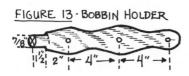

FIGURE 13 - BOBBIN HOLDER

Bearings

Three bearings are used in this design. The two bearings for the uprights have a 7/8" outer diameter and a 3/8" inner diameter. These can be made by cutting the side off of the narrow section of a bone and drawing the necessary disks. The centre needs to be clearly marked and drilled before the pieces are cut. (The cut pieces are hard to hold for drilling.) The outsides are then roughly cut on a band saw and shaped with a file or on a belt sander until they fit snugly in the appropriate hole. The other bearing is 5/8" outer diameter with a hole adequate to accommodate the end of the bobbin axle of the flyer assembly.

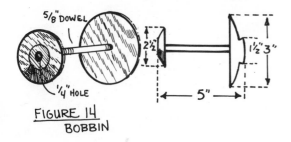

FIGURE 14
BOBBIN

Bobbins (Fig. 14)

The three bobbins are made from the same hardwood as the wheel. The dowel can be turned from 1" x 1" x 6" pieces. To get the hole centred, it is easiest to drill the 1" x 1" with a 6" bit. First make a 1/8" deep hole the diameter of the **dead centre** on the lathe. Then drill the main hole from the end drilled for the dead centre. I found it necessary to clamp the piece of a squared block with a corner on one side that the 1" x 1" fit into (Fig. 15). Since the drill press only had a 4" bite, I needed a shim that I could easily place under the jig to continue the hole. Before turning, saw a cross centred at the middle of the hole where it emerged from the piece. After the corners have been removed, the piece will fit on the lathe with the hole down the centre. The 5/8" dowel can then be turned. For the ends, mark appropriate circles on the leftovers from the wheel. Be sure to make the centre point clear. After the discs are cut out, drill the centre through with a bit slightly smaller than the

FIGURE 15

points of the lathe. After one side is crossed with a chisel, the pieces can be turned. With some lathes it is necessary to improvise a tool rest. For the pulley notch, some wood can be cut away with a chisel, but I used a small size round file for the most part.

The less wood in the bobbins the better they will work, providing they hold together. After the turning is finished, drill the centre to 5/8" and cut away anything left over from where the lathe was attached. A belt sander is useful for this. The pieces can then be assembled. Since I finished the batch I did, it was recommended that the bobbins be fitted with leather bearings. These would be 5/8" outer diameter and ¼" inner diameter. Their purpose is to keep the bobbin from clicking on its axle while spinning.

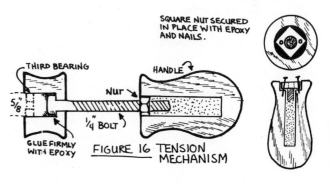

FIGURE 16 TENSION MECHANISM

Tension Mechanism (Fig. 16)

The part holding the bearing should be made out of hardwood. The bolt is firmly glued in with expoxy. The handle can be of any wood with the nut glued in and the hole drilled deep enough to receive the excess bolt. The length of the bolt can be determined by giving 3/8" or so beyond the widest point of the tension adjustment slot on the rear upright.

The Flyer Assembly (Fig. 17)

The orifice can be made from a 2¾ piece of 5/8" outer diameter pipe. The 3/8" diameter hole is about ¾" from the flyer end of the pipe. All burrs on the open end and

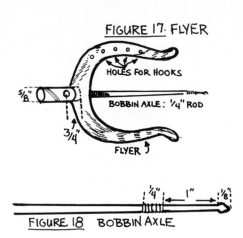

FIGURE 17. FLYER

HOLES FOR HOOKS

5/8"

BOBBIN AXLE: 1/4" ROD

3/4"

FLYER ♪

FIGURE 18   BOBBIN AXLE

1/4" 1" 1/8"

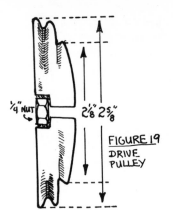

1/4" NUT

2 1/8" 2 5/8"

FIGURE 19
DRIVE
PULLEY

around the holes must be removed and smoothed to prevent the yarn from catching. The bobbin axle can be made from a 9" piece of 1/4" rod. One end needs to be turned (Fig. 18) for which a metal lathe would be optimal, but a wood lathe can be crudely adapted.

Turn a 2" 1" x 1" into dowel and cut it in half while still on the lathe. The saw marks will indicate the centre of each piece. Drill the dead centre end so that the 1/4" rod will fit in. Then drill the **live centre** end and glue in a 1/4" nut. With these adaptions, the 9" rod with a thread cut on one end can be turned. Cutting (possibly started on a grinder) should be done with metal files and finished with **emery** cloth. The part that rests on the bearing must be smooth or it will wear the bearing away.

The flyer must be shaped so that the opening encompasses the bobbin, but is not in the way of the strings. The point where the orifice and the axle attach should be at least 1" through.

It is important that the flyer be balanced. This can be worked out on paper by drawing one arm and folding it over. When shaping, saw squarely across the open end and cut along the outside edge. After locating and marking the centre point, drill a 5/8" hole 1/2" into the end. Take care to get it straight (check drill/table angle before starting). The 5/8" hole is then continued with a 1/4" drill. After the holes are drilled the inside edge can be cut out and the piece shaped and finished with a rasp, file and sandpaper. Before assembling is the best time to drill small holes to receive guide hooks.

Before assembly roughly clean the parts of metal to be glued. The axle needs to be measured to the actual size of your maiden tension bearing set up, and cut so that it does not protrude beyond the flyer base. These pieces can then be glued together with epoxy and set to harden as carefully aligned as possible.

The Drive Pulley (Fig. 19)

I made this piece from one of the corners cut off when the wheel was shaped. The 1/4" nut is to screw onto the bobbin axle, so the hole that continues must be large enough to accommodate the end of that axle. If the nut is in crooked the piece wobbles when it is being used.

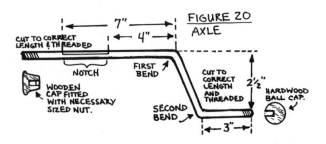

FIGURE 20
AXLE

7"

4"

CUT TO CORRECT
LENGTH & THREADED

NOTCH

FIRST
BEND

WOODEN
CAP FITTED
WITH NECESSARY
SIZED NUT.

SECOND
BEND

CUT TO
CORRECT
LENGTH AND
THREADED

2 1/2"

3"

HARDWOOD
BALL CAP.

The Wheel Assembly (Fig. 20)

The wheel axle can be made from a 17" piece of 3/8" rod. This is easily bent by putting a 3' length of pipe over the end and using its leverage. Be careful not to warp the section where the wheel will sit. The notch is for setting the wheel so that it is rigid with its axle. There are machines for making such grooves, but in their absence the job can be done with a **rotary file** and a drill press (Fig. 21). When

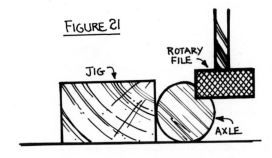

FIGURE 21

JIG

ROTARY
FILE

AXLE

the axle is bent, notched and **burrs** removed, it can be fitted and cut to length. The second bend should be directly above the end of the stand. The front end should be about 3/8" beyond the front upright. Both ends should be given 3/8" of threads. The axle is then put through the rear upright, a bearing, the wheel, another bearing, and the front upright. When the wheel is lined up with the drive pulley and the bobbin pulley, a small nail driven between the wheel and notch will fix it there. The front of the axle can be capped with a piece similar to the back piece of the tension mechanism but with the necessary sized nut. After the treadle is attached, the rear end can be capped with a 1" hardwood ball with a hole slightly smaller than 3/8". This will thread itself when it is twisted on.

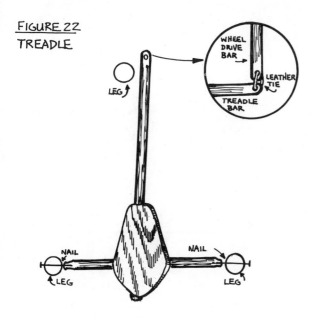

FIGURE 22
TREADLE

WHEEL
DRIVE
BAR

LEATHER
TIE

TREADLE
BAR

LEG

NAIL   NAIL

LEG   LEG

Treadle (Fig. 22)

The final thing to make, before yarn, is the treadle. I used pieces of branch with the bark left on for the connecting pieces, and masonite for the pedal. I have been told several times that the masonite is out of place, and if I do it again I will use a thin piece of maple. The piece connecting the crank to the treadle needs a hole for the crank larger than 3/8" so that it can move freely around.

The length of the wheel drive bar is determined to as follows. Drill the crankhole. Put it on the crank reaching toward the treadle bar. With the treadle bar one inch above the ground and the drive bar pulled towards it, mark, cut and drill the hole for the leather tie.

FIGURE 23

WHEEL DRIVE BAR (CONNECTS CRANK TO TREADLE)

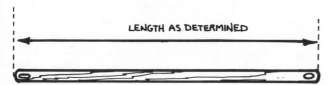

LENGTH AS DETERMINED

TREADLE HOLE
LARGE ENOUGH TO THREAD
LEATHER TIE

CRANKHOLE LARGER
THAN 3/8"

Stringing the Wheel

Take a fairly heavy string, wet it, and stretch it between two posts and let it dry. One length of string should go around the wheel, the drive pulley, the wheel again in the other groove and the bobbin pulley. The string should cross so that the one coming off of the drive pulley passes over

the other without rubbing. Pull the string taut with the tension mechanism near its low point, but not so low that the hooks or flyer touch the mother of all. Mark both ends at their meeting point and cut ¾" to 1" longer than the marks. I found the string too fine to splice like rope, so I just fitted the unravelled ends together with the marks aligned, worked in a little glue that dries pliable and wrapped a thread around the join.

When all is done, the whole thing should be treated with linseed oil. A 3" piece of stove pipe wire with a small hook on the end should be tied on a string from the base of the maiden so that it is handy to pull yarn through the orifice to start spinning.

A final touch which I add in order to communicate my initial inspiration is putting the name Bakavi on the stand. Bakavi is a way of life where people working in community produce from what grows around them the necessities of their existence. Materials which are not regenerative are managed in such a way that they are not lost. The energy that is needed by the community is provided from the sun, the wind and other continuous sources. To become a part of such a living situation is my objective. Perhaps others so inclined can get in touch through this article.

Mike Nickerson
P.O. Box 2011
Station 'D'
Ottawa, Ontario

A Colonial Spinning Wheel

by E.M. Love

Few people are fortunate enough to own a colonial wheel, but any handy person can make an excellent tool by following this article.

Most common hardwoods are suitable for material. Maple is perhaps the most desirable for the turned work, and oak or ash for the base, **treadle** and **pitman**. Glue up the wheel rim as a square frame from stock 1½ by 4¼ in. in the rough, the four pieces being 16 in. long. The ends are cut to an angle of 45°, as in fig. 1. Smooth one side and one edge of each piece for working faces, and gauge the ends with two lines, one 3/8 in. from the face; the other 7/8 in. for the sides of the **tenons** and **mortises**. Shoulder lines, 9½ in. apart, are scored with a knife square across the faces of the tenoned pieces, while pencil lines across the others limit the depth of the mortises. Rip the ends with the saw, splitting the line and cutting in the waste wood. Crosscut the shoulder, and chisel the mortise bottoms from both edges. Try for fit, apply glue liberally to all joining surfaces, and clamp up. Small clamps across the thickness of the joints will prevent wedging open. Set aside to dry until the turned work is done.

Rip 1½ in. strips from 1½ in. stock for larger spindles, and punch the centres of the ends with a nail. The illustration below fig. 1 shows a crude lathe driven by a washing-machine motor. The headstock is a piece of 2 by 4 inch wood, notched at one end to fit over the edge of another length of 2 inch material to which it is nailed. A 16 inch spike, driven through the centre 4 inches above the bed, forms a turning centre. The **tailstock** is like it, but left loose. The **tool rest** is a board of suitable width clamped in the vise. The **spindle**, drilled to fit the centres, and roughly rounded on one end to serve as a pulley, determines the distance between head and tailstocks. These,

when clamped to the tool rest, form a rigid assembly.

Bore a piece of hardwood to fit the motor shaft or collar, turning it to a groove diameter of 2½ in. Over this drive pulley, pass a round leather belt, or, lacking this, a piece of carpenter's chalk line woven into a chain stitch and knotted together for a splice.

If a motor is not available, tie a 2 ft. length of inner tube to the ceiling for a return spring, with the belt tied to the lower end. Loop the belt around the spindle, attaching it to a 1 by 4 in. treadle, 3 ft. long and hinged to the floor at one end by two spikes driven through ¼ in. holes. With a little practice, very good turning can be done on this primitive lathe. A more elaborately designed foot-powered wood lathe is featured in **Cloudburst 1**.

The average amateur has no turning tools, so shift must be made with common chisels. Sharpen a **gouge** to a razor edge. Fix the rest a little above centre. Lay the gouge on it, holding it level with the left hand close to the rest and steadying the handle with the right. Point the blade and incline its diameter somewhat in the direction of motion, taking a cut from one end to the other of the stick. A little practice will show how heavy a cut can be made without slipping the belt. Rough the spindle to the largest diameter.

Figures 3 and 5 illustrate the legs. Cut the stock 1½ in. longer than the finished length, to allow for the pulley. Lubricate the centres with hard oil. When roughed to round-ness, lay a rule on the rest, marking the divisions with a pencil while the piece turns. Work out the slender parts with the gouge to the finished diameter. If the tool is held well on edge in making the large **coves**, a shearing cut is obtained. Scrape the cylindrical portions with a ¼ in. chisel, holding it on edge to cut the shoulders and finishing with

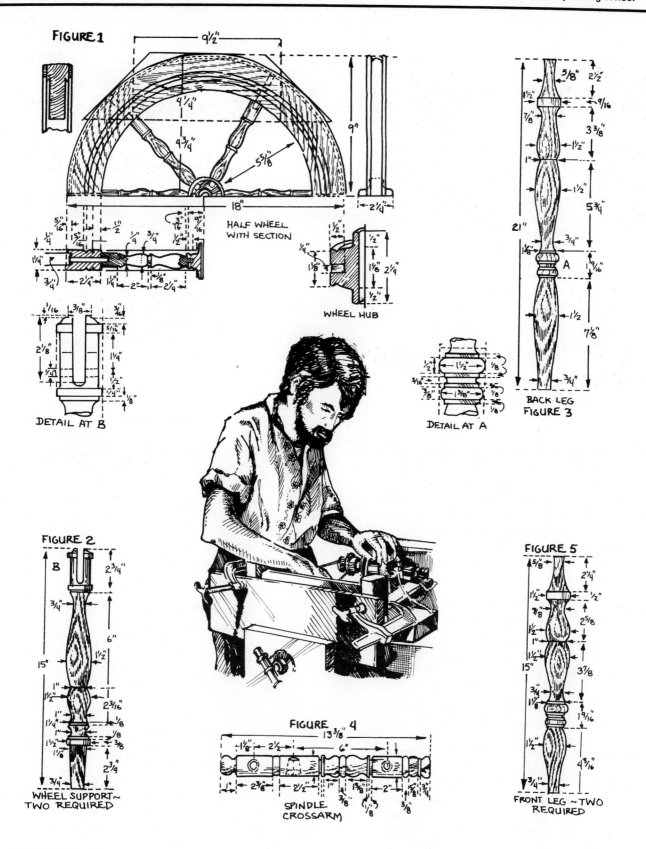

FIGURE 1

9½"

4¼"

4¾"

5⅝"

9"

18"

2¼"

HALF WHEEL WITH SECTION

WHEEL HUB

DETAIL AT B

BACK LEG FIGURE 3

21"

DETAIL AT A

FIGURE 2

B

2¾"

3/4"

6"

15"

1½"

1"

1½"

2³⁄₁₆"

1"

1¼"

1"

1½"

WHEEL SUPPORT~ TWO REQUIRED

FIGURE 4

13⅜"

SPINDLE CROSSARM

FIGURE 5

15"

FRONT LEG ~TWO REQUIRED

the blade held flat. For the beads, use the corner of the gouge, tipping the tool on edge as it nears the root depth. Cut the 1/8 in. coves with the tip of a rat-tail file. When the whole leg is shaped, smooth well with sandpaper. Lastly, cut to length.

Turn the two wheel supports, Fig. 2, in the same way. Rip the upper end of each through the diameter to a depth

of 2-1/8 in. Parallel to this, 3/16 in. from it on either side, make two other cuts. Bore the bottom with a 3/8 in. bit. File the slots smooth.

Figure 4 details the spindle crossarm, which fits over the tapered nut above the turned base, carrying the two spindle supports. The smallest coves are lines made with a three-cornered file. Centering 1-1/8 in. from the left shoulder, bore a ¼ in. hole, 1/8 in. deep. Bore through the diameter with a ½ in. bit, and with a ¼ in. chisel and round file taper the small hole to meet the larger upper one. Another hole, centering 8½ in. from it, is bored and tapered parallel to it. A third hole, tapering from 5/8 in. above to ¾ in. below, centres 2½ in. from the first, inclining at the rate of 3-3/8 in. horizontally with a vertical rise of 6 in. Clamp the piece in a vise with the end holes properly inclined, as determined by a single stick thrust through and compared with a square held upright on the bench. The bit can then be held vertical in the usual manner.

Figure 6 shows a mortise. 1/4 by 1 in., in each spindle support, receiving a sole-leather spindle bearing. One leather is pierced with a 3/8 in. hole, while the other, carrying the tapered end of the spindle, is 3/16 in. Glue these in. Turn the tapers to such a diameter that the lower ends, solidly seated, project ¼ in. below the crossarm. Fig. 7 illustrates the **distaff** support. Four and one-eighth inches from the lower end, a 1/2 in. hole, 1 in. deep, carries the distaff crossarm, also detailed in Fig. 7. A ½ in. hole, 1 in. deep, centred on the cylindrical part of the crossarm, receives the distaff.

For tightening the belt, a screw, shown in Fig. 8, must be made. If an old wood clamp is available, the screw and nut may be turned from it; but if not, turn the screw from 1½ in. stock, with the threaded part ¾ in. in diameter. The end bearing is ½ in. through. The ¼ in. groove engages a wooden **key** in the base, to prevent withdrawal when the belt is slackened.

To get the **pitch** of the thread, build a **mitre box**, 3/4 in. wide, 1 in. deep and 4 in. long. With a **backsaw**, inclining 1/16 in. from the square in the ¾ in. width, make a cut, 3/8 in. deep, across the middle. Insert the end of the screw blank and cut a groove about 1/16 in. deep, turning slowly and moving the saw in two or three short strokes. Next,

draw a pencil line midway between the grooves and whittle the thread roughly to shape. Smooth the groove with a saw file. A surprisingly accurate thread can be made in this way.

The nut, Fig. 8, having a square portion, 2-5/8 in. long, to slide in the base guide, is turned off on the corners to a diameter of 1¾ in. Bore a through hole 1-1/8 in. in diameter, centring 1¼ in. from the taper shoulder. Cast the threaded nut in plastic wood, as indicated below Fig. 8. Bore a 1½ inch hole through 2 x 4 inch piece, 1 inch from the end, and rip out the end. In the bottom, lay a thick bed of plastic wood. Press the oiled screw into it, mold the top and force the piece sawn out of the block against it. Cut the wooden mold to liberate the bushing, leaving it on the screw until well hardened. Afterward trim the **bushing** to fit the tapered nut and glue it in place.

The turned spindle base, Fig. 9, is best made from 4 by 4 in. solid stock, but if this is not available, glue two pieces of 2 in. stock together with the grain running at right angles, bore the hole and taper it, and drive it over the nut taper for an **arbor**. Turn to dimensions. It is recessed in the bottom ½ in. deep. The **bobbin**, dimensioned in the same drawing, is pierced with a ¼ in. hole, so as to turn freely on the spindle.

The spindle can be made from a 3/16 in. curtain rod, obtainable at most 10 and 15-cent stores. Split the end for ¾ in. bending the halves outward and back parallel, to give an inside width of 3/8 in. Cut the rod to 3¾ in., and file a taper, 1-5/8 in. long, on the solid end, reducing it to 1/8 in. Thread the rod for ¼ in. just above the taper where a nut sunk in the flier pulley engages. The eye bearing is a **ferrule** cut from the base of an oilcan spout and filled with plastic wood. When dry, fit the eye ends solidly and bore out the centre. The flier and pulley are also detailed in Fig. 9.

The flier is sawed from ¾ in. stock. Through a ¾ in. button, 3/8 in. long, and the slightly less than 3/16 in.

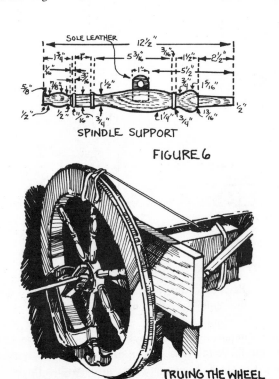

SPINDLE SUPPORT

FIGURE 6

TRUING THE WHEEL

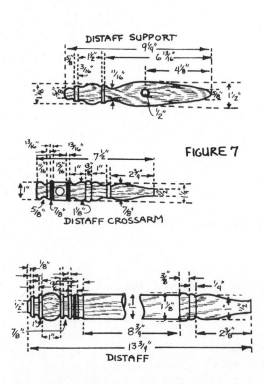

DISTAFF SUPPORT

FIGURE 7

DISTAFF CROSSARM

DISTAFF

MATERIAL LIST

1 piece, 1½ by 5 in. by 5 ft., maple.
1 piece, 1½ by 8 in. by 4½ ft., maple.
1 piece, 1 by 6 by 12 in., maple.
1 piece, 4 by 4 by 12 in., maple.
1 piece, 2 by 10 in. by 2 ft., oak.
1 hinge pin from loose-pin butt, 2½ by 2½ in.
1½ doz. small steel hooks.
1 leather shoelace.

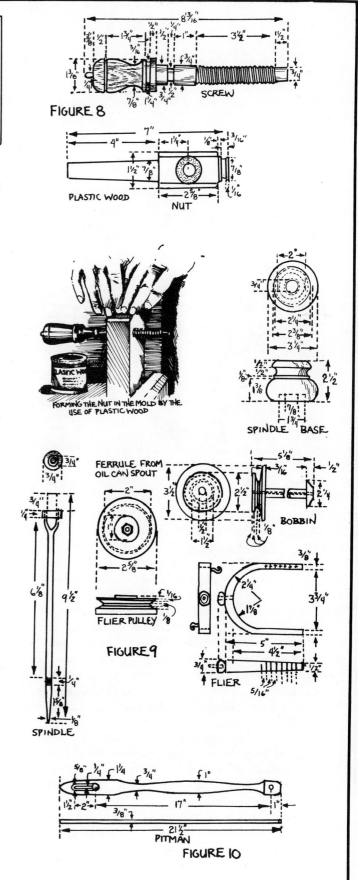

FIGURE 8

PLASTIC WOOD NUT

FORMING THE NUT IN THE MOLD BY THE USE OF PLASTIC WOOD

SPINDLE BASE

FERRULE FROM OIL CAN SPOUT

BOBBIN

FLIER PULLEY

FIGURE 9

FLIER

SPINDLE

PITMAN

FIGURE 10

hole in the flier, the spindle is forced until the eye sinks into the button enough to grip it strongly. Screw nine small iron hooks into each flier arm, and, lastly, screw on the flier pulley. (In use, the flax or wool is fed through the eye bearing and looped over the hooks, with the end tied to the bobbin. The flier, rotating, twists the yarn, while the bobbin, having a smaller pulley and revolving faster, winds it up.)

Two small pins, shown in Fig. 11, are turned to hold the wheel axle in the slots. The axle is a 5¾ in. piece of 3/8 in. round iron. For the crank, bend a 5/16 in. bolt to an arc of about 1-1/8 in., hammering it to a thickness of 3/16 in. Near one end, drill a 3/16 in. hole, to be filed square. Centering 2 in. from this, drill the crank-pin hole. File a square end on the axle for riveting to the crank. Use a piece of hinge pin for the crank pin, supplying washers, as in Fig. 13.

Scribe the inner and outer diameters of the wheel with a pivoted stick, as in Fig. 14, and cut the outside with a keyhole saw. Smooth with a spokeshave. Nail, across the two faces, pieces of 1 by 4 in. stock with the nails in the waste wood. Locate the wheel centre by scribing intersecting arcs from various points on the inner rim line. Bore holes in these temporary "spokes" to fit a piece of broomstick snugly; the spokes are nailed to the broomstick and a stout wooden crank is attached, after mounting in 2 by 4 in. bearings held in the vise. Stand on the floor a board long enough to serve as a tool rest, bracing it to the bearings. On each side of the wheel, with the least possible clearance, nail a guide piece, preventing side wobble with relation to the tool rest. If another person turns the crank, the belt groove detailed in Fig. 1 can easily be turned.

Turn the spokes and hub, bore 1/4 in. holes, 1/2 in. deep, in the large ends of the turned spokes, and locate the holes in the hub by stepping around the circumference with a pair of dividers spanning the radius of the hub. When the inside of the rim is cut and smoothed, bore 1/4 in. dowel holes through it at the proper points for the spokes. All being ready, glue up, inserting the spokes in the hub and inside the rim, driving the dowels from the outside.

The illustration below Fig. 6 shows a method of holding the wheel true until dry. Insert a 3/8 in. rod into the hub and clamp it level in the vise. Tack a board across the bench end, shimming it square with the rod, and place the wheel. If the spokes are tightly fitted, the hub will bulge outward. Force it into position and hold with sticks clamped to the axle. Rotate it until the part of the rim inclined outward is at the top, where it can be tied with a string, its position being proved by a square held along the shaft.

Figure 12 dimensions the oak base. Cut the stock 18 in. long, and work from a centre line. To make the molding, **rabbet** the top edge 1/8 by 3/8 in. Round the corners to a radius of 1/2 in. Plane off the bead corner and work it round. Bore 1½ in. holes for the ends of the guide, and

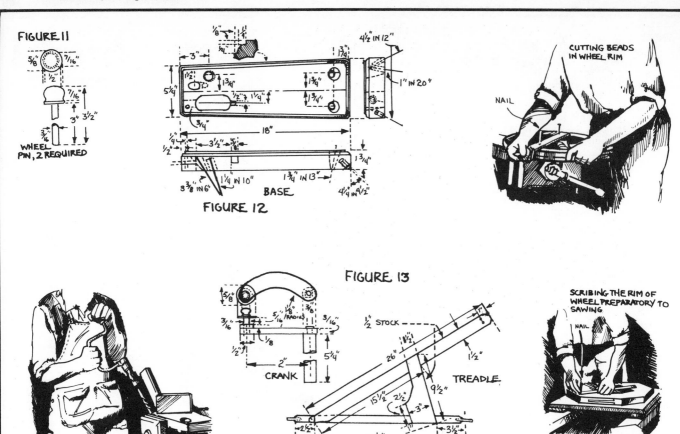

FIGURE 11

WHEEL PIN, 2 REQUIRED

FIGURE 12

BASE

FIGURE 13

CRANK

TREADLE

CUTTING BEADS IN WHEEL RIM

NAIL

BORING HOLES FOR LEGS

SCRIBING THE RIM OF WHEEL PREPARATORY TO SAWING

NAIL

FIGURE 14

saw out the material between. The screw bearing is 3/4 in. in diameter, 1 in. from the bottom and centred on the nut guide. A 3/4 in. hole, 5/8 in. deep, receives the end of the screw. Make a 1/4 in. square key hole 1/2 in. from the end and 1/4 in. from the screw centre. The nut is slipped into the slot in the base and the screw turned into the nut until the 3/4 in. nose on its end is fully seated in the corresponding hole in the bottom of the slot. Then a 1/4 in. key is inserted in the key hole above referred to, and driven in until it passes across the ¼ in. groove in the screw, locking the latter in place, and enabling the nut to be traversed back and forth by turning the screw. The spindle base fits on the taper portion of the nut, and the spindle crossarm on the upper part of the nut taper, above the spindle base. Next, the spindle supports are driven into the crossarm, and the spindle fitted into its leather bearings between them. Block the base in the vise at an angle of 3-3/8 in. rise in 6 in., and, holding the bit vertical, bore the distaff-support hole, centering 1½ in. from the narrow end and 1 in. from the base centre. This hole tapers from 3/4 in. at the top to 5/8 in. at the bottom.

The 5/8 in. hole in the bottom for the long leg is 3 in. from the narrow end and 1¾ in. from the centre leaning toward the wide end 1¾ in. in 10 in., and toward the centre 1 in. in 20 in. The angles of the front legs can be accurately bored by the use of a guide, as indicated in the illustration beside Fig. 13. They incline outward from the centre 4½ in. in 12 in., and, parallel to the base centre, 4¼ in. in 4½ in.

Assemble the legs with the base, stand on a floor, and

scribe the leg ends ¼ in. up for cutting.

Dress the wheel to thickness. Scratch the bead V's with a nail point in a pivoted stick. Clamp the axle in a vise, push the wheel against the bench end, and, holding a ¼ in. chisel against the bench top with the right hand, turn the bead by rotating the wheel with the left hand, pressing the rim against a stop on the bench end to secure a uniform cut. Sand the wheel, assemble the spindles and put the wheel on its axle. Align the grooves with the spindle and bobbin pulleys so as to mark the axle. Drill a 1/8 in. hole through hub and axle to receive a piece of nail as a key.

The pivoted member of the treadle (Fig. 13) is 1 in. square, with the ends turned to a taper. Use pieces of spikes as pivot pins, and hang 2 in. above the floor. The pitman, Fig. 10, has a ¼-in. slot at its upper end to accommodate the crank-pin body. In order that the head of the crank-pin with its washer rides on the shoulder. Attach the the latter terminates, at its lower end, in a 5/8 in. hole. Centering 2 in. from this, at the other end of the slot, is another 5/8 in. hole; this is drilled only ¼ in. deep. From this hole to the first, another slot is cut, 5/8 in. wide and ¼ in. deep, as indicated by the double lines in Fig. 10. This makes a shouldered slot, ¼ in. wide, on one side of the pitman and 5/8 in. wide on the other. The head of the crank pin with its washer rides on the shoulder. Attach the pitman end to the treadle with a leather thong tied underneath.

Give the wheel a coat of oil, and when dry and sanded off, give a second coat. Splice a single-string belt around the wheel and both pulleys.

The Lesotho Spinning Wheel

by C.J. Howse & M. Faulkner

Anyone wishing to produce a spinning wheel similar to the one described in this article must remember that the most helpful virtue to have is IMAGINATION. Any specific item in the material list that cannot be obtained easily should not be taken as the only thing that will suffice. The material list is a flexible one. If any material listed is not available, use the principle of the design, or modify it to suit those materials that are available.

Tools

The tools necessary for manufacturing the complete spinning wheel are listed below:

Pedestal drill — or a hand power drill with a drilling stand attachment.
Drill vise — 2" capacity is sufficient.
Twist drills — 1/8, 3/16, 1/4, 17/64, 5/16, 21/64, 23/64, 3/8, 1/2, 3/4, 49/64 and 1" dia. drills.
Circle cutter — consists of a pilot drill with a movable single point cutting tool which can be adjusted to a radius of 2".
Bench and bench vise.
Hacksaw.
Crosscut saw.
Mitre box and tenon saw to suit — an adjustable type if possible or a solid type that can cut right angles as well as mitres.
Large flat screwdriver.
Hammer — 8 oz.
Steel rule — 12".
Combination pliers.
Two 'C' clamps.
Wood chisel — 1½ inch dovetail.
Wood glue
Roll of masking tape.
Ball of bailing string.
Oxy-Acetylene welding equipment.
Afrox M15 bronze and flux — or other type of brazing spelter and flux.

Wheel Frame Parts List

Part	Quan.	Size	Material
A	2	1½ x 2 x 28	
B	4	1½ x 2 x 18	
C	2	1½ x 2 x 18	Cheap unplaned pine or any other cheap structural wood
D	2	1½ x 2 x 6½	
E	1	1½ x 2 x 24	
F	1	1½ x 2 x 20	
G	1	3 x ½ x 14	
H	2	6 x 6	Tempered Masonite ¼" thick (Hardboard)
J	2	7 x 6	
K	1	1½ x 2 x 3½	Cheap unplaned pine or any other cheap structural wood
L	1	1½ x ½ x 21	
M	2	4 - 5" nails	

Panel pins ¾" lg. 60
Woodscrews No. 12 x 3" lg. 20
Nails 1½" lg. 6

Wheel Frame Assembly Instructions

All pieces of pine are cut to length with square ends, using the mitre block.

Part A is then glued and screwed, using No. 12 x 3" woodscrews to part B. One at the end and one 22" further along part A, making sure that the edges are flush. This is repeated for the remaining parts A and B. Before screwing part A to part B, part A should be pre-drilled using a ¼" dia. drill (this is to take the screw shank) and part B should have 1/8" dia. spotted into it from those in part A. This provides easy alignment and screwing.

The gussets, parts H and J, are then cut to shape and glued and nailed onto parts A and B using ¾" panel pins.

Parts D are then attached 4" from the end of parts B, gluing, and nailing the two sides together, using part K as

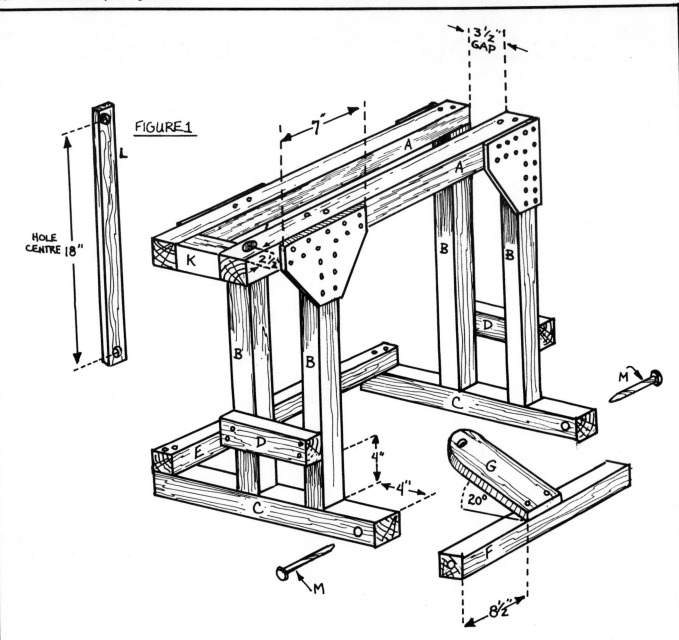

FIGURE 1

HOLE CENTRE 18"

3 ½" GAP

7"

2 ½"

4"

4"

20°

8½"

a spacer. Part K is also glued and nailed into position.

Parts C are then glued and screwed onto the ends of parts B using No. 12 x 3" woodscrews. This is done 4" from the end of part C and making sure that these parts are parallel. Before screwing, part C should be predrilled ¼" dia. for the screw shank and 1/8" dia. holes spotted through them into parts B.

Part E is then glued and nailed onto parts C at their extreme ends.

Part G is glued and nailed onto part F at its mid-point and at approx. 70 degrees. This is followed by drilling a ½" dia. hole through part G ¾" from the end, and 1/8" dia. holes centrally in the ends of part F.

Two holes clearance dia. to suit the 4" nails, are drilled into the sides of parts C 3/4" from the end and 1" from the bottom edge.

Part F is positioned between parts C and 4" nails are driven home (parts M in the assembly illustration).

Part L, the link between the foot pedal and the wheel

crank, is then drilled for two ½" dia. holes. One 1½" from the end and the other 18" further along (these sizes may have to be adjusted, so this stage should wait until final assembly of the spinning wheel).

FIGURE 2

WHEEL ASSEMBLY DIMENSIONS END VIEW

WHEEL BEARING CENTRES FRONT VIEW

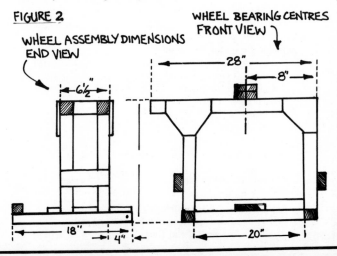

6 ½"

28"

8"

18"

4"

20"

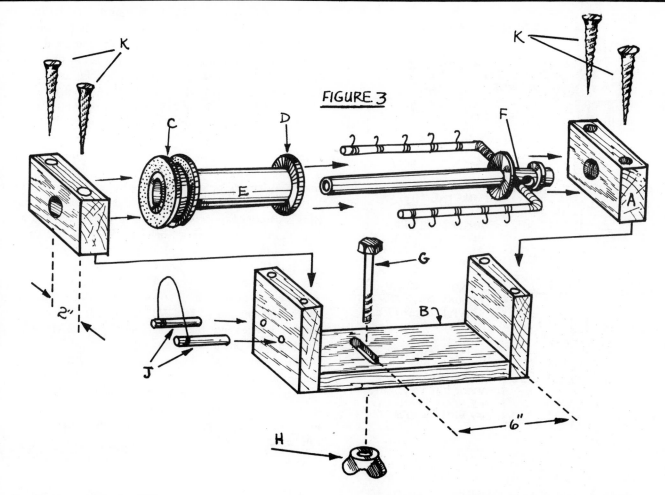

FIGURE 3

Cradle Assembly Parts List

Part	Quan.	Size	Material
A	1	x 2 x 3½	Meranti or some other hardwood
B		¾ x 4 x 9	Cheap unplaned pine or any
"		¾ x 4 x 3½	other cheap structural wood
C		3"dia. disc 1"hole	
"		3½"dia. disc 1"hole	Tempered masonite ¼" thick
D		3½"dia. disc 1"hole	(hardboard)
E		1" o.d. x 7½"	Aluminium or plastic tubing
F		¾" o.d. x 12"	Thin wall steel tubing (chrome plated curtain rod)
"	1	¼"dia. x 18"appx.	Concrete reinforcing rod
"	1	¾" i.d. x 1/16" thick	Mild steel washer
"	1	14S.W.G. x 40"appx.	Fencing wire
"	1	2½" dia. disc ¾" hole	Tempered masonite ¼" thick (Hardboard)
G	1	5/16"dia. x 3½"	These can be fabricated using the bicycle wheel spindle and nuts.
H	1	Wing nut to suit bolt	
J	2	3/8"dia. x 1½"	Wooden dowel rod
K	4	No. 12 woodscrews 2½" lg.	

Cradle Assembly Instructions

Part F. The ¾" o.d. tube is cut to length and then two holes are drilled through the tube. These holes must be on centre. One hole is 3/8" dia. and 1-3/8" from the end of the tube, the other is 17/64" dia. and is 2" from the same end of the tube.

The ¼" dia. reinforcing rod is cut to length, and bent at right-angles 8" from one end. The longer end is then threaded through the 17/64" dia. hole, in the ¾" tube, and then bent again to form a 'U' shape. This second bend, which is on the other side of the tube, is 4" from the first one. The finished operation leaves the tube loose in the centre of the 'U' shaped reinforcing rod.

Position the reinforcing rod equally each side of the tube, and with the arms of the reinforcing rod in line with the tube. The rod is then brazed in this position. After brazing the rod arms are trimmed to equal lengths. This stage is important as the centralising of the rod and the arm lengths affect the balance of the finished flyer (part F).

The ¾" i.d. washer is pushed on to the ¾" tube, the same end as the holes, until it is 1" from the end. The washer is then brazed in this position.

The 14 gauge fencing wire is cut to approximate length and then formed into the wire hooks shown below in Fig. 4. This can be done free-hand or by using the simple jig shown in Fig. 5. After the wire hooks have been manufactured, six are pushed on to each arm of the flyer (part F). These are spaced equally along the length of the arms and taped in position. Masking tape, Sello-tape or insulation tape can be used for this purpose.

A disc 2¼" dia. is cut from the sheet of ¼" thick masonite using the circle cutter. The disc is then drilled through its centre with a ¾" dia. drill, and pushed on to the ¾" tube (opposite end to the holes and washer) right up until it touches the reinforcing rod.

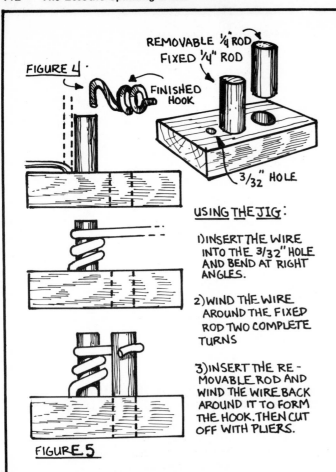

FIGURE 4

REMOVABLE ¼ ROD
FIXED ¼" ROD
FINISHED HOOK
3/32" HOLE

USING THE JIG:

1) INSERT THE WIRE INTO THE 3/32" HOLE AND BEND AT RIGHT ANGLES.

2) WIND THE WIRE AROUND THE FIXED ROD TWO COMPLETE TURNS

3) INSERT THE RE- MOVABLE ROD AND WIND THE WIRE BACK AROUND IT TO FORM THE HOOK. THEN CUT OFF WITH PLIERS.

FIGURE 5

Part E is then cut from the 1" o.d. aluminium tube, making sure that the ends are cut square.

Three discs 3½" o.d. (parts C and D) and one disc 3" o.d. are cut from the masonite, again using the circle cutter. All four discs are then drilled through their centres using a 1" dia. drill. Take two 3¾" dia. discs and smear glue onto one face of each, then smear glue onto both sides of the 3" dia. disc. The discs are then sandwiched together with the 3" disc in the centre of the two 3¾" discs. Insert part E into the 1" dia. holes in the discs to keep them central and clamp the sandwich together until the glue is dry. Push the remaining disc on to the other end of part E. This assembly is the completed bobbin.

Cut the pieces of pine for part B. Glue and nail the 3½" pieces to the ends of the 9" piece, making sure they are flush at the edges. The heights of the 3½" pieces above the 9" piece have to be the same or this will have an adverse affect on the bearings of the flyer.

Parts A are then cut from meranti (or some other hardwoods) and a 49/64" dia. hole is drilled 2" from the end and 1" in from the edge. This hole should be drilled through both blocks when they are clamped together (with their ends and edges flush) so that a matched pair is obtained. If there is any difference in the height of the holes this also has an adverse affect on the flyer bearings. Two holes are drilled in each block, ½" from both ends and midway on the 1" edge. Finally these holes are counterbored on the blocks' top face to suite the 2½" long woodscrews. Both blocks are then soaked in oil.

The bobbin (parts C, D & E) is slipped onto the flyer (part F), as shown on the exploded view. The two bearing blocks (part A) are then slipped on to the ends of the flyer. Place the bearing blocks onto the ends of the cradle (part B). Make sure that the flyer and bobbin both turn easily in the bearing blocks, and that the flyer is parallel to the cradle. After the blocks have been positioned the screw holes are spotted into the cradle using a 1/8" dia. drill. This gives the woodscrews a good location and eases effort required to screw them in. Just before the bearing blocks are screwed into position there are two final operations that have to be carried out on the cradle. One of these has to be done when the bicycle wheel has been positioned (this is described in the final assembly) so will have to wait, but the other can be carried out now. With the bobbin, flyer and bearing blocks in place on the cradle position two 23/64" dia. holes 1½" down from the cradle top and approximately 2½" apart. These holes are equally spaced either side of the ¾" tube as it protrudes through the rear bearing block. Two 3/8" dia. wooden dowels are then wedged into these holes, and a piece of string is attached from one dowel to the other.

This string acts as a drag or brake on the flyer, so giving the differential speeds of flyer and bobbin. This difference in speed is necessary to enable the yarn to be wound onto the bobbin, and by twisting the dowels, so loosening or tightening the string, the pull on the yarn can be adjusted (Fig. 6).

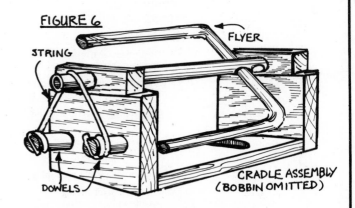

FIGURE 6
STRING
FLYER
DOWELS
CRADLE ASSEMBLY (BOBBIN OMITTED)

Wheel and Bearing Assembly Parts List

Part	Quan.	Size
A	1	Bicycle front wheel complete with spindle and wheel nuts – Approx. 26" dia. x 1-3/8" wide.
B	1	5/16" dia. Bright drawn mild steel x 12" approx.
C	2	Cone nuts from the wheel spindle
D	4	1½ x 1½ x 3½ Meranti or other hard wood
E	4	No. 12 woodscrew 2½" lg.

Wheel and Bearing Assembly Instructions

Bend the 5/16" dia. bright drawn mild steel to the shape shown in Fig. 8. This is the wheel crank, part B, and the curve on the crank arm is essential so that a smooth action is obtained on the wheel.

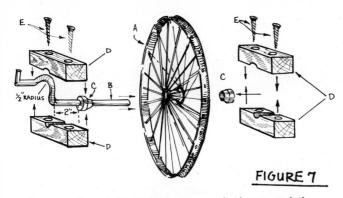

FIGURE 7

Remove the spindle, cone nuts, standard nuts and the ball bearings from the bicycle front wheel. The ball bearings can be put to one side as they will no longer be required.

Heat up the cone nuts (part C) with the Oxy-Acetylene equipment until they are cherry red, then bury them in sand and allow them to cool down. This will soften the steel so that they can be drilled. Next run a 5/16" dia. drill through the existing tapped hole in both cone nuts.

Push one cone nut on to the crank as shown in Fig. 3, so that the cone shape faces the end of the crank it was pushed onto. There should be a space of 2" between the curved arm of the crank and the square face of the cone nut. When this gap is correct, the cone nut is brazed into position.

The crank, with the cone nut brazed onto it, is then inserted through the wheel hub and the other cone nut pushed onto the crank. The second cone nut should have its cone end pointing towards the wheel. Press the second cone nut up against the wheel, clamp and braze. The wheel must be held tightly between the cone nuts, otherwise the wheel will not be centralised correctly and will run out of true. When the second cone nut has been brazed, the wheel is then brazed to the cone nuts.

The wheel bearings, parts D, are put into pairs and clamped together so that both their edges and ends are flush. A 5/16" dia. hole is then drilled through the blocks, so that half a hole is produced in each, 1¾" from their ends (see Fig. 7). While they are still clamped together, drill the two screw holes through both blocks using a ¼" drill. One part D in each pair has these holes countersunk on the top surface to suit the 2½" woodscrews. Both pairs are then soaked in oil. These parts must be kept together as they are manufactured, as they are matched pairs and are used as such. If they are piled in one heap it will take time and energy to sort them before use.

Final Assembly Instructions

The wheel bearings (part D wheel assembly diagram) are placed over the wheel shaft in their matching pairs.

The wheel and bearings are then placed on the frame with the wheel crank to the rear. The shaft is positioned 8" from the end of the frame (see Fig. 9) and screwed into position. The wheel should be parallel with the sides of the frame.

Place the cradle assembly on the frame as shown in Fig. 9, and position it until the pulley on the bobbin is in line with the bicycle wheel. When this position is obtained drill a 5/16" hole through the cradle base and frame. This hole should be drilled so that it passes through the centre of the frame side about 2½" from the end (see Fig. 1).

Take the cradle off the frame, and using a wood chisel elongate the hole in the cradle base, at right angles to the sides, for a length of 2½". The elongated hole provides adjustment on the cradle and should be 5/16" wide for its complete length, so that adequate clamping can be obtained from the bolt.

Using the 5/16" dia. bolt and wing nut (parts G and H of Fig. 3) secure the crade to the frame. The bolt is pushed through the cradle first and the wing nut is underneath the frame.

Adjust the hole centres on part L (Fig. 1) so that the pedal is clear of the ground when the wheel crank is at its lowest position. Slip one hole over the end of the crank and secure the other to the pedal with string. The string passes through the holes in the respective parts but is slack after knotting so that it provides a flexible joint.

Finally, string is threaded round the bicycle wheel, then the bobbin pulley, tied securely, and the surplus cut off. Any slack in the string can be taken up by moving the cradle.

FIGURE 9

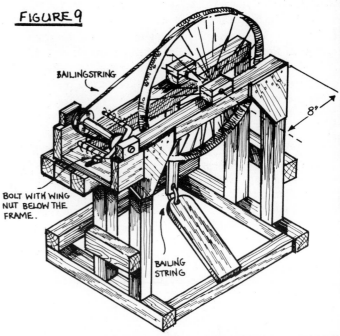

BAILINGSTRING

8"

BOLT WITH WING NUT BELOW THE FRAME.

BAILING STRING

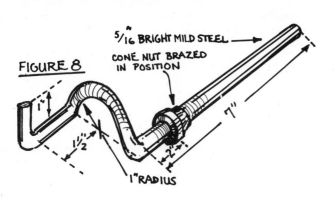

FIGURE 8

5/16" BRIGHT MILD STEEL

CONE NUT BRAZED IN POSITION

7"

1" RADIUS

½"RADIUS

A Hand Built Table Loom

by Stephen Lones

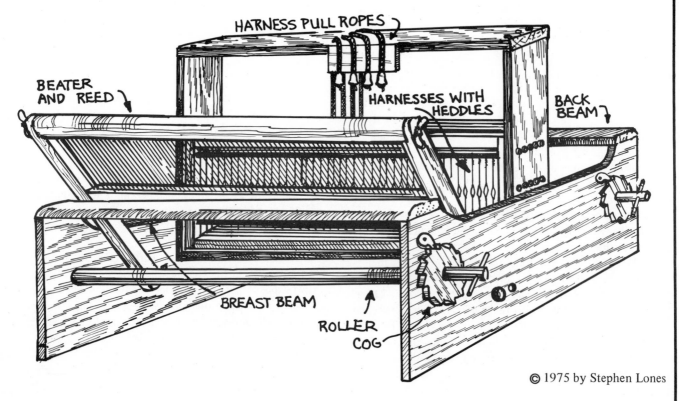

HARNESS PULL ROPES

BEATER AND REED

HARNESSES WITH HEDDLES

BACK BEAM

BREAST BEAM

ROLLER COG

© 1975 by Stephen Lones

Loom weaving involves the intertwining of fibres, both natural and synthetic, usually at right angles to one another. Synthetic fibres are usually purchased commercially spun, while natural fibres (such as wool, linen, cotton, mohair) can be purchased in the raw state and spun by the weaver. Spinning varies greatly depending on thickness, eveness, type of fibre and spinning equipment. Some weavers use handspun in conjunction with commercially spun yarns (either natural or synthetic), and others have a preference for one or the other.

In the same manner there is great variation in weaving styles. Pattern weaving is a focus for many, while colour and texture combinations hold interest for others. Hangings, tapestry, rugs, clothing and personal or practical articles may be woven. The number of threads per inch can vary from four to forty.

A table loom must accommodate a wide range of individual preference and style. It must be rugged enough to withstand heavy string rug warps and sensitive enough to weave something as fine and delicate as a bedsheet. Care put into the design and construction of a loom is well worth it. The weaver feels the difference and the finished product reflects it. If a loom is solidly built from hardwood, it will last a lifetime.

In loom weaving the **warp** threads, running front to back on the loom, are put on first. These threads are wound onto the rear roller (the **warp beam**) and brought forward to have the **weft** threads woven at right angles into them. As the cloth is produced it is wound forward and stored on the front roller (cloth beam). The rollers have cogs and ratchets which control the tension on the warp threads and allow the rollers to move freely one direction, but not the other.

Between the front and back rollers the warp threads pass through two parts of the loom. Starting from the warp beam each thread first encounters a **heddle**, a thin wire, string or piece of flat steel with an opening in the middle called the **eye** which the warp thread passes through. The heddle is held vertically in a frame called a **harness**. Looms have anywhere from two to twelve harnesses, four being a common amount. A typical way of threading the warp on a four harness loom would be to string the number one warp thread on the right side of the loom through the first heddle in harness one. The second warp thread is strung through the first heddle in frame two. Number three thread goes through number three harness and four goes through four. The fifth thread then starts with the first harness again, going through its second heddle; and so on until

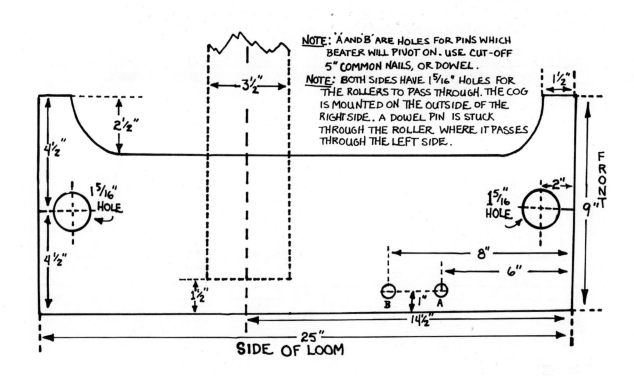

NOTE: 'A AND B' ARE HOLES FOR PINS WHICH BEATER WILL PIVOT ON. USE CUT-OFF 5" COMMON NAILS, OR DOWEL.

NOTE: BOTH SIDES HAVE 1 5/16" HOLES FOR THE ROLLERS TO PASS THROUGH. THE COG IS MOUNTED ON THE OUTSIDE OF THE RIGHT SIDE. A DOWEL PIN IS STUCK THROUGH THE ROLLER WHERE IT PASSES THROUGH THE LEFT SIDE.

SIDE OF LOOM

BREAST AND BACK BEAMS - TOP VIEW

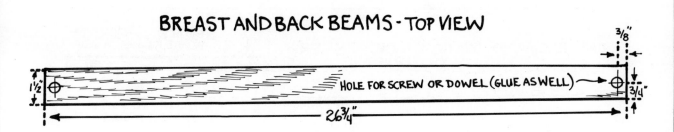

HOLE FOR SCREW OR DOWEL (GLUE AS WELL) →

the warp is entirely strung up. Threading the loom is tedious, but the actual weaving makes up for it.

When any harness is raised, it lifts up all the threads passing through its heddles; i.e. every fourth thread. In simple weave (called **tabby**) one half the threads are raised at a time. Harnesses one and three are raised and the weft thread is thrown through the resulting opening (called the **shed**). These harnesses are lowered, harnesses two and four are raised, and the weft is passed back the other direction. Such weaving could be done on a two harness loom also, as long as every other thread is to be raised. Pattern weaving involves using different combinations of harnesses, one, two or three at a time, and different methods of stringing warp threads through the heddles.

The threads also pass through the **reed**, which is held in a frame called the **beater**. The reed spaces the warp threads apart from one another. Usually one thread passes through each opening in the reed, and the number of openings per inch (the **dent** of the reed) determines the threads per inch of the cloth. The beater also pivots, allowing the reed to be swung through the warp until it packs the last weft thread woven against the cloth previously woven. The amount of force used in swinging the beater determines the **beat** or

pack of the cloth. The beater must be strongly made for packing heavy things like rag rugs. It is necessary that the reed can be easily replaced with one of a different dent. When the beater swings the reed should strike the cloth in a vertical position. There should be two sets of pins for the beater to pivot on so it will maintain a vertical position when striking the cloth near the harnesses as well as near the **breast beam**. That way, the cloth can be woven a longer distance before it needs to be wound forward onto the cloth beam.

Most table looms have a box within which the harnesses slide within slots cut into the uprights of the box. A problem arises when the harnesses need to be removed quickly so heddles can be added on or taken off. I use two sets of guide pins in each upright which can be pushed back to allow the harnesses to be removed. The system used ultimately depends on the preference and ingenuity of the builder. Somehow the harnesses must be guided so they don't strike each other.

In North America wire heddles are commonly used on table looms. String heddles could also be used but would require a different set-up and loom design. Wire heddles (and reeds) can be obtained through any dealer of Leclerc

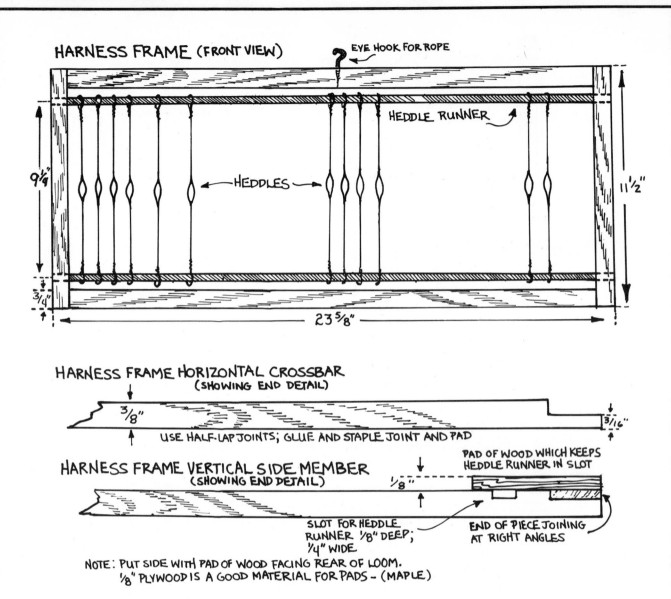

HARNESS FRAME (FRONT VIEW)

EYE HOOK FOR ROPE

HEDDLE RUNNER

HEDDLES

9¼"

11½"

¾"

23⅝"

HARNESS FRAME HORIZONTAL CROSSBAR
(SHOWING END DETAIL)

⅜"

3/16"

USE HALF-LAP JOINTS; GLUE AND STAPLE JOINT AND PAD

HARNESS FRAME VERTICAL SIDE MEMBER
(SHOWING END DETAIL)

⅛"

PAD OF WOOD WHICH KEEPS
HEDDLE RUNNER IN SLOT

SLOT FOR HEDDLE
RUNNER ⅛" DEEP;
¼" WIDE

END OF PIECE JOINING
AT RIGHT ANGLES

NOTE: PUT SIDE WITH PAD OF WOOD FACING REAR OF LOOM.
⅛" PLYWOOD IS A GOOD MATERIAL FOR PADS - (MAPLE)

Looms of Quebec.* Heddles must be able to move sideways within the harness frame so they can line up with the openings of the reed. Bars called **heddle runners** allow sideways motion. These bars are mounted within the frame in such a way that they can be easily removed to add on or take off heddles.

Loom Basics

Most table looms are **jack** type. This means the harnesses are controlled individually and are raised to produce a shed opening. It would also be possible to use a **counterbalance** tieup where harnesses one and two are connected by rope to each other via a pulley, and the same with harnesses three and four. Then the two sets of harnesses are connected by rope via another pulley or over a bar. If harnesses one and three are pulled down, harnesses two and four would be raised. Jack type seems most practical for table looms.

One problem is how to raise and lower several harnesses at once while only using one hand and one motion. This

operation is performed after each throw of the weft thread and must not become tiring. A common method is to run a rope from the top middle of each harness through a hole in the top of the box and have it catch in a slotted piece of wood mounted top front on the box. Pulling each rope and catching it in a slot can become tedious, but at least such a system is easy to build and can be improved upon later. Leclerc's 22" table loom uses automatic metal changes which work with one motion of one hand. Unfortunately they work hard and produce enough noise to give a headache. Some Swedish looms employ a method which solves all these problems. Each rope coming through the top of the box is connected to a handle which pivots in a semi-circle around a pin. When the harness is raised the handle is in such a position that the rope can gain no leverage to pull the handle around its pivot point. Try to find a loom using this system and study it. The concept is difficult to explain.

A 2½" shed opening is wide enough to take the **shuttle** (a flat piece of wood with the weft thread wrapped around it). A bigger shed would create too much tension on the warp threads. The threads tend to remain on the **warp line** (a straight line drawn between the tops of the **back** beam

* If there is no authorized dealer near by, you may write direct to: Leclerc Looms, L'Isetville, Quebec, Canada

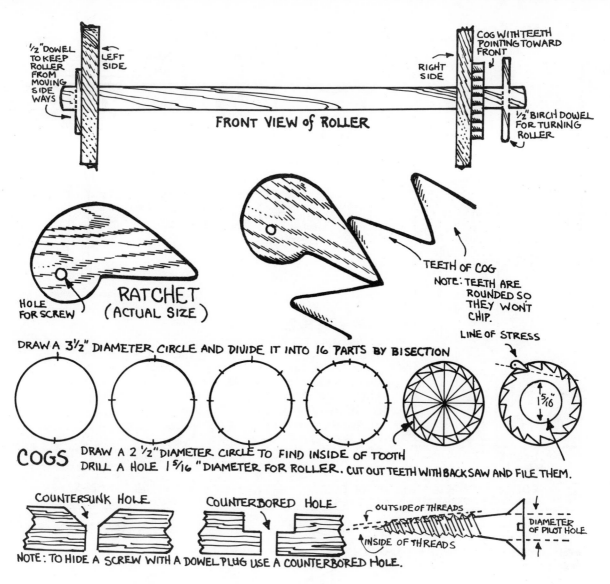

FRONT VIEW of ROLLER

½" DOWEL TO KEEP ROLLER FROM MOVING SIDE WAYS

LEFT SIDE

RIGHT SIDE

COG WITH TEETH POINTING TOWARD FRONT

½" BIRCH DOWEL FOR TURNING ROLLER

RATCHET (ACTUAL SIZE)

HOLE FOR SCREW

TEETH OF COG

NOTE: TEETH ARE ROUNDED SO THEY WON'T CHIP.

LINE OF STRESS

DRAW A 3½" DIAMETER CIRCLE AND DIVIDE IT INTO 16 PARTS BY BISECTION

1 5/16"

COGS DRAW A 2½" DIAMETER CIRCLE TO FIND INSIDE OF TOOTH DRILL A HOLE 1 5/16" DIAMETER FOR ROLLER. CUT OUT TEETH WITH BACK SAW AND FILE THEM.

COUNTERSUNK HOLE

COUNTERBORED HOLE

OUTSIDE OF THREADS

INSIDE OF THREADS

DIAMETER OF PILOT HOLE

NOTE: TO HIDE A SCREW WITH A DOWEL PLUG USE A COUNTERBORED HOLE.

and the breast beam). When the threads are pulled away from this line, their tension increases. Since Jack type looms have a **rising shed** (the harnesses only move upwards), the harness frames are kept half the height of the shed below the warp line when they are in the lowered position. Then the harnesses which are raised will be half the shed height above the warp line and the tension in warp threads both raised and lowered will be the same. The weight of the harness (including heddles and heddle runners) should be sufficient to depress the heaviest warp threads to be used down the necessary 1¼". They should not be heavier than this minimum or raising the harnesses will become unnecessarily difficult. I use yellow cedar (3/8" x 3/4") for the frames because the heddle runners (1/8" x 1/4" cold roll steel) are heavy. Just consider your own needs and available materials and experiment with it.

The warp line is also used to position the height of the reed and beater. If the middle of the reed is at the warp line when the beater is in a vertical position then everything is positioned correctly and there should be no need to make the height adjustable. Do remember to have the beater adjust front to back. There should be no side-to-side free play. Use wooden washers if necessary to keep the beater firmly centred between the sides of the loom.

Cogs and ratchets are needed on the cloth and warp beams to adjust tension on the warp. The positioning of the ratchet is very important. If the ratchet just catches the top of the tooth, it may chip or break it. The tip of the ratchet should solidly contact the base of each tooth. Stress must be directed into the body of the cog rather than just into the tooth. The cog must turn freely one direction and the ratchet must engage fully on each tooth when turned the other direction. The cog can be attached to the roller with glue and pins. First bore a 1-5/16" hole in the cog. Then cut out the teeth with a back saw and round all their edges with a file. The cog should fit snugly on the roller. Beware of drilling the hole too small or the cog will break when you tap it on. Maple is a good wood for cogs since it is tight grained. Douglas Fir dowel 1-5/16" diameter makes adequate rollers. Hardwood dowel of that size would be extremely expensive.

Assembly Procedure

Cut all material to length. I use red oak, but you may use whatever is available and suitably strong.

Drill all holes which the head of a screw or bolt will

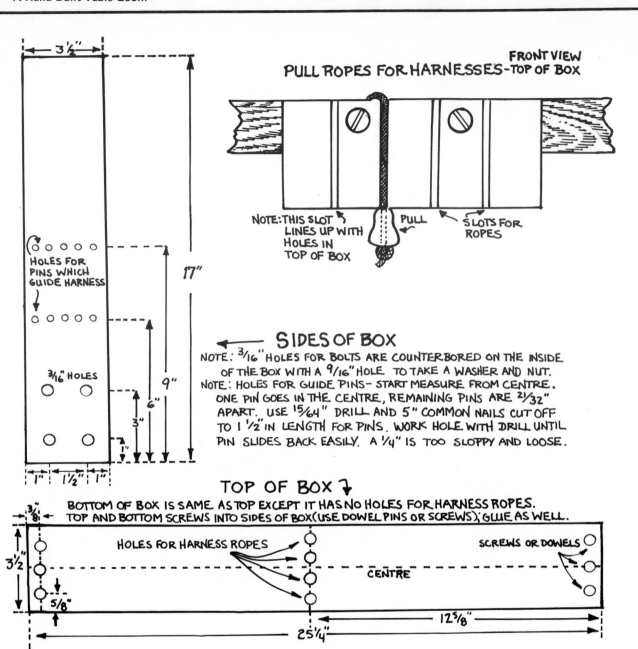

3½"

FRONT VIEW
PULL ROPES FOR HARNESSES-TOP OF BOX

HOLES FOR
PINS WHICH
GUIDE HARNESS

17"

NOTE: THIS SLOT
LINES UP WITH
HOLES IN
TOP OF BOX

PULL

SLOTS FOR
ROPES

9"

6"

3"

1"

3/16" HOLES

SIDES OF BOX

NOTE: 3/16" HOLES FOR BOLTS ARE COUNTERBORED ON THE INSIDE
OF THE BOX WITH A 9/16" HOLE TO TAKE A WASHER AND NUT.
NOTE: HOLES FOR GUIDE PINS- START MEASURE FROM CENTRE.
ONE PIN GOES IN THE CENTRE, REMAINING PINS ARE 21/32"
APART. USE 15/64" DRILL AND 5" COMMON NAILS CUT OFF
TO 1 1/2" IN LENGTH FOR PINS. WORK HOLE WITH DRILL UNTIL
PIN SLIDES BACK EASILY. A 1/4" IS TOO SLOPPY AND LOOSE.

1"   1½"   1"

TOP OF BOX ↗

BOTTOM OF BOX IS SAME AS TOP EXCEPT IT HAS NO HOLES FOR HARNESS ROPES.
TOP AND BOTTOM SCREWS INTO SIDES OF BOX (USE DOWEL PINS OR SCREWS), GLUE AS WELL.

3/8"

3½"

HOLES FOR HARNESS ROPES

SCREWS OR DOWELS

CENTRE

5/8"

12⅝"

25¼"

bear against. If you are using a #8 - 1½" countersunk
woodscrew, these holes would be drilled 11/64" and then
countersunk for the screw head. The bolt holes on the
insides of the box uprights need a 9/16" counterbore to
accommodate a 3/16" washer and nut flush with the inside
surface (use 1½" 3/16" diameter bolts with these to join
loom sides to the box). Drill a 1/8" hole first and then
counterbore. Then drill the 1/8" hole out to 3/16".

As you assemble the loom, mark for pilot holes in each
piece which takes the threaded end of a screw. A good
marking technique is to place a predrilled and countersunk
piece exactly onto the piece it will join and tap a screw
inserted into each hole so the screw tip will mark for the
pilot hole. Such a mark also helps guide the drill bit in the
same manner as an impression made by a counterpunch.
A pilot hole is necessary to prevent the screw from splitting
the wood. The hole should equal the inside diameter of
the screw threads so they will engage the wood completely.
If you plan to use dowel instead of screws then different

procedures will be necessary.

Assemble the box for the harness frames first. Lay one
of the loom sides down on the workbench with its inside
facing up. Place the box on its side on top of this and position and square the two pieces correctly together (middle
of box sits 14½" from front of the loom side; bottom of
box is up 1½" from bottom of side). Put bolts in the four
bolt holes in the box and tap them firmly so they make
impressions on the side of the loom. Centrepunch the centre
of each impression and drill out to 3/16". Do the other
side in the same way. Label parts with a pencil when assembling them so they can be put back together correctly if
disassembled. Bolt the sides onto the box with the nuts
inside the counterbored holes of the box. Use washers with
the bolt head and the nut.

Install the breast and back beams, again using a screw to
mark the pilot holes. Push the rollers through the 1-5/16"
holes in the loom sides. They should turn freedly but not
too loose. The rollers should protrude 1" through the left

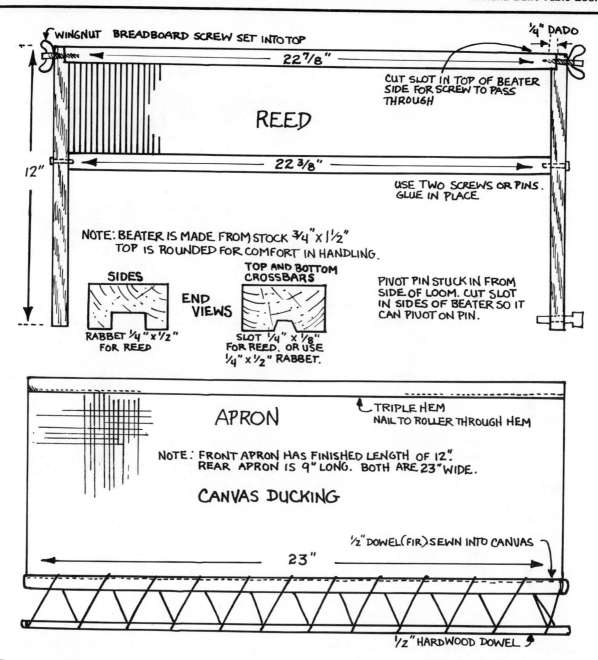

REED

22 7/8"

WINGNUT   BREADBOARD SCREW SET INTO TOP

1/4" DADO

CUT SLOT IN TOP OF BEATER SIDE FOR SCREW TO PASS THROUGH

12"

22 3/8"

USE TWO SCREWS OR PINS. GLUE IN PLACE

NOTE: BEATER IS MADE FROM STOCK 3/4"x1/2" TOP IS ROUNDED FOR COMFORT IN HANDLING.

SIDES

TOP AND BOTTOM CROSSBARS

END VIEWS

RABBET 1/4" x 1/2" FOR REED

SLOT 1/4" x 1/8" FOR REED, OR USE 1/4" x 1/2" RABBET.

PIVOT PIN STUCK IN FROM SIDE OF LOOM. CUT SLOT IN SIDES OF BEATER SO IT CAN PIVOT ON PIN.

APRON

TRIPLE HEM
NAIL TO ROLLER THROUGH HEM

NOTE: FRONT APRON HAS FINISHED LENGTH OF 12". REAR APRON IS 9" LONG. BOTH ARE 23" WIDE.

CANVAS DUCKING

1/2" DOWEL (FIR) SEWN INTO CANVAS

23"

1/2" HARDWOOD DOWEL

side. Draw a pencil line on the rollers where the outside of the left and right sides hit them. Cut out the cogs and fit them on rollers so they are touching the pencil lines on the right sides. Insert a 1/2" birch dowel between the cog and the end of the roller so it can be turned when winding on during weaving. Install the rollers into the loom and insert the dowel in the left side which keeps them from moving sideways. Position and install the rachets.

Construct the beater, being sure the reed can be easily removed. Set the beater on its pivot pins and check whether both sides of the beater strike the breast beam at the same time. If not, then check the distance of both the left and right sides of the breast beam to the box. Also double check the positioning of the pivot pins for the beater. They should be 6" and 8" back and 1" up. (When installing the pivots in the loom sides, use a 7/32" drill and work the drill around in the hole so it is bigger than 7/32". The next drill size larger is too loose.) Insert the pin slowly by tapping it, taking care not to split the wood. This applies for using a

5" common nail cut off to 2 1/4" for a pin. (Different procedures would apply if dowel were used.) Height of the reed must also be doublechecked. Be sure the beater is centred between the sides, using wooden spacers on the pins if necessary.

Assemble the harness frames. Fit the guide pins for the harnesses into the box. The pins on each side must slide freely so the harness frames can be removed. Work the holes with the 15/64" drill until the pins slide properly. Tie ropes onto the eyehooks of tops of harness frames. These ropes go through their respective holes in the top of the box and are tied to pulls or are knotted so the harnesses are raised when the ropes are caught in their slots. If handles are used then set those up and adjust them, using patience and ingenuity. Handles are difficult to work out but they sure work well when properly done.

Round edges on breast and back beams and on the top of the beater. Sand the loom carefully and oil it with Danish or Teak oil, or a suitable substitute.

Log Falling & Bucking

Falling a tree requires a great deal more consideration than merely bringing it to the ground.

Considerations

1. Falling each tree in the safest possible manner.
2. Falling each tree with consideration being given to its subsequent safe bucking.

Before starting to fall timber, you should determine the best face or position to start the quarter or strip, generally with the timber stand's prevailing lean, if any, and in a manner which will allow the timber to fall into the clear. You should have knowledge of your falling position, in relation to roads in use, and to other equipment and workers in the area.

Finally you should have a thorough knowledge of the written procedures as explained on pages 120 to 125 inclusive.

1. Brush and debris adjacent to the tree to be felled shall be cleared away to permit the free and safe use of tools and to allow a quick, safe, unobstructed path to safety.
2. Assess the tree or snag to determine the apparent situation with regard to:
   a) Loose limbs, chunks, or other overhead material.
   b) Logs, saplings, or chunks on the ground that could constitute a hazard.
   c) Other trees or snags being involved by contact when the tree being cut falls.
   d) The best escape route to a predetermined place of safety.
   e) Lean, if any.

Considerations at the Base of the Tree

A sufficient undercut shall be made in each tree being felled. You should ensure:
1. That the undercut is complete and cleaned out.
2. That appropriate measures are taken to control the fall of the tree.

The Undercut

Properly sawn, the undercut will allow the tree to fall freely in its chosen direction. A clean, uniform undercut should be used on all trees. The following guide is useful:
1. As a minimum, the undercut should be one-quarter of the tree's diameter.
2. As a minimum, the opening of the undercut should be one-third of the undercut's depth, or one inch vertical for every three inches horizontal.

Note:

1. Both undercuts shown in Fig. 1 are correct. However, some people like the "Humboldt" undercut for closer utilization.
2. The horizontal part of the undercut must be level and well cleaned out where the cuts meet to prevent "barber-chair" and/or unintended "Dutchman".
3. The undercuts shown are based on a one-inch opening

TREE 48" DIA.   FIGURE I   TREE 48" DIA.

UNDERCUT DEPTH 12" MINIMUM

OPENING 4" MINIMUM

"HUMBOLDT" UNDERCUT (UNDERCUT BLOCK TAKEN FROM STUMP)

UNDERCUT BLOCK TAKEN FROM BUTT

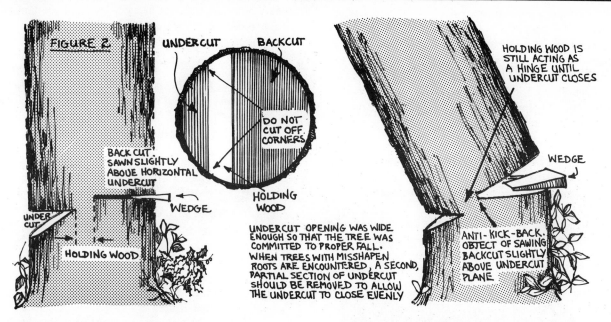

FIGURE 2

UNDERCUT   BACKCUT

DO NOT CUT OFF CORNERS

BACK CUT SAWN SLIGHTLY ABOVE HORIZONTAL UNDERCUT

WEDGE

UNDER CUT

HOLDING WOOD

HOLDING WOOD

UNDERCUT OPENING WAS WIDE ENOUGH SO THAT THE TREE WAS COMMITTED TO PROPER FALL. WHEN TREES WITH MISSHAPEN ROOTS ARE ENCOUNTERED, A SECOND, PARTIAL SECTION OF UNDERCUT SHOULD BE REMOVED TO ALLOW THE UNDERCUT TO CLOSE EVENLY

HOLDING WOOD IS STILL ACTING AS A HINGE UNTIL UNDERCUT CLOSES

WEDGE

ANTI-KICK-BACK. OBJECT OF SAWING BACKCUT SLIGHTLY ABOVE UNDERCUT PLANE

for three inches of horizontal cut.

4. The two cuts which form the undercut must **not** cross at that point where they meet, in order to prevent formation of "Dutchman".

The Backcut

Sufficient holding wood must always remain to maintain control of the tree so that it does not break, slip, or twist off the stump, and fall in any direction other than that intended — no matter how heavy the lean.

1. The backcut must be level and sawn-in slightly above the horizontal plane of the undercut to form an anti-kick-back step.
2. Care must be taken not to saw the corners off when side notching (see Fig. 2).

Falling Against the Lean May be Necessary on Occasion to:

1. Avoid unnecessary breakage
2. Place the tree in a favourable bucking position
3. Avoid falling a tree into other adjacent standing trees

4. Keep a tree from falling on a road grade, or
5. Avoid crossing the lead or falling pattern.

To establish hard and fast guidelines for falling a tree against its lean would be most difficult because of the variations in lean, height, diameter, species, etc. In extreme cold weather, frozen wood becomes brittle and undependable as holding wood.

Make a habit of plumbing the tree before commencing falling, even if you feel sure you know where the lean is.

A large tree with heavy lean may be felled against its lean by inserting steel wedges in the **kerf** of the backcut, driving the wedges alternately as the backcut is sawn. (Always use eye protection when driving metal wedges, and keep your head above or below the wedge.)

Most trees can be felled away from their lean by using the normal falling wedges and by retaining additional holding wood as shown in Figs. 3 and 4.

"Dutchman" in the Undercut is caused by:

1. The undercut not being fully cleaned out, or
2. The two saw cuts of the undercut not meeting properly

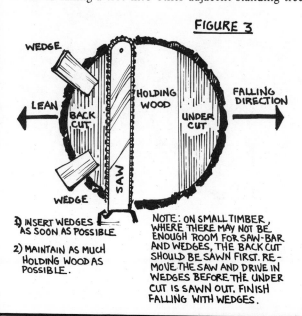

FIGURE 3

WEDGE

LEAN

BACK CUT

HOLDING WOOD

UNDER CUT

FALLING DIRECTION

WEDGE

SAW

1) INSERT WEDGES AS SOON AS POSSIBLE.

2) MAINTAIN AS MUCH HOLDING WOOD AS POSSIBLE.

NOTE: ON SMALL TIMBER, WHERE THERE MAY NOT BE ENOUGH ROOM FOR SAW-BAR AND WEDGES, THE BACK CUT SHOULD BE SAWN FIRST. REMOVE THE SAW AND DRIVE IN WEDGES BEFORE THE UNDER CUT IS SAWN OUT. FINISH FALLING WITH WEDGES.

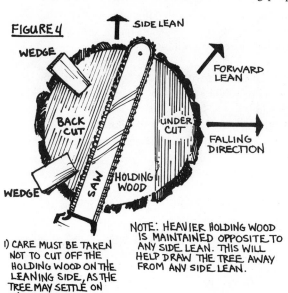

FIGURE 4

SIDE LEAN

WEDGE

BACK CUT

UNDER CUT

FORWARD LEAN

FALLING DIRECTION

SAW

HOLDING WOOD

WEDGE

1) CARE MUST BE TAKEN NOT TO CUT OFF THE HOLDING WOOD ON THE LEANING SIDE, AS THE TREE MAY SETTLE ON THE SAW BAR.

NOTE: HEAVIER HOLDING WOOD IS MAINTAINED OPPOSITE TO ANY SIDE LEAN. THIS WILL HELP DRAW THE TREE AWAY FROM ANY SIDE LEAN.

by allowing the top or bottom cut of the undercut to be sawn past the other.

The result is that, as the tree starts to fall, the Dutchman closes, usually throwing the tree away from its intended direction of fall. This action may allow the tree to fall among other adjacent standing trees or snags, creating a hazardous situation for you from broken limbs or tops being thrown back towards you.

Intentional "Dutchman" has been used by fallers to help them overcome a particular falling problem when the need to pull or throw a tree could not be achieved by other means; and then, only after understanding and evaluating the hazards involved.

Even for the most seasoned and skillful faller, the amount of pull or throw created by the Dutchman cannot always be determined — thus a lack of control could ensue. For this reason the use of Dutchman, even intentional, is not advocated (see Fig. 5).

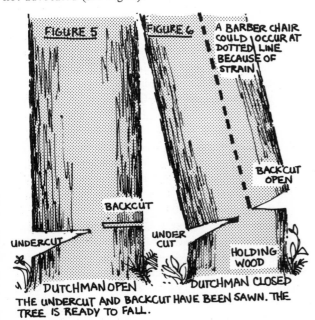

Poor Falling Practices

1. The practice of hanging one tree in another, deliberately, for the purpose of holding pressure to eliminate wedging while working on the forward tree is excessively hazardous and therefore prohibited.
2. Excessive pushing or "domino" falling. The practice of pushing one tree with another must only be done to overcome a falling difficulty, or where there is no better method.
3. Working within range of a tree which has been "cut-up" (except work processes required in order to get the tree down).
4. Standing under the lean or loose material while making the falling cuts.
5. Failing to move quickly away from the falling tree on a predetermined and prepared escape route.
6. Falling without having wedging equipment immediately available, or neglecting to place a wedge in the backcut as soon as possible.
7. Falling timber during periods of high wind, dense fog,

heavy snowfall, or when heavy snow is on the limbs.
8. Falling trees too close to adjacent fallers, other workers or equipment.

Bucking

Before starting any bucking cut, buckers should plan the work by analyzing log movements and other hazards that may develop as a cut log is released, such as pivot points, natural skids, soundness of log being bucked, etc. You should:

1. Make sure of firm footing. Avoid standing on loose chunks or logs with bark or material that will roll when a log is sawn off. (Peel away loose bark underfoot.)
2. Stand to one side of the power saw while cutting. Avoid standing directly behind saw to prevent a blow to the body from a kick-back. Be able to handle a saw either right or left-handed.
3. When a falling tree brushes a snag, or other weak or unstable tree, leave the tree unbucked until the snag or defective tree is felled.
4. Always be on the look-out for limbs or other objects hanging above in standing timber.
5. When bucking blown-down trees, or where windfalls are present, fall the snags to prevent them being struck by rolling logs released during bucking.
6. Buck the bottom windfalls of a "jackpot" first, to avoid top logs or material from rolling.
7. Avoid bucking any windfalls on hillsides above the immediate falling area or face.
8. When working in a windfall area, be mindful of loose bark which could result in a serious fall.

Top Bind

When a tree is lying in a position in which the top side is compressed while the bottom is under tension, the tree can be safely bucked without any wood splitting, or the saw bar being pinched, by making cuts in the following sequence:

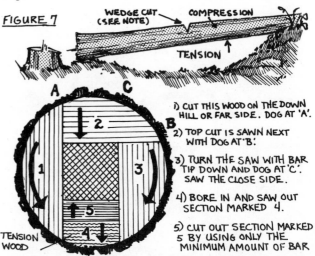

Bottom Bind

Cuts are made in almost the same manner as for top bind, except for the top and bottom cuts which are reversed.

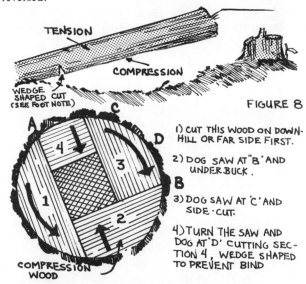

FIGURE 8

1) CUT THIS WOOD ON DOWN-HILL OR FAR SIDE FIRST.

2) DOG SAW AT "B" AND UNDER BUCK.

3) DOG SAW AT "C" AND SIDE·CUT.

4) TURN THE SAW AND DOG AT "D" CUTTING SECTION 4, WEDGE SHAPED TO PREVENT BIND

NOTE: ARROWS INDICATE SAW TRAVEL DIRECTION AND CROSS-HATCHING INDICATES HEARTWOOD WHICH WILL BREAK. AS IN TOP BIND, A WEDGE SHAPED SECTION COULD BE TAKEN OUT WHEN SAWING CUT 2 TO ALLOW FOR CLOSING ON SEVERE BIND.

Bucking Large Logs

In the cutting of big logs, buckers have a tendency to buck off as much of the far side of the log as they can by reaching over the side from the top of the log (see "B", No. 2 Position). This practice quite often results in a section of the lower left side of the cut remaining unbucked.

The diagram below indicates a safe method of bucking a large log.

1. Saw into the top of the log about 12-14 inches from Position "A".
2. From Position "B" cut off the lower side of the log right into the heart wood.
3. From Position "C" cut off all remaining wood on the low side of the cut.
4. Return to safe Position "A". Cut off balance of wood to complete the cut.

Note: You should carefully size up log lie and condition of log before adopting the third bucking position to ensure that no untoward event could take place which could endanger you.

FIGURE 9

A. FIRST AND LAST BUCKING POSITION
B. SECOND BUCKING POSITION
C. THIRD BUCKING POSITION

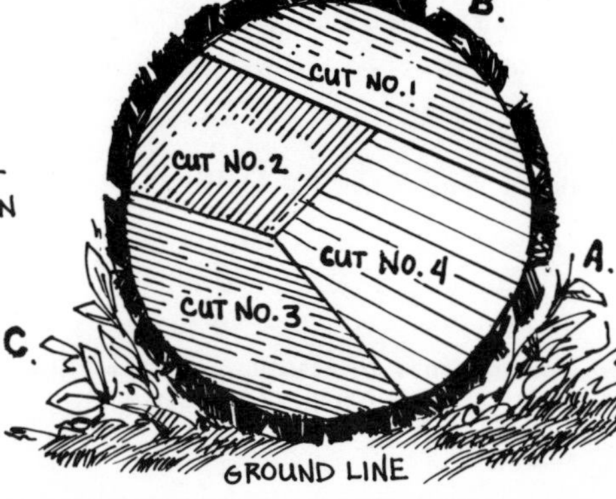

End Pressure

When a tree is lying flat on steep terrain, straight up and down the slope, a bucked log would have a tendency to slide down, causing the bar to be pinched as the log was bucked off. Matching top and bottom cuts can be made without end pressure on the bar by inserting a wedge as shown in Fig. 10.

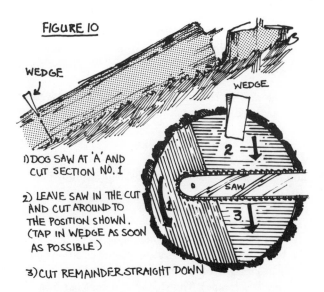

FIGURE 10

1) DOG SAW AT "A" AND CUT SECTION NO. 1

2) LEAVE SAW IN THE CUT AND CUT AROUND TO THE POSITION SHOWN. (TAP IN WEDGE AS SOON AS POSSIBLE)

3) CUT REMAINDER STRAIGHT DOWN

NOTE: THE ENTIRE CUT CAN BE MADE WITHOUT REMOVING THE SAW. THE WEDGE CAN BE TAPPED OUT AFTER CUTTING IS COMPLETED.

Pivot Points

As an example of unexpected action, a faller was killed when the windfallen tree he was bucking swung uphill, crushing him under the butt. The windfallen fir tree, 30 inches in diameter by 90 feet in length, was lying across a steep sidehill. The butt end was rooted while the small end was resting on chunks. The first cut was made 12 feet from the root. The faller, expecting both the tree and root to roll away from him, finished the cut from the uphill side. As the cut was released, the butt end of the tree swung uphill because of a small stump located under the windfallen tree.

Bind

Bind can be expected in most trees that are felled because of uneven terrain and other material already on the ground. The bind can also be present in combinations of top bind and side bind, or bottom bind and side bind.

The best defence you can have in order to avoid personal injury or equipment damage caused by bind and/or poorly chosen cut is to examine the felled tree carefully and determine any bind which may be present, and what action will take place when, or as, the bucked log is released.

Many serious and fatal accidents have occurred because fallers or buckers failed to recognize side bind during bucking activities. They had positioned themselves on the side to which the bucked log "sprung" or swung upon release.

Falling and Bucking Difficulties

Tree Sits Back

Just as you are completing the backcut, the tree starts to sit back on the bar. This can happen because:

1. You misjudged the tree's lean.
2. The stump contained hidden rot.
3. An unexpected gust of wind took it backwards.
4. You neglected to place a wedge in the backcut as it was being sawn.

If sufficient holding wood remains, the tree may be wedged-over in its intended direction. Be sure to clean the bark away, above and below the back-cut, to allow wedges to bear on solid wood.

The tree may be leaning backwards heavily, and wedges cannot be started in the back-cut. You are left with several choices:

1. You may fall the tree over backwards.
2. You may use a hydraulic jack.
3. You may "push" this tree over by falling another tree into it.

The Second Undercut

Fig. 11 depicts a large tree which has "sat back" heavily on the backcut. The faller has sawn a good-sized second undercut at an angle on the right or left side (depending on best lay and escape). The second undercut has been sawn from the stump, but the topcut of the new undercut is the original backcut. By sawing the second undercut at an angle, part of the backcut will remain intact to support the tree while the second undercut is sawn in. When the second undercut is well cleaned out, the faller should run the saw into the original undercut and saw off the holding wood.

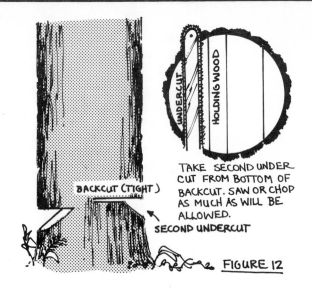

TAKE SECOND UNDER CUT FROM BOTTOM OF BACKCUT. SAW OR CHOP AS MUCH AS WILL BE ALLOWED.

FIGURE 12

more control can be maintained by sawing the holding wood over its entire width. The small undercut would act as a lip to help prevent the butt from sliding backwards. The choice of these two methods would depend largely on the direction in which the tree appears to be leaning, obstructions to its free fall, steepness of terrain, and the location of the new escape path.

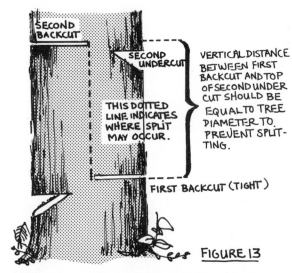

VERTICAL DISTANCE BETWEEN FIRST BACKCUT AND TOP OF SECOND UNDER CUT SHOULD BE EQUAL TO TREE DIAMETER TO PREVENT SPLITTING.

FIGURE 13

Figure 13 will allow for most control being maintained as a proper undercut, backcut and holding wood can be sawn in above the original cuts. Maintain as much vertical distance between the first falling cuts and the new falling cuts — at least the measurement of the tree's diameter. A danger exists that a vertical split may occur between the first and second set of cuts.

Pushing One Tree by Falling Another Into It

Because of the hazards involved, this practice should only be done to overcome a falling difficulty when:

1. The tree may be limb-tied to another.
2. The tree may be leaning against another.
3. The tree has settled backwards and you are unable to start wedges.

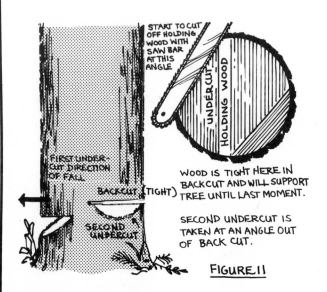

START TO CUT OFF HOLDING WOOD WITH SAW BAR AT THIS ANGLE

WOOD IS TIGHT HERE IN BACKCUT AND WILL SUPPORT TREE UNTIL LAST MOMENT.

SECOND UNDERCUT IS TAKEN AT AN ANGLE OUT OF BACK CUT.

FIGURE 11

As the tree falls, very little control can be maintained because of the large "Dutchman" which developed, and because all the remaining holding wood has been sawn off.

Fig. 12 depicts the same situation, except that a bit

Hazards

1. You may only brush the tree being pushed, which may sway and fall over into the area where you are standing.
2. A dry top or limbs may be broken off and thrown back towards you.

If pushing becomes necessary, ensure that:

1. The pushing tree is at a good angle — no more than 20 degrees off the imaginary centre line behind the tree being pushed.
2. Extra protection with regard to the undercuts and holding wood of both trees is taken.
3. An unobstructed get-away path is located and the surroundings well sized-up.

When difficulties arise with an incompletely felled tree, you should direct all your efforts to getting the tree down safely. Under no circumstances should you continue with unrelated work in the area of the "cut-up" tree.

Heavy Leaners

A tree with a heavy lean develops enormous tension in the wood directly behind the lean. When an undercut is put into the tree, in the direction of the lean, then the tension is further aggravated. As soon as a conventional backcut is started, this tension is immediately relieved and the tree starts to fall. However, too much holding wood remains, and instead of the holding wood breaking off normally, the tree trunk will split vertically from where the backcut is started. A huge slab will develop and kick backward at the same time, causing the "barber-chair".

To prevent barber-chairing it is necessary to leave that part of the wood which is most under tension, located behind the lean, until more of the holding wood is sawn out. Several methods may be employed in removing the excessive holding wood.

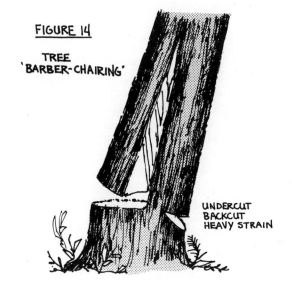

FIGURE 14

TREE
'BARBER-CHAIRING'

UNDERCUT
BACKCUT
HEAVY STRAIN

Side Notching

After the undercut block has been removed cleanly, the sides of the tree are side cut or side bored as shown in Fig. 15.

The remaining holding wood of the backcut will be sawn faster, with less likelihood of the tree splitting.

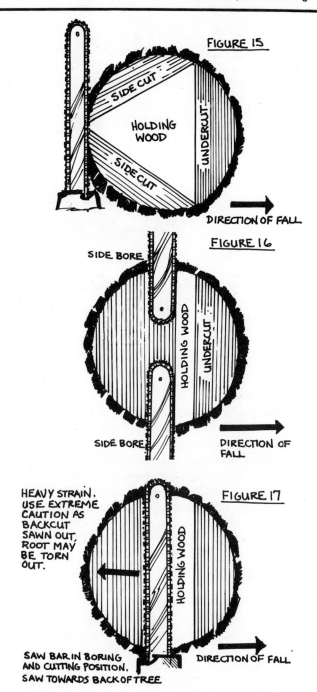

FIGURE 15

SIDE CUT
HOLDING WOOD
UNDERCUT
SIDE CUT

DIRECTION OF FALL

FIGURE 16

SIDE BORE
HOLDING WOOD
UNDERCUT
SIDE BORE

DIRECTION OF FALL

FIGURE 17

HEAVY STRAIN.
USE EXTREME
CAUTION AS
BACKCUT
SAWN OUT.
ROOT MAY
BE TORN
OUT.

HOLDING WOOD

SAW BAR IN BORING
AND CUTTING POSITION.
SAW TOWARDS BACK OF TREE

DIRECTION OF FALL

Boring the Backcut

After the undercut block has been removed, the tip of the saw bar is bored into the tree on the same plane as the horizontal of the undercut. You must ensure that you leave a few inches of holding wood between the start of the boring cut and the back of the undercut. It may be necessary to bore in from both sides if the tree is wider than the length of the bar, (see Fig. 16). The saw is worked backwards, cutting from the inside out, until the point is reached where the normal backcut would have been started (see Fig. 17).

At this time, the wood directly behind the lean will be under enormous tension as all other holding wood has been severed. Trees have been known to fall at this time, before the saw has cut through, pulling a large section of root out of the ground.

Raising Large Stones

by William Hood

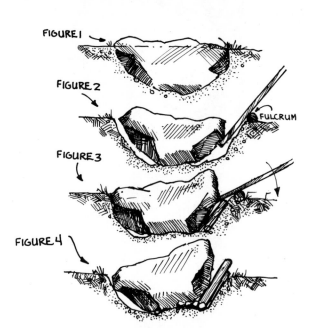

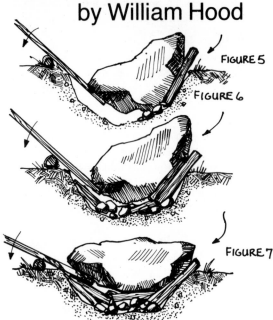

The area which we chose for a site for our garden was underlain with a number of glacially deposited boulders weighing up to 500 pounds. We could have, as did the previous owners of the property, ploughed around these encumbrances but, being perfectionists, we could not tolerate unwanted materials of such density lying below the surface of our soil. Consequently, as the neighbour's plough bounced off each boulder, we set a marker at the spot and later with probes outlined the area of the stone and calculated our chances of raising and removing same. Of the fifteen or so we encountered, none appeared too large to handle, so we commenced digging with long handled shovels around the boulders and, where possible, to their full depth. When the boulders were suitably exposed, we started levering them from the underlying matrix with an old car axle, using pieces of suitable square timber for fulcrums. When a boulder proved unyielding, we found that a few buckets of water poured into the hole and allowed to settle also helped to free the boulder from its bed.

Two persons are necessary to efficiently raise the stones. One or both can use the pry to lever the stone upwards to a point where a new bite and a larger fulcrum becomes necessary. As one person with the pry holds the stone at its new position, the other person packs suitable material under the stone to prevent it slipping back into the hole. Pieces of firewood or short pieces of scrap lumber will hold most stones until a new bite is obtained on the opposite side of the stone. The process is repeated from side to side until the stone is at ground level, at which time it is wise to bridge the hole with plank or poles so that the stone can be manipulated away from the hole.

We were fortunate to have the hood from a vintage Pontiac which we use most effectively as a stoneboat. It is quite simple for us to push the open end of the hood up tight to the stone and to roll or pry it onto our stoneboat. Our 14 horsepower garden tractor easily draws this appartus with the stone on board away from the garden site, and it becomes a simple matter to roll the stones off the hood when the stone-pile is reached.

Of course if the stones to be raised and moved are anything but large granite cobbles, as in our case, which defy conventional breaking, one can usually break them, particularly in winter, if they are well heated under a scrap wood fire and doused with buckets of cold water while hot. This method will usually break the stones along their lines of cleavage into manageable pieces.

Another method for breaking large boulders is by the use of dynamite in a method called mud capping. However I would not advocate the use of blasting materials unless a person is thoroughly familiar with blasting techniques and safe handling of powder, detonators and fuse. The method is simple when done by an experienced blaster and is accomplished by placing a charge on top of the stone and forcing the explosive force downwards, thereby shattering the stone. The dynamite is removed from its waxed paper cylinder and according to the size of the stone to be broken, is placed on top of the stone in a quantity from one half to a suitable number of whole sticks. The dynamite is arranged as compactly as possible on the stone at a place where the stone would be struck with a hammer if it were possible to break it that way. A detonator with a suitable length of fuse is embedded in the dynamite and this, known as the charge, is then covered with mud to a convenient thickness, but not less than five inches. The end of the protruding fuse (not less than three feet long) is split to facilitate lighting and ignited with a match or spill. The resulting blast will usually fracture the stone.

Glossary

apron Piece of canvas attached to the warp and cloth beams to which the warp ends are tied.

back beam Bar at back of loom over which warp passes from warp beam.

backcut Final falling cut. The backcut will progress until the tree starts to fall in its intended direction.

backsaw Handsaw with a thin blade having 11 to 16 teeth/inch. It is primarily used for finishing work in which precise cutting of straight lines is important.

bar or blade The part of the chain saw on which the cutting chain travels.

barber-chair The configuration of a tree stump (shaped as a chair) resulting from a tree splitting as it is felled; usually the result of poor falling cuts.

beam A wooden cylinder forming that portion of a weaver's loom on which the warp is wound before weaving; also, the cylinder on which the cloth is wound during the process of weaving.

bearings Any part of a machine in or on which another part revolves, slides, etc.

beater Frame holding reed. Used to "beat" weft thread back into place in the web.

bevel The sloping edge of a board which forms an angle greater or less than 90° with the surface.

bind or bound Compression created in a tree or a log due to uneven terrain or contact pressure from other trees or logs.

bit A sharp-edged tool for drilling or boring, having a shank for attachment to a brace, drill press, etc.

blow-down An area of standing timber which has been blown over by strong winds or storms.

board foot A unit of measurement by which board lumber is priced, represented by a piece 1" by 1' by 1' or its cubic equivalent.

bobbin(s) A spool or reel holding thread (or yarn) for spinning, weaving or machine sewing.

boring Cutting with the nose of the power-saw bar to cut from inside the log or tree.

breast beam Bar at front of loom over which fabric passes before it winds on the cloth beam.

buck or bucking To saw lengths from a tree after it has been felled.

burrs(metal) A roughness or rough edge, especially one left on metal in cutting or casting.

bushing Metal lining of circular orifice.

butt That end of the log or tree sawn from the stump, i.e., butt-end.

calipers An instrument resembling a pair of compasses, usually with curved legs, used for measuring diameters.

channel A shape which is like a dado or groove.

chimney flue A passage housed in a chimney through which smoke and gases are carried from a fuel burning appliance, fireplace or incinerator to the exterior.

cloth beam The front roller on which the cloth is wound as it is being woven. The roller holds the web at the correct tension.

countersink To drill a conical depression at the mouth of a screw hole to set a flathead screw flush with or below the surface. Also, the tool employed to accomplish this purpose.

cove Inward sloping arch.

cull A tree or log which is considered unusable because of defects.

dead centre A non-rotating centre, as on a lathe. See **spindle.**

dent Single space in a reed.

distaff A staff on which flax, wool, etc., is wound for use in spinning.

dogs Pointed teeth located between the chain saw blade and motor for use when falling or bucking to pivot saw and maintain position while sawing.

dowel A wooden stick 1/8" to 1½" in diameter used for making furniture joints, plugging screw holes and other purposes.

draft Drawing on ruled paper indicating the placement of the threads in the harnesses used in threading loom.

dutchman Portion of the undercut not removed. Can change falling direction of the tree. Very hazardous if improperly used.

edge grain Lumber that is sawn along the radius of the annual rings or at an angle less than 40° to the radius is edge-grained; this term is synonymous with quarter-sawn.

emery A very hard black or greyish-black variety of corundum, used as an abrasive.

end grain The face of a piece of lumber which is exposed when the fibres are cut transversely.

eye A loop of wire, metal or thread used for securing a warp thread in a heddle.

face Edge of area formed along standing timber as timber is felled.

faceplate A disc that holds and rotates work, as on a lathe or boring mill.

fascia Long wood board under eaves.

feathering Reducing gradually to a very thin edge.

ferrule A bushing; a metallic lining for a hole as in the hub of a wheel, designed to insulate or to prevent abrasion between parts.

fire clay A clay of high heat-resisting qualities used to make fire brick and the mortar in which fire brick is laid.

flange A projecting edge, rib, or rim; the top and bottom of I-beams and channels are called flanges.

flashing Sheet metal or other material used in roof and wall construction to shed water.

footing The widened section, usually concrete, at the base or bottom of a foundation wall, pier, or column.

gable The upper triangular-shaped portion of the end wall of a house.

gable end The entire end wall of a house having a gable roof.

gauge A standard for measuring e.g. diameter

of nails or wire and thickness of metal sheets.

gouge A chisel having a scoop-shaped blade used chiefly for carving or cutting wood.

harness Frames on which heddles are hung.

heddles Wire, twine, or flat pieces of steel with holes or eyes in center through which warp ends are threaded.

hip The sloping edge of a roof formed by two intersecting roof slopes.

hip-rafter The rafter which forms the hip of a roof.

holding wood Hinge of wood left uncut between the back of undercut and the backcut.

jack-pot A pile of haphazardly felled trees.

jack type looms A rising type loom in which only the harnesses which are to rise are attached to any heddle.

kerf The width of any saw cut.

kick-back When the power saw is jerked out of the faller's control, common cause of saw cuts on the arms and legs. Also, when a tree being felled slips backwards off the stump toward the faller.

lam Horizontal bar between heddle frame and treadle used to keep the heddle frames balanced.

lap joint Uniting two pieces of wood by overlapping their surfaces, usually by cutting away half the thickness of each piece so their surfaces are flush.

lay The position in which a felled tree is lying.

lead The established direction in which all trees in a quarter or strip are to be felled, usually governed by general slope or terrain.

lean Outward slant of a tree with reference to its base.

leaner A tree which leans, not growing perpendicularly.

lintel A horizontal structural member (beam) that supports the load over an opening such as a door or window.

live centre The centre of a rotating spindle, turning with the work, as on a lathe. See also **spindle.**

masonite Masonite are hardboard panels produced from by-product wood chips reduced to the cellulose fibres by high steam pressure.

mitre box A device used as a guide in sawing wood at an angle for mitre joints.

mortise A space hollowed out in a piece of timber, stone, etc., and shaped to fit a tenon to which it is to be joined.

mortise and tenon joint A furniture joint accomplished by fitting a tenon on one member into a mortise on another.

offside Opposite side to which the faller stands when falling or bucking.

peen To shape with the round end of a ball-peen hammer.

pitch Distance between successive points or lines, e.g., between successive teeth of cog wheel or threads of a screw.

pitman A rod that connects a rotary with a reciprocating part; a connecting rod.

plate A beam or piece of timber laid horizontally in a wall to receive the ends of other timbers.

rabbet An L-shaped cut in the edge of a board.

ratchet Wheel at end of warp and cloth beams to facilitate winding.

reed Comblike part of the beater, made of metal.

rest A device for supporting the turning tool or the work in a lathe.

ridge board A horizontal member usually ¾" thick at the upper end of the rafters, to which these rafters are nailed.

scantling Small beam under five inches in breadth and depth.

school-marm A tree stem which branches into two or more trunks or tops.

set-back Occurs when a tree settles back opposite to the intended direction of fall; hazardous situation when faller loses control of a tree.

shed Opening formed in warp, by raising or depressing harnesses, through which the shuttle is passed.

shed roof A sloping roof having its surface in one plane.

shims A piece of metal or other material used to fill out space, as where joints are worn loose, or between something and its support.

shoulder In carpentry the square end of an object at the point where the tenon commences, as of a spoke, the stile of a door, etc.

shuttle A device used in weaving to carry the weft to and from between the warp threads.

side-notch Additional side saw cuts made to prevent "barber-chair" or to facilitate sawing large trees to logs.

sidewinder A tree which does not fall in the required direction while being felled.

sill The horizontal member forming the bottom of an opening such as a door or a window.

sleeve To be enclosing rod of smaller tube.

snag Any dead or dying tree, ten feet or more in height.

spiked top The top of a tree may die and lose its branches, leaving a tall, dry spike of dead wood (usually occurs in cedar).

spindle In a lathe, a shaft-like part (live spindle) that rotates while holding the thing to be turned, or a similar part (dead spindle) that does not rotate.

tabby Usually used to describe plain weave. Can also apply to thread inserted between pattern threads.

tailstock That standard or stock of a lathe through which passes the nonrotating spindle or dead centre.

tenon A projecting part cut on the end of a piece of wood for insertion into a corresponding hole (mortise) in another piece to make a joint.

tie-up Tying of lams to treadles.

treadle A lever operated by the foot, usually to cause rotary motion.

trunnion Supporting cylindrical projection on each side of an object such as a cannon, moveable saw, etc.

turn To shape (an object) in rounded form by turning on a lathe or other cutting tool.

vise A clamping device, usually of two jaws made to be closed together with a screw, lever, etc., used for grasping and holding objects being worked on, glued, etc.

warp The threads running lengthwise in the loom and crossed by the weft or woof. Also, to arrange threads or yarns so as to form a warp.

warp beam The roller or beam in a loom on which the warp is wound.

whip beam Beam at back of loom directly above warp beam; corresponds in position to breast beam at front of loom; also called "slab" or back beam.

widow maker Limb or other loose material dropped or thrown from a tree toward the faller as the tree is felled; a constant hazard for fallers.

wind falls Trees blown over by the wind, etc., lying among standing timber.

Metric Conversion Table

METRIC SYSTEM

Length
Meter	= 1.093 yards
	= 3.281 feet
	= 39.370 inches
Kilometer	= 0.621 mile

Surface
Square meter	= 1.196 square yards
	= 10.764 square feet
Square centimeter	= 0.155 square inch
Square Kilometer	= 0.386 square mile
Hectare	= 2.471 acres

Volume
Cubic meter	= 1.308 cubic yards
	= 35.314 cubic feet
Cubic centimeter	= 0.061 cubic inch
Stere	= 0.275 cord (wood)

Capacity
Liter	= 0.880 Imperial liquid quart or
	= 1.056 U.S. liquid quarts
	= 0.908 dry quart
	= 0.220 Imperial gallon or
Hectoliter	= 0.264 U.S. gallon
	= 2.75 English bushels or
	= 2.837 U.S. bushels

Weight
Gram	= 15.432 grains
	= 0.032 troy ounce
	= 0.0352 avoirdupois ounce
Kilogram	= 2.2046 pounds avoirdupois
Metric ton	= 2204.62 pounds avoirdupois
Carat	= 3.08 grains avoirdupois

ENGLISH

Length
Yard	= 0.9144 meter
Foot	= 0.3048 meter
Inch	= 0.0254 meter
Mile	= 1.609 kilometers

Surface
Square yard	= 0.836 square meter
Square foot	= 0.092 square meter
Square inch	= 6.45 square centimeters
Sqare mile	= 2.590 square kilometers
Acre	= 0.405 hectare

Volume
Cubic yard	= 0.764 cubic meter
Cubic foot	= 0.028 cubic meter
Cubic inch	= 16.387 cubic centimeters
Cord	= 3.624 steres

Capacity
Imperial liquid quart	= 0.7883 liter
U.S. liquid quart	= 0.946 liter
Dry quart	= 1.111 liters
Imperial gallon	= 4.543 liters
U.S. gallon	= 3.785 liters
English bushel	= 0.363 hectoliter
U.S. bushel	= 0.352 hectoliter

Weight
Grain	= 0.0648 gram
Troy ounce	= 31.103 grams
Avoirdupois ounce	= 28.35 grams
Pound	= 0.4536 kilogram
Short ton	= 0.907 metric ton